Zoophysiology and Ecology
Volume 2

Laurence Irving

Arctic Life of Birds and Mammals
Including Man

With 59 Figures

Springer-Verlag
Berlin · Heidelberg · New York 1972

Laurence Irving
Professor of Zoophysiology
Institute of Arctic Biology
University of Alaska
Fairbanks, Alaska/USA

ISBN 3-540-05801-X Springer-Verlag Berlin · Heidelberg · New York
ISBN 0-387-05801-X Springer-Verlag New York · Heidelberg · Berlin

Typesetting, printing and bookbinding: Druckerei Georg Appl, 8853 Wemding.

Contents

VIII

Chapter 1

Introduction

After travel through Alaska during the Second World War, in 1947 I went to Barrow with a very lively group of biologists. From their productive research developed the Arctic Research Laboratory. While we examined the rather surprisingly modest metabolic rates of arctic warmblooded animals in cold, PER SCHOLANDER proposed and then carried out measurements of metabolism of some tropical animals in Panama. The differences could be formulated to show the basis of adaptation to arctic cold and to tropical warmth. Imagination and logic were required to formulate the comparison so that it could become a part of science, but the essential measurements were derived from animals and plants in their own arctic and tropical environments. Characteristics that adapt the forms of life to climatic conditions of various environments appear clear in the large dimensions of extremely differing climates.

At the time of my arrival in Alaska many of the arctic Eskimos were still largely dependent on natural resources of their immediate and local environment, in which great seasonal changes in temperature and solar radiation appeared as dominant factors. The living environment on which they subsisted was also markedly affected by the changes of the seasons, in particular by the change in state of water to ice that terminated summer and by the melting that brought the late transition from winter to summer.

The magnitude of these changes and their rapid progress emphasized the adaptive compensations of animals that are requisite for arctic life. Adaptation that occurred after the arrival of winter would be too late to make adaptive compensation required by the arctic seasons. Arctic people remembered their experience of earlier seasons and, in social groups, anticipated the progress of the seasons by preparing shelter, clothing and implements. They secured their supply of food by prediction and interpretation of the seasonal movements of fish and game from remembered earlier experience and traditions. Places of residence were carefully chosen for convenience to food and fuel and in favorable exposure. The sand dunes along the Killik River in the Brooks Range of Alaska are marked with the scars of sudden and violent winds. SIMON PANEAK, who was born there, related that his father early warned him that it was dangerous to make camp in the valley except in sites that had been used earlier and found safe.

So the old Eskimo people, dependent for subsistence upon their immediate and local surroundings, were so familiar with the seasonal changes in their environment that they could prepare in advance the requirements for each time of the year. Without experience and traditional skills they could not have lived on the natural resources of the Arctic. Now the old ways of Eskimo life are being suppressed and physically improved, as the Eskimos are shielded from the environment by imported contrivances, fuel and food.

Having seen traces of the ways by which the old Eskimos prepared for the changing arctic seasons I can vaguely understand how knowledge transmitted through generations enabled them to anticipate and prepare for the most extreme climatic changes encountered by human societies. The other arctic animals must also make adaptive preparations for the sudden onsets of winter and spring, which come on more swiftly than they can prepare for by initiating the slow adaptive processes of physiology and behavior after the new season has arrived. Easiest to record, if we could follow them attentively, would be migratory movements to localities favorable for shelter and subsistence. Some small arctic mammals store food and contrive shelter. Larger mammals and the few winter-resident birds improve their insulation. All birds and mammals go through prolonged anticipatory physiological preparations to bring forth their young in a location and at a date favorable for their specific requirements. I shall not be able to indicate in any way how animals make their forecasts of the coming seasons, but I have tried to see some of the programs and physiological processes by which birds and mammals are readied for conditions of arctic life.

Without our awareness of their social deliberations, societies of animals maintain traditions that lead them to migrate over regular courses at appropriate dates. In spite of changes in landscape by agriculture and urbanization, migrations of birds continue to lead them in season to localities of earlier resort even after the terrain is completely altered by the construction and destruction effected by man. The arctic terrain is now beginning to be altered by the powerful technological processes of exploitation. Life may become impossible for some arctic species, but others will adjust their habits to changing conditions of the land. They will still encounter the arctic seasonal regimes of temperature and light and will retain predilections for territories formerly occupied.

Within a few decades the lives of arctic people have been altered by importation of goods, technology and power that are rapidly relieving them of dependence upon their immediate and local environment for subsistence. But the light and cold of arctic seasons are still there and arctic people must sometimes go out of doors to exploit an environment in which imports are costly and from which exports must be cheap enough to allow for their transportation. I am relieved that I am not expected to consider the monetary economy and sociology of arctic life.

Historically biology has developed through compilations of descriptive observations of species and their parts in apparent relation to each other, to their circumstances and activities, and to time. Without observed facts of life there is little that imagination can project to suggest an orderly biology. I had only vague preconceived ideas about the Arctic until I saw arctic Alaska and its animals, although information published by many scientists was available. My experience in other arctic areas is so limited that I surely err by projecting my views from Alaska to generalization on ways of life in the entire arctic region. It is even more difficult for the biologist to speculate backwards into the times when animals were developing their present habits. But in spite of recognizing the difficulty of projecting ideas from here to there and from now to then, speculation is still the most rapid way to enlarge one's thoughts. It is an especially useful practice for scientists.

In proposing themes that I think are common to arctic life I have the advantage of some years of familiarity with life in Alaska along with time to think about it in relation to the complex regulations that govern the development of order in biological information. Often I have speculated upon ways by which animals

2

would encounter arctic conditions only to find that they did not in fact operate in the manner that I had postulated from a few observations. After more experience and time I have discarded many speculative generalizations as based upon errors in observation or on inadequate hypotheses. Having been convinced that attempts at scientific ordering of records of animal populations are likely to discard the important diversity in the activities of individuals and their momentary appearance, I have often tried to preserve such observations by narrative descriptions of their occurrence. I regret that my art is inadequate to picture them realistically.

I have enjoyed the scenes of arctic life, which I could not have seen without support by funds, supplies and transportation derived from a society that so generously sustains scientific research. I do not know what use the results may have, but for me the views of arctic life have been interesting, and I have a feeling that, like art, science is as valuable as it provides pleasurable interest.

In their complete dependence upon communication with others, scientists are perhaps socially the most highly organized of people. A scientist in the Arctic depends so closely on other persons for information, transportation, food, shelter and companionship that his communication with them is especially sociable and friendly. For the pleasure of these associations I am grateful.

In many places in the following text I have referred by name to sources of information, but even more often I have been instructed by conversations with friends who more significantly than with words have pointed to animals, scenes and events of arctic life. I especially appreciate and acknowledge the great help of Mrs. HELGA WILM in preparation of these comments on arctic life.

Chapter 2

Environment of Arctic Life

Geographical Characteristics

Small Extent of Polar Regions

The Arctic is now a familiar sight to many people who have looked down during flights over intercontinental arctic routes on uninhabited regions and have gained an impression of the vast extent of their frozen surface. As a matter of fact the two frigid zones within the Arctic and Antarctic Circles comprise the smallest areas of the earth's climatic zones. Vague recognition of their small extent impelled explorers in the 16th through 19th centuries to sail eastward and westward from Europe in search of usable short arctic sea routes toward sources of the luxury goods of China. During the 20th century transarctic air routes have been established between America and Europe with attendant networks of communication to assure information about weather and navigation. Transport by sea has been established along the long coasts of arctic Asia and is under preparation over the shorter but more complex ice-filled sea routes north of America. These routes circumnavigate the Arctic Ocean, which forms a polar basin with bordering Eurasian and American coasts and with large islands projected northward from each continent.

Geographic Asymmetry between Arctic and Antarctic

Quite opposite is the distribution of land and sea in Antarctica, where a massive south polar continent is separated by wide seas from other continents in the southern hemisphere. This asymmetry between the two polar regions makes conditions entirely different for the distribution and kinds of arctic and antarctic life. In fact Earth would be a dull and perhaps lifeless globe if its surface masses had been symmetrically fixed.

In Antarctica, international relations among scientists, commercial whaling, and measures for conservation on land have ben pursued in political accord. In the Arctic, bordering nations claim separate national jurisdictions. Scientists collaborate and exchange information as far as political interests permit. But arctic traffic for science has been constrained within separate national European, Asian and American sectors.

Eurasian and American Arctic Compared

Ice-free waters border the arctic Scandinavian coasts throughout the year. The low-arctic coasts of Europe eastward to the Ural Mountains are colder extensions of northern Europe. East of the Ural Mountains in Asia, great rivers rise deep in the forests and dry steppes of the interior and flow northward through steppes, forests and tundra, providing communication northward to the arctic seas. In Siberia mountains approach the coasts but they are still traversed by northward-flowing rivers nearly to its eastern promontory. These routes led to sparse ancient human settlement of arctic Asia from the south.

In America the Mackenzie River forms the only great valley communicating through forested lands with the plains of the western interior. Unlike Scandinavian coasts, the coast of arctic Alaska is long ice-bound in winter. Its Arctic Slope is separated from the interior by the Brooks Range, which closely borders the sea at the boundary with Canada. Only narrow Bering Strait separates Alaska from Siberia, and this contiguity with Asia has decisively influenced the life of America.

Central and eastern arctic Canada and the Canadian arctic islands do not offer easy communication with the south through their cold seas, the Barren Grounds, forest and muskeg. Eastward of the Canadian arctic islands and separated from them by the deep waters of Davis Strait and Baffin Bay lies Greenland. A few hardy land mammals, such as reindeer *(Rangifer tarandus)* and Eskimos, could in winter, cross the narrow ice-covered straits separating Ellesmere Island from north Greenland. For the ubiquitous polar bears *(Ursus maritimus)* and arctic foxes *(Alopex lagopus)*, the ice of the arctic seas is a circumpolar habitat. East

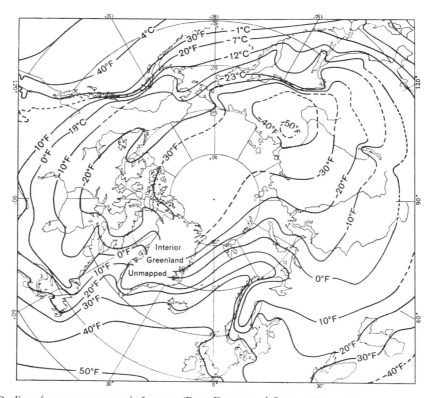

Fig. 2.1. Outline of mean temperature in January. (From KIMBLE and GOOD, 1954, p. 74)

5

of Greenland, broad and long unfrozen seas bar exchange of land animals with Europe.

Climate, ice, seas and varying terrain visibly limit the distribution of some animals. But the highly mobile birds, seals and whales migrate along routes established by past experience as serving for their sustenance. Experience of natural populations as well as specific capabilities of individuals constrain them within ranges that they have found suitable, and the conservative ways of animal societies retard venture into new territory.

Arctic Seasons

In contrast with the even seasonal temperature at tropical sea level, arctic air cools below −50° in winter and warms well above melting temperature in summer. Arctic birds and mammals keep their bodies 90° warmer than coldest winter air

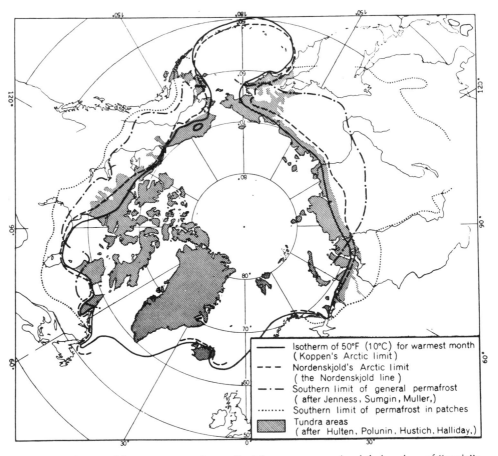

Fig. 2.2. Isotherm 10° in warmest month, usually July; some conventional designations of "arctic"; extent of permafrost and tundra. (From KIMBLE and GOOD, 1954, Fig. 21)

6

but only some 20° warmer in summer. Mean temperatures recorded in global isotherms provide indication of thermal stress but they conceal the vagaries of weather that fluctuates during each day and differs from place to place. Air temperature (Fig. 2.1) is the simplest of several distinguishable indicators of environmental conditions (Fig. 2.2). Considering the complexity of climates and weather it is surprising that mean temperature of air can so usefully indicate conditions for life unless we think of air temperature as a thermal potential of the local atmosphere.

Isotherms: East-West Asymmetry

As temperatures decline northward meridionally, it is evident that their gradients are not zonally arranged along parallels of latitude. Variation of isotherms from latitudinal distribution is more evident in the Arctic than in Antarctica and occurs in relation to land masses, mountains and ocean currents, with greatest seasonal changes in the interior of continents. Conspicuous is the latitudinal asymmetry by which warm poleward currents in the North Atlantic extend waters free of ice north along the southwest coast of Greenland and along Scandinavian coasts into the Barents Sea. On these west-facing coasts, waters free of ice extend farther north and warming in spring is earlier than in east Greenland. Eastern Siberian coasts are colder than Alaskan coasts below the Arctic Circle, but the barrier of the Aleutian Islands reduces the small climatic tempering of Alaskan coasts of Bering Sea.

Arctic coasts are long ice-bound from eastern Europe over Asia and over America. The coldest winter air occurs in the interior of continents, with warm or even hot summer days. In the forested interior of Alaska, as in northeastern Siberia, during the transition from winter to summer the air suddenly warms through nearly 20° in April and by a nearly equal amount in May (Fig. 2.3). The daily rate of warming in spring and the rate of cooling in autumn distinguish the high latitudes.

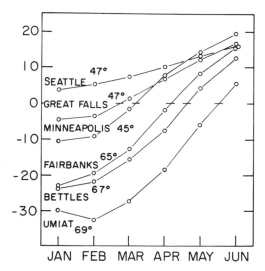

Fig. 2.3. Winter-to-summer progress of monthly mean temperature in three Alaskan localities and in three northern cities. North latitude shown in degrees. (From IRVING, 1960)

7

At this point it will be apparent that I have not defined the extent of arctic conditions occupied by what I call arctic life. The only unequivocal definition is by the area within the Arctic Circle (latitude 66° 33'N). But because of the zonal climatic asymmetry and related asymmetric distribution of living conditions I will take arctic animals as we find them in northern regions that are dim or dark during long and very cold winters.

Annual Solar Cycle

The annual solar cycle brings sunlight to earth for 12 continous hours at the equinox. On the Arctic Circle there are 24 hours of insolation on the midsummer day and 24 sunless hours at midwinter. At Barrow, Alaska (latitude 71°N), sunless midwinter lasts two months as does midsummer without sunset. Winter darkness is agreeably relieved by a night sky lighted by stars, moon and aurora that show objects in contrast with the brightly reflecting snow. In the dim light of noon at Barrow in winter one may identify as a dog an object one hundred meters distant, but not distinctly enough to aim at the object with a rifle. Under the commonly overcast sky and wind-blown snow, arctic winter day can be really dark.

Freezing and Prolongation of Winter

As the lowering sun in summer ceases to warm the arctic lands and waters, they lose heat and water freezes. Heat loss from ground and water is lessened by the insulation afforded by snow and ice but cooling is much increased by the diminished incident heat of winter radiation from sun and sky, which is largely reflected by the snow covering polar lands and ice. Only a part of the water in deeper arctic lakes and rivers remains liquid, restricting the winter range of free swimming animals. The heat released by freezing water retards autumnal progress toward winter beyond the equinox and radiative losses extend the thickening of ice beyond midwinter to reach a maximum in February or early March.

As sunlight returns in spring part of its warming is expended in melting ice and snow, which delays warming of air toward midsummer. As a result, snow lingers on at Barrow, Alaska (latitude 71°N), into June and sea ice does not open for coastal navigation until August. Seasonal air, ground and ice temperatures lag behind the annual cycle of solar radiation.

In the annual cycle of the Arctic the usual summer gain of solar heating about equals the winter loss (FLETCHER, 1965). Years vary in warmth, with shorter or longer periods suitable for the growth of plants on which all life depends. In the northern situations periods of warmth in summer approach the minimum extent for completion of life cycles. Near the northern limit of life a years's reproduction may be lost in a cold summer and a sequence of cold seasons leads toward elimination of shortlived animals and plants.

Permafrost

On polar lands not covered by perennial ice the frozen surface thaws in each summer. Over one fifth of the extent of the world's land area (Fig. 2.2) the ground is only superficially thawed in summer and is underlain by perennially frozen ground called permafrost (PéWé, 1966). In northern Alaska and Asia borings have penetrated over 400 meters through frozen ground. The frozen depth diminishes southward to a terminus that is more irregular in Asia than in America.

Even in high-arctic regions the antiquity of permafrost is not uniform over the surface of the land, for it may have been eroded by rivers and modified by geological changes and varying climate. Although some permafrost may be a relic of glacial times its present extent by no means coincides with the maximum extent of Wisconsin glaciation (Fig. 2.4), and existing permafrost can be related to no single past climatic event. Rather it is a product of the entire thermal and geological background of the locality in which it occurs.

Permafrost is perennial rather than permanent, and indicates a balance derived from climates of previous years. In Ogoturuk Valley of northwestern Alaska it

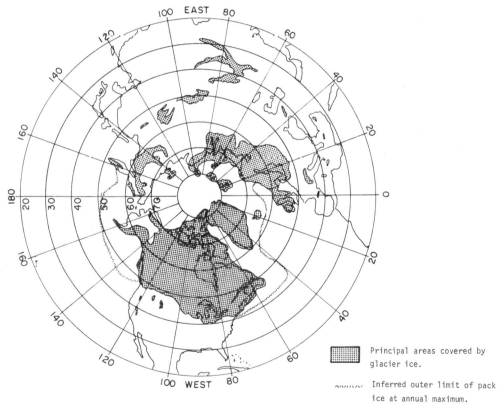

Fig. 2.4. Extent of large glaciers and pack ice at the time of maximum of glacier ice. (From FLINT, 1957, pt. 3)

9

was estimated by measurements of heat flow that during several thousand years of the present climate permafrost would have formed to a depth of 260 meters. In fact the measured depth is 367 meters, suggesting that one quarter of that permafrost is a relic of earlier and colder climatic regimes (LACHENBRUCH et al., 1966). Solidly frozen ground is impermeable to water but its surface cracks with cooling. It has been subjected to erosion by weathering and to covering by deposition of sediments from water and air.

Roots of vegetation and burrows of animals do not penetrate frozen ground. The depth to which ground thaws in summer limits biological activity by the extent of active soil that is available. Northern forests and their undergrowth flourish in the shallow soils that overlie frozen ground. In fact thick covering vegetation insulates the ground against thawing. When a forest and its undergrowth are cleared for cultivation or building, the bare ground thaws progressively deeper each summer. If the formerly frozen ground contained much water or if, as is common, actual layers of ice lie near the surface, the ground and the structures built upon it subside, distorting roads and leaving buildings at crazy angles.

Thick layers of well-drained gravel may effectively insulate the firmly frozen bases of roads, but their construction and maintenance are difficult and costly. Recently large buildings erected on permafrost have been supported on piles that penetrate into the frozen layer and elevate the building several meters above the surface in order to provide an air space to prevent heat from the structure from melting the frozen foundation. Water and sewer lines must likewise be carried above ground in heated utilidors. These problems of arctic development can be met only by careful engineering and at costs that can only be provided by especially valuable productions. Judging from reports that do not clearly reveal the economy of exploitation of arctic lands, large enterprises are in progress in arctic Asia. In arctic America and Greenland establishments for communications are maintained by governments and eager exploration is proceeding, supported by venturesome private capital.

Fires in northern forests lead to rapid erosion, and recovery, which never quite restores the former state, is prolonged. The thawed surface of tundra can remain long disturbed by even a single year's trails formed by migrating caribou (*Rangifer*) and the consequent erosion in the channels formed by their sharp hooves. About a former overnight camp the tracks of a few Eskimos may remain visible for several seasons. A village – old arctic villages consisted of only a dozen or so families – leaves a lasting impression. A settled town brings about melting of its underlying permafrost in summer to mud plus accumulated filth, from which the ancient residents preferred to scatter to fresh tenting places in summer. As settlements become stabilized about stores, churches and schools they cannot escape from the damage and pollution of the terrain. For millenia the Arctic was only affected by the power of a few men with their dogs and reindeer, and their fires. Now the application of the enormous power and implements of civilization is suddenly showing its effect on the Arctic.

Spring Breakup

The rapid warming in spring melts arctic snows to water that, running over impermeable frozen ground, fills water courses and floods depressions. The "spring breakup" in arctic rivers is an awesome spectacle as the stream of melt-water flowing over the ice suddenly floats ice that had been fast-frozen to the river bottom and bears the tumbling blocks of ice crashing in the current. In narrow channels the ice may jam and form a dam that spills ice and water over adjacent flat land with destructive erosive effects. The loads of silt and debris carried by floods build flood plains over the flatlands of arctic valleys. The native people who settled along streams learned to choose sites safe from flooding, but often newcomers build on the flood plains, which in summer appear deceptively to be suitable sites for buildings. Disastrous floods that follow disregard for the prospect of flooding, however, are afflictions not peculiar to arctic settlers.

Because of the small capacity for storage of water in the thin layer of unfrozen ground, arctic spring floods soon subside. Precipitation during arctic summers is generally only 10 centimeters. But since all run-off flows over impermeable frozen ground, sudden floods in summer have had conspicuous effects on the landscape and on the ways of arctic residents.

Sea Ice

Most arctic seas are frozen to the shores in winter, but open water extends from the Atlantic Ocean north of Scandinavia into the Barents Sea. The annual depth of freezing of the arctic seas is said to amount to four meters. Throughout the winter, ice fields, moved by winds and currents, form jams as they encounter more stable masses of ice. At these encounters blocks of ice are thrust over each other to form the pressure ridges that obstruct travel on ice. If one is so fortunate as to have clear weather during a transarctic flight in winter he will be impressed by the number and extent of open leads in the ice of arctic seas. Ice forced against arctic shores forms pressure ridges that may rise for 20 meters as they ground at much greater depths. In summer the ice slowly retreats from arctic shores and open leads become more frequent in the sea ice.

Over their main extent, arctic seas are sufficiently ice-covered to prevent complete melting by reflection of summer radiation. Although the arctic ice-cover is an ancient condition, sea ice is impermanent. Parts of it persist for years; but it is nevertheless renewed each winter at a rate to balance summer melting and transfer of heat by currents from the Atlantic and by limited currents from the Pacific through Bering Strait. Changing weather alters the southern extent of sea ice from year to year, with some northward or southward trends prolonged for years. Balance in the apparent impermanence of arctic sea ice has, nevertheless, long preserved ice-covered arctic seas (FLETCHER, 1965). Speculative but logical calculations indicate that were the reflection of radiation by the ice-covered arctic seas once removed by melting, the persistent arctic ice cover would not reform under present climatic conditions. The estimated consequences for world climates would be so considerable (and yet so uncertain) that even the speculators sound anxious lest an experimental attempt be made to melt the polar ice.

11

Passage of an ice-breaking ship in late winter through continuous ice near the margin of the polar ice exposes extensive brownish discoloration of lower layers of thick sea ice. This material includes diatoms and other phytoplankton that had grown in the cold brine under the dim illumination penetrating to the bottom of the ice. Even in winter some photosynthesis proceeds to add an as-yet-unmeasured amount of productivity that contributes to the sustenance of crustaceans, fishes, bottom fauna and, eventually in the marine food chain, it contributes to the support of seals. Polar bears (*Ursus maritimus*) derive sustenance from the production of the underlying waters, and their circumpolar distribution is affected by their ability to obtain food and travel on the frozen arctic sea. Men like Eskimos, adapted by their culture to live and travel on ice, have traversed short distances between arctic lands. Caribou (equivalent to reindeer, *Rangifer*, of Europe) annually migrate over the ice between Canadian islands, but are limited in distance by the frequency of their need for herbivorous nutrition obtainable only on land. A few hardy land mammals wander short distances over ice. Many sea birds, however, venture far northward in summer to feed in open leads, and a few land birds annually migrate far over ice to arctic island shores.

Ice Caps and Glaciers

Accumulated snow packed to ice covers Antarctica with a massive ice cap flowing outwards as glaciers into the surrounding sea. Limited ice fields in North America and the Greenland ice cap discharge into the seas through glaciers. Arctic islands north of Eurasia and Canada are partially covered with ice fields. The massive Greenland ice cap is still far inferior in size to the ice cap of Antarctica. Ice caps on land are the results of ancient precipitation sequestered during millenia by accummulated excess of freezing over melting. While sea ice is proposed to represent accumulation of a few years (BUDYKO in FLETCHER, 1965), glacial ice is the product of centuries and millenia in which accumulation has exceeded melting. As melting polar ice at the end of Wisconsin glaciation raised the level of the seas, great marine transgressions have occurred that within a few tens of thousand years have profoundly modified arctic coasts and living conditions on land and sea. In the past million years there have been sequences of glaciation and ablation, accompanying world climatic variations, that made several rapid and tremendous changes in the lands and coasts of the northern hemisphere (FLINT, 1957). Recent in the background of northern life are the profound changes in lands, seas and climates of Quaternary time, and the Arctic is an immature and changing environment.

Areas Occupied by Life

Looking at the Arctic of the present we see some general indicators of the extent of conditions suitable for arctic life. Polar sea ice sustains no herbivores but supports polar bears *(Ursus maritimus)* and foxes *(Alopex lagopus)* on products of the underlying sea, a few species of sea mammals (see p. 28–32) and, in summer, several species of carnivorous migratory birds (see p. 75). Coastal regions, open in summer, have supported sea mammals, many species of migratory birds and several races of arctic men. Ice fields on land and the most northern inclement areas support vegetation so sparse that they are practically arctic deserts. Two types of arctic vegetation can be named.

Tundra

The poor soil of arctic tundra, with precipitation amounting to only 10 cm, permits only low plant growth. Tundra varies from sparse herbs, grasses and lichens to extensive cover with grasses and sedges. Herbivorous animals subsist in relation to density of vegetation, which varies in supporting a few large colonies of small animals, but usually small localized colonies. Concentrated in rare favorable arctic plains and valleys are occasional suprisingly large populations of a few species of birds and mammals. At high elevations tundra-like vegetation extends far southward into the continents, affording possible routes of communcication between residents of arctic and temperate alpine tundra.

Swept by cold and often violent winds, the winter tundra, thinly covered by the meager arctic snowfall, is a bleak range for animals. Where snow drifts around hummocks of sedge and low herbs and willows, local areas of subnivean shelter are provided for small rodents and shrews. Over areas swept bare by wind, caribou (*Rangifer*) and ptarmigan (*Lagopus lagopus* and *mutus*) and their retinue of predators have access to exposed vegetation. In order to exist on this meager production a population of large animals must be able to range over wide distances and have habits of dispersal that prevent prolonged local feeding that would soon terminate the tenuous existence of the vegetation of the tundra.

Large winter inhabitants of tundra (caribou, wolves, foxes, ravens and ptarmigan) have ability and habits for ranging widely. Tolerant of cold and wind, they are permitted by the bare ground and wind crusted snow to travel unobstructed over regions sufficiently large to provide their sustenance. Arctic men, protected by their skill at clothing and shelter, likewise find that firm winter tundra permits their travel for hunting over long distances in order to obtain sufficient game. Only small snowshoes are needed on winter tundra and sleds move easily over the firm surface. In wooded lands, soft snow impedes winter travel of men and animals and requires different habits that cannot be formed by some species and are inconsistent with the practices of tundra-dwelling animals and people.

Taiga

A rather abrupt northern termination of tree growth marks the tree line, which in turn is found at increasing elevations in southern mountainous country. Boreal forested lands (Fig. 2.2) bordering on tundra, called taiga, are composed of spruce and some birch trees in North America, with undergrowth of willow, alder and varying heath and swamp shrubs, herbs, grasses, mosses and lichens. In northern Scandinavia pine trees (*Pinus*) extend near to the arctic seas. Eastward in Eurasia

13

conifers dominate the taiga. Trees of the taiga modify life conditions and bring about its occupation by several animal species of the forests and by people with culture differing from that of tundra peoples.

Accummulation of snow is favored in the shelter of forests. Snow shields against convective loss of heat and insulates against conduction of heat from the ground. A layer of mossy vegetation affords further insulation to such effect that a few centimeters beneath the snow-covered surface of moss, the range of annual temperature may be restricted to − 10° to + 10° while temperatures in air above the moss range from − 50° to + 35°. Subnivean taiga is moderately cool, windless, dark, humid and quiet, a well-tempered habitat for its small denizens. Before the cover of snow accumulates in autumn, voles and shrews of the mossy ground may encounter their most severe climatic stress. Venturing above snow they encounter large climatic gradients, and they avoid this exposure (PRUITT, 1957).

Bare tundra is difficult or impossible for the life of small arctic mammals because it is untempered from the cold and winds. Where snow accumulates locally over vegetation, lemmings, voles and shrews find discontinuously sheltered areas for runways and food as they do in the near-continuous shelter of snow under northern forests. Rare tracks on the snow show that they seldom venture from these subnivean shelters in winter, but seasons of late or sparse snowfall can be severe trials for small northern mammals.

Tree line is not zonally distibuted along lines of latitude. It appears to correspond closely with the July isotherm about 10°, which is taken to indicate the least warmth in the growing season that can accommodate growth of trees. Winter cold is not a limit for northern forest trees, for the coldest continental winter weather occurs in forested northeastern Siberia and in the well wooded interior of eastern Alaska and Yukon Territory (Fig. 2.1).

In the northern interior of Asia cold, dry, treeless steppes extend northward locally to verge upon tundra without passing through the taiga and forest that prevail in the northward vegetational transitions of America. The maritime climates of treeless western Alaska and the moderate cold of treeless Aleutian Islands illustrate other climatic conditions as well as arctic that affect the extent of forests.

The northern tree line in North America has changed in recent millennia. In Keewatin remainders of ancient burned forests, now covered by tundra, show that forests extended 280 km north of their present limit. The date of the fire, afforded by dating the charcoal, was 3500 years ago, when presumably a corresponding northward extension of a warmer climate allowed the extension of forest (BRYSON et al., 1965). Palynological studies further indicate that the tree line in this part of Keewatin extended north of its present limit from 6000 to 3500 years ago and again from 1500 to 600 years ago (NICHOLS, 1967).
Within this century noticeable northward movements have extended ranges of birds, mammals, and fishes northward in eastern and central Canada, along the coasts of Greenland (HARPER, 1961) and also in Scandinavia. It is less clear that forest or taiga has extended northward in some parts of America, but it is quite apparent that during this century, boreal animals have been moving into lands and waters of eastern America that were formerly considered in the domain of arctic life. Thus the regions of arctic life have changed, probably globally, and asymetrically in time as well as in geographical location.

14

Similarity in Circumpolar Arctic Conditions

Seeking to generalize upon conditions affecting arctic life, by the sacrifice of geographical detail, we can pick upon a few characteristics common to the Arctic and in contrast to the temperate south. A long cold and dark winter, with snow and ice covering frozen ground, alternates with a shorter summer when water is fluid and warmth briefly permits vegetational production. Arctic life must be adaptable to these common and seasonally changing conditions which selectively limit the number of species and the total production of populations. Polar bears *(Ursus maritimus)* and arctic foxes *(Alopex)* are virtually restricted to arctic ice and shores. Willow ptarmigan *(Lagopus logopus)* are denizens of low arctic and subarctic habitats, and rock ptarmigan (*Lagopus mutus*) reside in low and in some high arctic lands. The ubiquitous raven *(Corvus corax)* occurs in high arctic lands and southward to tropical deserts. Caribou are creatures of the snow, but the versatile wolf *(Canis lupus)* and red fox *(Vulpes fulva),* like the raven, can extend from cold arctic lands to southern steppes, plains and deserts. We are tempted to think that adaptation of a species for arctic life might make it unfit for life in temperate climates, but that can be suspected in only a few cases. Animals trail a variety of past experience and inheritance, but they move only through ranges that are now tolerable. Furthermore they occur in regions to which their ancestors had access.

History of Arctic Climates

The margin of arctic life, which I have taken as the range of arctic animals, changes conspicuously with the seasons as many migratory birds move northward in spring to arctic nesting grounds. Caribou migrate in vaguely known paths that change their seasonal occupation of arctic lands. Many populations of the sea move northward in summer. Gray whales (*Eschrichtius gibbosus*) that breed in winter in coastal waters of Baja California move into northern and arctic seas in summer. These seasonal movements are related to annual climatic changes.

During the 20th century northward displacement of southernmost populations of seals and northward extensions of some land mammals and migratory birds have occurred along coasts of Greenland. In other arctic regions recent changes in the ranges of birds and mammals have been less apparent for want of records.

Norse settlements in southwest Greenland left written records of conditions suitable for their European style of subsistence by sheep-raising in the 11th century. By the 15th century climatic deterioration reduced the possibility of this form of subsistence below levels practical for survival, and the Norse settlers, inadaptable for living by hunting like Eskimos, were replaced by these adaptable indigenous arctic people. Records pertinent to climatic influences upon distribution of life were vaguely kept and have had to be dug out by historians from the further obscurity and confusion caused by the effects of northward-expanding human power on the land and its life. The history of changing climatic influence on northern life is still vague (LAMB, 1965), but it shows clearly in general terms that the arctic environment and its populations have passed through enormous changes in ten millenia of Recent time.

15

Pleistocene Glaciation

Conspicuous in northern land forms is the evidence for the extensive masses of ice that covered large parts of northern continents during times of Pleistocene glaciations (Fig. 2.4). During the better known last glacial events (Wisconsin in America or Würm in Europe), tremendous masses of ice covered much of northern America and Europe and large extents of Asia. Ice-covered lands were lifeless and barred access from the south to the limited arctic ice-free regions in North America and Europe. Large ice fields restricted communication between arctic and southern Asia to ice-free corridors.

Land Bridge between Alaska and Siberia

It is becoming increasingly evident that the contiguity of Siberia and Alaska has been the site of intercontinental exchange of life that leaves large traces in present life, particularly in northern America. Withdrawal of water from the oceans into northern and southern ice caps during the Wisconsin epoch lowered the level of the sea by over 100 meters and exposed the shallow continental shelf between Alaska and Siberia to form dry lands as broad as Alaska between the two continents (HOPKINS, 1967). As a path for movement of populations the common designation of the intercontinental land as a land bridge indicates its service for intercontinental communication, but it was a bridge as broad as Alaska.

The bridge remained dry land during many thousand years late in the last (Wisconsin) glaciation, to be submerged with the sudden melting of continental ice caps that flooded continental shelves before 10 000 years ago. Reconstruction of conditions on the bridge from pollen in adjacent shore deposits (COLVINAUX, 1967) indicates an arctic climate and vegetation on the land bridge resembling that now prevailing north of the Brooks Range in arctic Alaska. The impression given by accounts is that grassy and sedgy tundra without trees covered much of its extent and the adjacent shores of Alaska and Siberia.

Because flooding of the bridge now submerges the tracks of intercontinental migrations, inferences about the moving traffic are derived from the relations of existing plants and animals of America with those of Asia. The evident continental exchange of flora and fauna impressively indicates results but leaves open questions about processes and their dates.

The extent of cover by the ice cap plausibly explains the predominant movement of Asiatic life toward America. Through Wisconsin time the massive Laurentide ice sheet extended westward over Canada to coalesce with the western Cordilleran ice sheet at the maximum of ice cover, isolating arctic America from the south. In Asia, however, unglaciated corridors persisted from southern steppes and taiga to the Arctic tundra between separate large ice masses, allowing communication between the great extent of the interior and arctic Asia and thence eastward over the land bridge.

16

Refuges in Glacial Periods: Beringia

Changing glaciation confuses and renders incorrect any simplified summary of the traffic over the land bridge, for there seem to have been several Pleistocene stages in which the bridge was dry and then again more or less submerged by marine transgressions. There existed in Alaska and Siberia a region not covered by the ice sheet of Wisconsin time. This region was called Beringia by HULTÉN (1968). In Alaska it extended over land north of the Alaska Range and served as a refuge for plants and animals moving from Asia over the land bridge. The unglaciated land bridge and adjacent Alaska were, however, isolated from the rest of America by massive ice south of the Alaska Range and probably eastward in the region of Mackenzie Valley. Here the migrants to America from Asia were confined in an arctic tundra and grassland that presumably extended across the land bridge with access to the tundra and southern interior of Asia. When the Wisconsin ice cover melted rather rapidly before 10 000 years ago, a residue of arctic life with Asiatic affinities became cut off from Asia by submergence of the land bridge and could extend to resettle the great extent of northern North America as it became free from ice. Populations with prolonged arctic backgrounds moved eastward and southward into America, encountering also a northward flow from populations that had been confined by ice sheets in areas south of Canada. A great area of North America is thus rather newly populated and is occupied by plants and animals derived from relicts in northern refuges and by others from south of the glaciers in temperate America.

Migrations of Man to America

Early: Indians

American Indians show characteristics of mongoloid people of Asia. The diversity of local types of Indians in North and South America indicates that they have become differentiated through a long time and in the course of wide geographical distribution. As they are further differentiated than are Eskimos from Asiatic mongoloids it is proposed that the predecessors of Indians came to America separately and in an earlier movement over a land bridge.

Artifacts of stone and bone found in the northwestern plains of the United States are fashioned in ways that suggest relation and derivation from styles that were spreading eastward and northward through Asia in the late Pleistocene (MÜLLER-BECK, 1967). Implements found in northern Asia show that man was at that time culturally adapted for life by hunting large mammals over cold steppes and arctic tundra (MÜLLER-BECK, 1967). At some imaginable but undocumented time when the land bridge was passable and the Laurentide and Cordilleran ice sheets had not yet coalesced, an ice-free corridor may have existed through which these early immigrants could have reached the southwestern plains to begin their differentiation as American Indians. As the corridor closed by coalescence of the eastern and western ice sheets, isolation and geographical distribution over North and

17

South America led to their diversification from the earliest settlers in the western plains.

Charcoal in the hearths where the first instruments of these ancient Indians were found, along with bones of extinct mammoths and bison, is dated from 12 000 to 9 000 years ago. Evidence for rapid extension of the culture of old Indians in America leads to speculation that these early hunters on land had been preceded by people who had come from Asia at a still earlier date, but these earlier tracks remain invisible. Carbon in what are suspected to have been earlier hearths of man has been dated older than that in ancient remains attributable to Indians, but the interesting evidence is too vague to support a generally acceptable hypothesis about the oldest American Indians.

There are as yet only a few fragments of evidence dating man's occurrence in interior Alaska 11 000 and perhaps 13 000 years ago, which is considerably later than the time thought likely for the earliest mongoloid migration to America, from which Indians are suspected to have developed. At this date the land bridge was just about in the course of its final submergence, and the receding glaciers of the Alaska Range might have been about to open a land route from Alaska southward through the prairies of Canada. Artifacts have not yet been found in sequences sufficient to indicate the predecessors of these ancient Alaskan artisans, nor is the information adequate to indicate their relation to the later Eskimos and Indians of Alaska and to the Indians of the rest of America.

The land bridge is now submerged and the route of a suspected migration from Beringia to the American plains has been scoured by glaciation. The early travellers were probably small groups of families moving toward favorable hunting on land without long-established abodes, and possessing only their own muscles and fire with which to leave marks upon their environment. It is hardly to be suspected that they knew they were migrating. But in the relics of their industries and prey we can feel that these ancients have unwittingly left evidence of their ways somewhere in the changing environment. Imaginative speculation prompts the search toward our enlightenment about conditions during the Pleistocene movements that brought so many Asian influences into the life of America.

Eskimos

On Umnak Island in the eastern Aleutians, successions of strata show sequences of human occupation over 8 000 years (LAUGHLIN, 1967). The implements and bones are for use in coastal residence and suggest dependence upon seafood. Styles of workmanship bear resemblances to those of eastern Asia. Found near present sea level, these artifacts imply occupations that could have developed from maritime residents about Bering Sea only after the land bridge was submerged. They precede widespread cultural remains that may reasonably be taken to represent origins of Eskimos.

For several thousand years people with cultures appearing logically to be precursors of Eskimos have variously occupied arctic and northern American coasts from Siberia to Greenland (GIDDINGS, 1967). Their main occupation was coastal with dependence upon sea life, but bands penetrated into and occupied the arctic interior. In historic times Eskimos have been rather clearly separated by culture from Indians of the bordering interior forests, and the separation of the two races has been sufficient to develop genetic distinctions between blood types. Life on arctic coasts and tundra differed from forest living. Whether it was their two manners of life or distinct origins that brought about differentiation of Indians and Eskimos, the two peoples adapted to their adjacent ranges in the Arctic in different manners.

Extinction of Large Land Mammals

Shortly after the termination of the last (Wisconsin) glaciation there came about rapid extinction of many species of large mammals of the northern hemisphere (GUTHRIE, 1969). Huge mammoths, large bison, horses and some 95% of the species in the North American megafauna ceased to exist. Clearly something, and evidently very much, was going on in these first millenia after the continental ice caps melted, and the removal of the great herbivores and their predators in itself could contribute to environmental change as the effects of their grazing were removed. In the last few centuries of history man has eradicated many species, large and small, but whether prehistoric men possessed the power for such extinctions is conjectural. During many prehistoric years a principal prey of arctic man has been caribou (*Rangifer*), which happily still exist wild in North America.

Following melting of the continental ice caps came reestablishment of northern vegetation in sequences that would progressively change the environment. Erosional rates differed with age of the system as well as with the climate. Post-Pleistocene climatic change was conspicuous in the warm millenia 5000 years ago. I have already mentioned the likely environmental effect of the extinction of large herbivores. It is debatable whether it was a cause or result of environmental change. Implicit in the description of environmental instability is the evolution of animal and plant associations that result from environmental change as well as influences modifying evolution of the environment to its present condition.

Adjustments to Climatic Change

It seems that many species of mammals and birds in their present forms lived through the late Pleistocene. Resettlement of the Recent Arctic was effected by spread from arctic refuges and from areas south of the ice fields. In America, Europe and Asia major portions of the glaciated lands have recovered vegetation and animals. To this degree the Arctic is a new environment that has been resettled within some 10000 years by animals and plants that are close to the forms of their predecessors, which often lived in distant localities and circumstances. Their environment has passed through great physical changes to which some populations have reacted by notable expansion of ranges and numbers.

It is a common and useful practice to describe ancient climates in terms of the characteristic thermal requirements of species. Foraminifera preserved in an-

19

cient sediments are used to depict ancient climates by their apparently limited thermal requirements. Were it not for the attested usefulness of this method of interpreting climate from the denizens prevalent in residues a physiologist would question the reasoning, for we see clearly that climatic adaptability of many species of animals differs with season and even clinally within some latitudinally widely distributed species. Here is raised a question that you will not find answered in succeeding pages.

Populations that could retreat before the ice and subsequently return north-ward, and these form the bulk in numbers and kinds of residents of the Arctic, must have had plastic adaptability to meet latitudinal and temporal environmental changes. Could populations unexercised in encounter with cold by life in the climate of a southern retreat long preserve adaptability for the north to which they have returned? Evidently some did. Speculating further afield, how did some forms of life in a long mild Tertiary climate prepare the flexibility required to meet the extreme fluctuations encountered during Pleistocene glacial and intergla-cial epochs? These questions impinge upon problems of genetic and evolutionary processes in populations which physiology is not now prepared to face, but which may become decipherable in the light of the great seasonal and secular changes of the arctic.

Some arctic residents display great versatility in their encounters with their environments. Some find protective shelter, others, such as birds, annually retreat from arctic winter and punctually return in the season appropriate for nesting. In all cases they must time the changes in their habits to fit conditions of the great changes in arctic seasons. Populations must accurately distribute themselves in time and place over arctic ranges that provide rather sparse sustenance unevenly distributed in localities and seasons. Many of the adjustments involved in current life we can see, but contemplation of the development of these adjustments in the kaleidoscopic environmental changes through which present populations have evolved should stimulate inquiry into processes of adaptation.

References

Armstrong, T. E.: Russian Settlement in the North. Cambridge (England): University Press 1965.

Bryson, R. A., Irving, W. N., Larsen, J. A.: Radiocarbon and soil evidence of former forest of the southern Canadian tundra. Science 147, 46–48 (1965).

Colvinaux, P. A.: Quaternary vegetational history of arctic Alaska, 207–231. In: The Bering Land Bridge. Ed. by D. M. Hopkins. Stanford, Calif.: Stanford University Press 1967.

Fletcher, J. O.: The Heat Budget of the Arctic Basin and Its Relation to Climate. Santa Monica, Calif.: The Rand Corporation 1965.

Flint, R. F.: Glacial Geology and the Pleistocene Epoch. New York: John Wiley & Sons, Inc. 1955.

Flint, R. A.: Glacial and Pleistocene Geology. New York: John Wiley & Sons, Inc. 1957.

Freuchen, P., Salomonsen F.: The Arctic Year. New York: G. P. Putnam 1958.

Giddings, J. L.: Ancient Men of the Arctic. New York: A. A. Knopf 1967.

Guthrie, R. D.: Pleistocene Extinctions: The Search for a Cause. Ed. by P. S. Martin and H. E. Wright. Reviewed in Arctic 22, 82–84 (1969).

HARPER, F.: Changes in climate faunal distribution and life zones in the Ungava Peninsula. Polar Notes: Occasional publication of the Stefansson Collection, Hanover, N. H., U. S. A. (1961).

HOPKINS, D. M.: The Cenozoic history of Beringia – a Synthesis. In: The Bering Land Bridge, 451–484. Ed. by D. M. HOPKINS. Stanford, Calif.: Stanford University Press 1967.

HULTEN, E.: Flora of Alaska and Neighboring Territories. Stanford, Calif.: Stanford University Press 1968.

IRVING, L.: Birds of Anaktuvuk Pass, Kobuk, and Old Crow – A Study in Arctic Adaptation. United States National Museum Bulletin 217. Washington, D.C.: Smithsonian Institution 1960.

KIMBLE, G. H. T., GOOD, D. (eds.): Geography of the Northland. New York: John Wiley & Sons, Inc. 1954.

LACHENBRUCH, A. H., GREEN, G. W., MARSHALL, B. V.: Environment of Cape Thompson, Alaska, 149–164 (Permafrost and Geothermal Regimes). Ed. by N. J. WILIMOVSKY. Oak Ridge, Tenn.: U. S. Atomic Energy Commission 1966.

LAMB, H. H.: Britain's changing climate. In: The Biological Significance of Climatic Changes in Britain. Ed. by C. G. JOHNSON and L. P. SMITH. London and New York: Academic Press 1965.

LAUGHLIN, W. S.: Human migration and permanent occupation in the Bering Sea area, 409–450. Ed. by D. M. HOPKINS. Stanford, Calif.: Stanford University Press 1967.

MÜLLER-BECK, H.: On migrations of Hunters across the Bering Land Bridge in the Upper Pleistocene, 373–408. In: The Bering Land Bridge. Ed. by D. M. HOPKINS. Stanford, Calif: Stanford University Press 1967.

NICHOLS, H.: The post-glacial history of vegetation and climate at Ennadai, Lake Keewatin, and Lynn Lake, Manitoba (Canada). Eiszeitalter und Gegenwart 18, 176–197 (1967).

PÉWÉ, T. L.: Permafrost and its Effect on Life in the North. Corvallis, Oregon: Oregon State University Press 1966.

PRUITT, W.O., JR.: Observations on the bioclimate of some taiga mammals. Arctic 10, 131–138 (1957).

Chapter 3

Mammals of the Arctic

A dramatic event in the history of scientific exploration occurred in 1741 when
STELLER, naturalist in Bering's exploration for lands east of Siberia, recognized
a dark blue, crested jay (now *Cyanocitta stelleri)* from Kayak Island, in the Gulf
of Alaska, to be unlike Asiatic jays but like those of North America (STEJNEGER,
1936). His recognition came about from his recollection of an illustration of the
eastern American crested blue jay in CATESBY (1731), a work that he had seen
in St. Petersburg. STELLER did not question that the presence of a North American
land bird showed that the Russian explorers had found the American continent.
Uncertain navigation with no existing chart left the navigators in much confusion,
while STELLER accepted identification of a continent by a single conspicuous species
of bird.

Palaearctic and Nearctic Regions

The role of the Arctic in the distribution of life is emphasized by the naming
of the two life regions of the northern hemisphere as Palaearctic (Eurasia north
of the tropics) and Nearctic (North America north of tropical Mexico) by A. R.
WALLACE (1876), utilizing earlier regional definitions proposed by SCLATER (1858).
As facts about geographical distribution have multiplied these early generalizations
have gained significance. Designation of an old and a new region does not refer
to the historical time of the European discovery of America but to the apparent
priority and predominance of origins of groups of animals in Eurasia. The inclusion
of 'arctic' does not imply that the regions are arctic in climate or that arctic life
is more abundant, but it foreshadows the view that intercontinental diffusion of
lifeforms on land passed through the arctic contiguity of Asia and America.

Arctic Native Human Populations

At present, while the world's ethnic groups are becoming less distinct, there are
still recognizable differences among the native populations of arctic Eurasia and
America (FREUCHEN and SALOMONSEN, 1958) (Table 3.1). One people, Eskimos,
occupy northern and arctic coasts of America. In speaking of Eskimos, SIR JOHN
RICHARDSON (1852) was impressed by their continental uniformity in contrast
with the diversity among adjacent European nations. 'Outside of (south of) Bee-
ring's Straits, on the North Pacific, their language and customs have undergone
considerable changes ...; but elswhere there is no substantial variation in either;
the modes of life being uniform throughout, and the differences of speech among
the several tribes not exceeding in amount the provincialisms of English counties.'

In Eurasia arctic people appear derived from and have mingled with many peoples of the wooded taiga and steppes along the ancient lines of travel provided by the great rivers draining northward into arctic seas.

Table 3.1. Arctic peoples

Ethnic group	Population size
Eurasian	
Lapps	33000
Samoyeds	20000
Yakuty	10000 (but 300000 in forest)
Dolgany	600
Lamuty	2000
Yukagiri	500
Chukchi	12500
Koryaki	7500
Eskimo	1500
	85600
Eskimos	
Alaska	16000
Aleuts	4000
Canada	10000
Greenland	23000
	53000

(From FREUCHEN and SALOMONSEN, 1958, p. 22)

Russian Arctic Settlement

In the great extent of arctic Asia (approximately north of latitude 60°) ARMSTRONG (1965) estimated that 40000–50000 Russians had settled by the beginning of the 20th century, forming a small minority in relation to native residents and mainly concerned in the export of furs. By 1959 Russians in the north had increased to some 1600000, achieving a 4:1 majority over native residents. The great movement of population came about through development of mines, communications and attendant services organized by government. The influx is new and politically sustained for exploitation and the Russian population cannot be considered established residents like the old northern native peoples.

Northern American People

ROGERS (1967) estimated that in 1740–80 the population of native people in Alaska was 74000, which had diminished to about 1/3 as many by 1900–1920, but thereafter had increased to 2/3 of the 18th century numbers by 1960. Probably at all times the arctic people were considerably less than half of the Alaskan totals.

Decline in aboriginals after contact with more elaborate technological and economic ways seems to have been common in history. At the worst it now appears attributable to exploitation of the less advanced people. It may be that the sudden upturn in numbers at the beginning of this century represents adaptation of the native arctic people to the newly introduced ways or improved concern from outside for their welfare. In the period 1952–63 ROGERS (1967) estimated the annual increment of the Alaskan native population at from 3.0% to 3.6%, compared with an annual increment in the United States of 2%. The arctic people show the recent large increments that characterize many so-called underdeveloped human populations. The changing numerical status of arctic people is not unique to their environment or race and is an illustration of problems of numerical growth of human populations in which confusion about causes is compounded by concern about whether and how regulation of numbers should be attempted.

Figures on the population of North America north of latitude 60° would now show about 200000 people in Alaska, 50000 in Canada and 30000 in Greenland. White newcomers to Alaska now outnumber Eskimos and Indians many times, but north of the Arctic Circle established white residents are rare and still mainly transient for seasonal technical and scientific activities. The warm summers of the interior northward to the Tanana and Yukon valleys in Alaska favor forests, permit some agriculture and exploitation of minerals and are extending small urban communities gradually northward as accessibility by land, water and air increases and transarctic intercontinental air traffic develops. In contrast, the summer climate of northern Canada cools east of the Mackenzie, limiting the tree line and possible agriculture and restraining settlement by urbanized people in the center and east of North America to south of the latitude of James Bay.

Recent intense exploration for minerals and petroleum raises prospects of a large influx into arctic Alaska and Canada of men strange to northern life, carrying on technical operations in the exploitation of natural resources. In comparison with the modest earlier physical effects of the arctic fur trade, the tremendous application of power and heat involved in exploitation of minerals and oil is already radically modifying the northern tundra. It is as yet impossible to predict the changes in the northern environment or how they can be constrained within limits compatible with satisfactory (and profitable) human life. There are grave unsolved economic and social problems for the future of native arctic people.

In arctic Alaska and Canada it is doubtful that there could be found a white man truly settled in residence unless he had married into an Eskimo family and become incorporated in one of their villages. The future of the newcomers in the American arctic is uncertain, for present prospects indicate a growing population of men in transient residence in a region strange and essentially difficult for men accustomed to urbanized ways of living. Exploitation of the American Arctic is directed by private, highly organized and intensely competitive managements, in contrast to the political direction of exploitation in Asia.

Arctic Mammals

According to DARLINGTON (1957) the northernmost land homeotherms are slightly modified hares, rodents, wolves and foxes, bears, weasels, deer and birds. He further remarks that the northern kinds are members of dominant groups requiring small modification for adaptation to northern life. Dominant groups, in the terms of the zoogeographer, are evidently adaptable in extending ranges and multiplying their kind. To a physiologist this is like saying that they possess climatic adaptability, for otherwise they would not occupy the short roster of arctic mammals nor would they thrive in the cold and limited ranges of northern productivity.

Arctic species are relatively few: of a world list of 3,200 mammals, DUNBAR (1968) names 23 land residents north of the tree line, with five or six mammals of arctic seas. Within a limited arctic land region, 40 kilometers south of Barrow, Alaska (latitude 70°), BEE and HALL (1956) figure 17 kinds of mammals, as compared with 55 kinds about Lawrence, Kansas, and 140 in Panama. Extending the view of the northern area from coastal waters for 160 kilometers over the Arctic Slope enlarges the roster to 42 species (BEE and HALL, 1956), which includes six whales, one walrus and five seals (only four of these marine species are common).

Polar Bears and Arctic Foxes

Two species of mammals, the polar bear *(Ursus maritimus)* and arctic fox *(Alopex lagopus)*, stand out for ranging over the whole extent of arctic sea ice and lands (MACPHERSON, 1965). Many bears winter on sea ice and along coasts even in the high Arctic, but pregnant females bear their young in snow caves on certain coasts of America, Europe and Asia. The foxes likewise bear young in burrows on land, where some of the population are present throughout the year. Strong but not swift swimmers, bears or their tracks have been encountered by explorers in highest latitudes. In summer bears are occasionally transported far southward on ice floes, having reached Newfoundland and Hokkaido (45°). From ice floes that grounded in late summer 1947 off the Alaskan coast near Barrow, some 25 bears were killed along 80 kilometers coast within a few days, illustrating the prompt extermination facing southward-venturing bears.

The living prey of bears on ice are ringed *(Phoca hispida)* and, nearer shore, bearded *(Erignathus barbatus)* seals, but they also eagerly consume carrion remains of whales and walrus. I saw a bear approach the edge of an ice floe a kilometer off shore and pause to wave its head until it located by scent a long dead white whale on the beach. It then launched itself and swam directly to the beach near the putrefying whale and began to devour it. According to reports (PERRY, 1966) polar bears in summer roam over arctic shores feeding on vegetation as do other bears. Foxes appear to follow bears in winter over the ice to feed on the residue of their kills. The foxes, a hundred times smaller than the bears, appear equally tolerant of arctic cold. There are few observers abroad during the extremes of arctic gales but there have been reports that bears and foxes occasionally sought shelter under snow in protecting crevices in the ice.

The major part of the population of foxes is on land, where the numbers taken annually by intensive trapping for their valued fur vary with the cyclical abundance of lemmings, on which they subsist (MACPHERSON, 1969). The relation of the far-wandering foxes of the sea ice to a fixed range is uncertain. Subspecific and specific names applied to a number of populations of arctic foxes indicate that geographical distinctions have occurred within the species. Subspecific names reported for polar bears are dubious evidence of subdivisions of the species established in reference to territorial ranges that restrict gene flow within their limits. Concentrations of reproducing females in rather regularly favored breeding areas do indicate territorial reference that orders components of the species population of bears. In their wide and seldom surveyed range, the annual program of geographic reference of these bears remains obscure. It would be a unique species, however, if its individuals were not constrained within geographical ranges that are better defined than is now apparent.

Survey of Arctic Land Mammals

An offhand tabulation of high-arctic land mammals illustrates their kinds and distribution. Of the nine kinds listed in Table 3.2 a few wild musk oxen have escaped extinction by man in north and northeast Greenland, on Canadian arctic islands and on the continental Barren Grounds. Man is ubiquitous and caribou,

Table 3.2. Land mammals extending to high-arctic islands

	Weight (kg)	Species	Distribution	Nutrition
Man	60.0	one	ubiquitous	C
Lepus (Arctic hare)	2.0	several	Arctic	H
Dicrostonyx (Lemming)	0.100	several	Arctic, temperate	H
Canis lupus (Wolf)	50.0	several	Arctic, temperate	C
Alopex (Arctic fox)	4.0	several	Arctic	C
Mustela (Weasel)	.100	several	Arctic, temperate	C
Ursus maritimus (Polar bear)	500	one	Arctic	C
Rangifer (Caribou)	100.0	one	Arctic, temperate	H
Ovibos (Musk ox)	250.0	one	Arctic, temperate	H

C = carnivorous – H = herbivorous

formerly in North Greenland and still on Canadian arctic islands, extend to British Columbia and were only recently exterminated in Maine. In Eurasia wild reindeer (caribou [*Rangifer*]) have been so intermingled with domesticated reindeer that natural ranges scarcely exist. This species and dogs are the only domestications by arctic man. Arctic hares (*Lepus* spp) of America and Eurasia comprise rather similar species of the tundra. Brown lemmings (*Lemmus* spp) do not extend north of the American continent but penetrate into northern forests. The hardy collared lemmings (*Dicrostonyx*) exist on Canadian arctic islands and North Greenland. Wolverines (*Gulo*) are widely distributed in the north temperate world but their extension north of the American continent is localized. The other three arctic carnivores, wolf (*Canis lupus*), ermine (*Mustela erminea*) and least weasel (*Mustela rixosa*), are represented by ubiquitous relatives. Probably musk oxen (*Ovibos*), arctic hares and collared lemmings can be added to polar bears and arctic foxes as animals presently confined to regions of arctic climate, ice and tundra. In the late Pleistocene, however, related musk oxen left remains far southward, and imposing arrays of large mammals that are now extinct dwelt at times in arctic lands during interglacial and even in glacial epochs, and in some periods resorted far southward.

It is of interest to see that the order of size in the high arctic list extends from small to large without, however, including the smallest of mammals, shrews. A number of species (Table 3.3), including very small shrews, extend from southern climates to continental American and Eurasian tundra. Even later than the Pleisto-

Table 3.3. Land mammals commonly found only as far north as arctic continental coasts

	Weight (kg)	Species	Distribution	Nutrition
Soricidae (Shrews)	0.004	several	widespread	C
Cricetidae (Mice)	0.025	several	widespread	H
Citellus (Ground squirrel)	0.800	several	widespread	H
Lemmus (Lemming)	0.070	several	northern	H
Mustela rixosa (Least weasel)	0.030	several	widespread	C
Vulpes sp. (Red fox)	2.0	several	widespread	C
Lynx (Lynx)	8.0	one	northern	C
Gulo gulo (Wolverine)	25.0	one	northern	C

C = carnivorous   H = herbivorous

cene, elephants (*Mammuthus*) of almost the largest mammalian size were arctic dwellers, so that we cannot designate size as a common requirement or limit of arctic life. It should be considered, however, that we are mammals of medium size, impressed as exploiters by the dimensions of the larger ones that produce greater yield per capture. Their large forms are exposed, visible and leave conspicuous remains that long endure weathering which soon destroys traces of the smaller kinds.

Among the kinds of mammals that live in arctic tundra and over wide southern ranges, beside those listed in Table 3.2, a number of northern mammals reside in some localities north of forested lands (Table 3.3). The whole list of mammals (Tables 3.2 and 3.3) demonstrating common capability for life in arctic lands includes representatives of only 6 orders. I have listed in Table 3.4 eight kinds of land mammals widely distributed in northern forests that venture locally onto

Table 3.4. Land mammals extending residence in some localities just north of forests

Lepus (Varying Hare)
Marmota (Marmot)
Ondatra zibethicus (Muskrat)
Ursus arctos (Brown bear)
Mustela (Mink)
Mustela (Marten)
Lutra (Otter)
Alces (Moose)
Ovis (Mountain sheep)

the edge of tundra. These show their capability of meeting arctic cold seasons, although closely-related kinds also live in warm, low latitudes. The entire roster of living arctic mammals is comprised within 6 taxonomic orders among which man is the only primate.

Migrations by Arctic Land Mammals

Among the land mammals, only caribou make fairly well-known seasonal migrations. Polar bears and some arctic foxes may likely be found to move to breeding areas with the recurrent regularity that I call migratory behavior. Collared and brown lemmings multiply in periods of three or four years to numbers exceeding their food supply. At these times they may scatter widely or even move in ordered groups. The movement seems to be erratic and ends in destruction, without the return to a locality characteristic of a true migration. For the remainder of arctic mammals, individuals may be called sedentary in the sense of keeping within a territory, although the radius of a wolf's range may be large, and some individuals of every population stray from their natal localities and bring about considerable extensions (and contractions) of occupancy of land from year to year. Quite otherwise is the commonness of long annual migrations on regular schedules among the sea mammals and birds.

Sea Mammals

Seals

At the risk of generalization by personal judgment I have listed six species of seals with known arctic habits (Table 3.5). They are all short-haired members of the family Phocidae. Four southern species of this family of hair seals breed on antarctic ice. None of the fur seals and sea lions (Otariidae) will be considered to be of arctic habit. The seals prized for fur *(Callorhinus* and *Arctocephalus)* have populations breeding from Bering Sea (57° N) over equatorial Galapagos to the so-called antarctic islands (about 50° S). All arctic seals are of the size of man or several times larger. They have been so basic to the subsistence of coastal Eskimos as to have largely influenced their ways of living. As European men acquired seamanship, their vessels pursued seals to the limit of the developing ability of navigation in order to harvest populations that congregated seasonally at the margins of arctic sea ice; and arctic explorers have in various degrees depended upon seals for food, oil for heat, and skins. Commercial exploitation of seals continues to be important in the economy of northern Europe, Asia and America, a pursuit that has been a support for arctic exploration and scientific studies. As a result of their direct importance to man much is known about seals in spite of aquatic habits that only rarely bring them into view.

28

Table 3.5. Arctic seals (Phocidae) and walrus

Species	Birth place	Distribution		Fur of pups	Population size
Phoca vitulina (Harbor seal)	ice margin	A	P	white	45 000
Pusa hispida (Ringed seal)	land-fast ice	A	P	white	2 000 000
Histriophoca (Ribbon seal)	sea ice		P	white	20 000
Pagophilus (Harp seal)	ice margin	A		white	4 500 000
Erignathus (Bearded seal)	sea ice	A	P	dark	25 000
Cystophora (Hooded seal)	breeding on northern ice	A		white	300 000
					6 870 000
all Phocidae (including those of Antarctica)					10 900 000
Odobenus – 2 species (Walrus)	sea ice	A	P	bare	45 000

A = Atlantic – P = Pacific

(From Irving, 1969)

Numbers of Seals and Ice-breeding

Although long exploitation by man has likely unbalanced the natural numbers of seals and walrus it has afforded bases for estimating their numbers with more significance than for any but a few circumscribed populations of land animals. I have quoted Scheffer's (1958) estimates of minimum numbers, which he believed unlikely to be actually as much as twice as great (see Table 3.5). Hair seals breeding on arctic ice constitute nearly 70% of the world's Phocidae. If we add the estimated minimum numbers of four species of antarctic hair seals breeding on ice, quoted as 2 320 000, the remainder of the world's population (some 5 percent of the Phocidae) not breeding on ice is impressively small. Furthermore, among arctic ice-breeders I have not included the several ice-breeding populations (near 1 000 000) of ringed seals *(Pusa)* now confined in large lakes and seas of temperate Eurasia. The populations of ringed seals of Lake Baikal and the Caspian Sea still resort to breed on landfast ice formed in winter along the northern shores. These disjunct populations are now regarded as relicts of southward displacements from the arctic that occurred during Pleistocene ice ages. During many millenia of life in a temperate climatic regime they have retained the habit of breeding on ice. The eared seals (Otariidae – sea lions and fur seals) only approach arctic waters in Bering Sea, where they breed on shores in summer, when ice is far northward.

Ice-breeding Harbor Seals and White-coated Pups

Only in arctic harbor seals *(Phoca vitulina)* and, to a degree, in gray seals *(Halichoerus)* does the ice-breeding habit appear to be adopted by the northern members of a species. Harbor seals have, in addition, extensions of shore-breeding populations far southward. I have made a guess that half of the species in the Pacific breeds on ice. In Bering Sea the northernmost harbor seals breed near the margin of sea ice in April or May, producing pups with white fur, while the southern pups born on shore molt this infantile coat before birth. Ice-breeding and production of fur-covered pups are changeable within the range of this species, which is able to have arctic and non-arctic components distinguishable by choice of breeding platforms and by important modification of insulative protection of the pups during the several weeks when they are developing capability for living in cold water.

Gray Seals

Gray seals *(Halichoerus grypus)* that breed about the British Isles bear their pups on shores free of ice. On northeastern Atlantic and Baltic coasts, on coasts of Canada and Newfoundland, some may bear pups either on bare or ice-covered shores or even on ice floes. In all of these stocks the pups bear coats of white fur, a condition suggesting their relation to the arctic seals (SCHEFFER, 1967). The white-coated condition continues to prevail in the pups of gray seals breeding on shore, unlike the harbor seals of Bering Sea.

White-coated Pups of Other Arctic Seals

Only one of the six arctic seals named does not produce white-fur coated pups. The large bearded seal *(Erignathus)*, which ranges into high-arctic ice, produces its large (33 kg), dark-coated pups exposed on ice, where they grow rapidly, molt and soon develop aquatic capability (BURNS, 1967). The other five species produce white-fur-coated young, with only the ringed seals sheltering their young in lairs protected by snow (McLAREN, 1958).

Migrations of Arctic Seals

Harbor, Ringed, and Bearded Seals

Migrations from breeding places on ice of Bering Sea carry numbers of harbor, ringed and bearded seals northward in summer with the retreating ice, converging through the Straits and then diverging along Siberian and Alaskan coasts. Well programmed migrations also transport many of these species northward into arctic Atlantic ice. But many ringed and bearded seals winter in ice-covered arctic seas, where they breed on shore-fast ice. These two seals sustained the clever coastal Eskimos in their highest-arctic residences. Many factors in the sea ice determine the arctic seasonal distribution of these two seals, but the entire populations of these two species do not so evidently carry out organized migrations as do harp and hooded seals.

Harp and Hooded Seals

The most numerous seals, harp seals *(Pagophilus)*, congregate for pupping in spring in three regions on the southern margin of Atlantic pack ice. One resort for breeding is off Newfoundland, another in the Greenland Sea between Iceland and Svalbard, and a third in the White Sea and Barents Sea between Svalbard and Novaya Zembla (SCHEFFER, 1958). White-fur-coated pups in great numbers are slaughtered for fur and adults are taken for shorthaired skins and at times for blubber and flesh. Pups grow rapidly to the strong swimming ability that enables them to join the adults in pelagic bands that follow the northward-retreating ice in summer into high-arctic waters. As winter approaches they move southward at the margin of ice until spring finds them again at their respective breeding grounds. West Atlantic ice margins annually move over 25° of latitude, which sets the longest latitudinal migrations of these seals.

Unlike the harp seals, hooded seals *(Cystophora)* do not aggregate in large numbers to breed, but bear their pups rather as individuals scattered over the ice packs off Newfoundland and Jan Mayen. In summer they are said to penetrate more deeply among arctic ice floes than do the harp seals. Like harp seals their range off shore obscures the order and courses of their migration, but resort of each species to breeding regions at special dates indicates a high degree of temporal and geographic organization in these far ranging populations.

Walrus

European and American populations of the walrus (*Odobenus*) are denizens of icy waters off eastern and western arctic Atlantic coasts. A disjunct Pacific population breeds on the late-winter margin of ice in the Bering Sea and moves eastward and westward over Alaskan and Siberian continental shelves in summer on apparently regular migratory schedules. Associating normally in herds, individual walrus have ventured rather far southward, where, even if they could abandon their ice-dwelling habits, human predation for centuries has pretty well eliminated chances for southern colonization. The dependence of walrus upon ice for breeding and resting restricts their range to the seasonally moving edge of arctic ice floes. Their range is further restricted to the shallow depths of the continental shelves that provide the molluscan food that they can reach by diving for about a hundred meters. Still utilized by arctic residents for flesh, hides and ivory, the small numbers and social habits of these huge mammals would expose them to extinction if commercial exploitation were permitted.

Whales

Arctic Residents

Narwhals *(Monodon)* and bowhead whales *(Balaena mysticetus)* are considered resident among arctic ice floes (FREUCHEN and SALOMONSEN, 1958). Narwhals in the Atlantic frequent arctic coasts but are little known except to a few arctic

31

people. The large bowhead, feeding on plankton through its baleen filtering system, has been nearly exterminated in arctic Atlantic waters as a result of intensive commercial whaling initiated in the 17th century and culminating with the 19th century. A Pacific population of bowheads follows leads opening in spring from Bering Sea westward and eastward. Regular spring and occasional fall hunting by Alaskan Eskimos in their skin boats shows the program of migration of Pacific bowheads. Although these whales show skill at manoeuver in leads among ice floes, neither they nor walrus are able to break through heavy ice or maintain breathing holes with teeth or clawed flippers as do ringed and bearded seals. These whales are thus restricted by seasonal movements of ice within the limits of their abilities to navigate among ice floes. Their range in the loose ice at the margin of pack ice moves widely with the seasons and requires related extensive seasonal migrations.

Migrants to Arctic Waters

Many of the numerous white whales *(Delphinapterus)* of north temperate Atlantic and Pacific waters migrate northward in schools along arctic coasts and into estuaries, where they are hunted by resident arctic people for meat and hides. Their summer arctic appearances indicate regularity of arctic migrations. White whales do not penetrate ice floes as deeply as narwhals and bowheads; occasionally schools are trapped in winter by freezing of the mouths of estuaries.

In summer gray whales (*Eschrichtius*) migrate from their breeding lagoons in Baja California, through open leads in the ice along the coasts of Alaska and Siberia. The smallest of the arctic whales, the harbor porpoises *(Phocoena)*, occasionally appear in the arctic waters of America and Europe. These examples show that some whales range over wide latitudes and that numbers of some species more or less regularly venture close to summer arctic ice.

Arctic Mammals of the Late Pleistocene

In the late Tertiary twice as many taxa of mammals migrated from Siberia to Alaska as in the opposite direction. During the late Pleistocene some 20 taxa moved from Siberia into Alaska and none are established to have moved in the opposite direction (HOPKINS, 1967). A common opinion is that the predominant eastward migration was related to the great area (and evolutionary productivity) of Eurasia.

Fossils from late-Pleistocene deposits of northern Alaska include large grazing mammals such as horses *(Equus)*, bisons (*Bison*) and mammoths *(Mammuthus)*, which exceed in numbers the remains of non-grazing or browsing moose *(Alces)*, caribou *(Rangifer)* and elk *(Cervalces)*, suggesting that there was then more grass in the tundra vegetation than is now available (HOPKINS, 1967; GUTHRIE, 1968). It is also apparent from fossil records that the present mammalian fauna of the Arctic has been much impoverished by Pleistocene and even post-Pleistocene extinctions. Large carnivorous cats *(Felis)*, species of wolves *(Canis)* and bears *(Ursus)* seem to have been present in numbers greater than could be sustained by the numbers of existing herbivores.

It is said that extinctions of large mammals occurred later in America than in Europe and that the American survivors are mainly Pleistocene newcomers from Asia such as caribou *(Rangifer)*, sheep *(Ovis* sp), and wolverine *(Gulo)*. Ancient American horses *(Equus* sp.), cattle *(Bos* sp.), camels *(Camelus* sp.), and ground sloths *(Mylodontidae)* did not survive the Pleistocene (MARTIN, 1970).

Causes of these major and apparently sudden extinctions are inconclusively debated because of lack of clear information about the environment and distribution of the ancient and seemingly richer mammalian fauna of the past. It is of no great help to postulate that either favorability of the arctic environment for mammals has deteriorated or the adaptability of mammals for arctic conditions has run its course. Those who consider man as a cause of extinction might speculate that the earlier development of European hunters, or of their ability to misuse resources, brought about the earlier extinctions of large European mammals.

Resettlement of Lands as Wisconsin Ice Caps Melted

As the massive Wisconsin ice sheets melted from the northern continents, in a rather sudden change culminating about 10000 years ago, great regions of northern Eurasia and America became exposed for resettlement and coast lines regressed inland as the sea level rose. Evolution did not meet this change by inventing new species of mammals to reoccupy the new and much altered lands. Many species that had existed through the glacial and interglacial episodes of the Pleistocene did not survive. Extinctions of large mammals and changes in range rather than new evolutionary developments, marked the biological transition from Wisconsin to Recent time.

It can be surmised that the provision of great new northern land areas as they became vegetated brought increasing numbers to the new northern populations of mammals. We do not have a census of comparative numbers of Wisconsin and Recent individuals, but we have many records of geographical distribution of species, then and now, that indicate the spread of populations from species stocks relict in ice-free, northern refuges.

Resettlement from Beringia

RAUSCH (1963) says that of 21 species of living holarctic mammals, the present distribution in North America of eight indicates post-Pleistocene dispersal from Beringia. It must be recalled that Beringia included land in Alaska and Siberia along with the broad continental shelf between the two continents that is now submerged. Rausch would have the collared (varying) lemming *(Dicrostonyx)* spreading eastward over Canadian arctic islands to north Greenland and Labrador, a remarkable extension of this hardy little (50–80 g) rodent.

Ordinarily sedentary in local communities on Alaskan tundra, in the spring of a year of climaxing abundance a lively and pugnacious lemming came to my camp on sea ice east of Barrow, on a gravel bar two kilometers from shore.

Tracks and an unmarked dead lemming were seen on the ice several kilometers from shore. The seaward direction of this mad movement was pointless but it illustrates stamina that could lead to far dispersal of a population even by random wanderings. How lemmings might cross the ice or water between islands and over straits to Greenland and Labrador is hard to imagine.

The periodic movements of masses of brown lemmings *(Lemmus)* in Norway result in massive destruction of dispersing local populations. It might be suspected, however, that during the course of post-glacial time the periodic eruptions of lemmings from discrete relict populations have sent out such numbers that by chance and luck they have become widely distributed. Several smaller rodents (species of *Microtus* and *Clethrionomys)* appear to have spread from Beringia to Hudson Bay.

Post-Wisconsin Invasion from a North Greenland Refuge

Subspecific designations show geographical taxonomic deviations in local populations of lemmings, mice and others that are suspected of having been formed by settlement and differentiation in deglaciated lands after emerging from the Beringian refuge. These taxonomic designations are helpful in postulating the direction of spread of a species if specimens are sufficient and when agreement exists among taxonomists. Opinions do differ, however; for example, MACPHERSON (1965) proposes that collared (varying) lemmings (*Dicrostonyx)* from an unglaciated Wisconsin refuge in north Greenland repopulated northern Canadian arctic islands. Several other arctic unglaciated refuges have been proposed to account for taxonomic relationships among species populations presently inhabiting arctic tundra. It is not so much to be thought that evidence from taxonomy for sources and directions of resettling populations is in conflict as that still incomplete information is being revised and extended.

A great deal of skill and art is required in the preparation of taxonomic information for indicating progress in the dissemination of species. This confusion resulting from the growth of knowledge will continue to fascinate devotees of the subject, and it is steadily or even rapidly advancing reasonable ideas about the origins and relations of populations of mammals. There is also a vast body of related information from the taxonomy of fishes, invertebrates and plants. There are further exciting indications from beginnings of genetic studies and from still less advanced comparative views of organic molecular structures and activities. Unfortunately I must admit that methods of analysis of physiological processes do not yet point far toward comparison of developing adaptations within populations of a species.

Recapitulation of Views upon Post-Wisconsin Populations

Having opened the subject of the spread of mammals from their resorts in Wisconsin time over the broad lands that became deglaciated, we can say that without doubt the lands have become reoccupied but that the ancient environmental conditions and processes of resettlement are unclear. Probably all of the present arctic mammalian species were in existence during the late Pleistocene, along with many others now extinct. Some species certainly sat out the Wisconsin glaciation in ice-free arctic refuges of America and Eurasia. Others resorted in lands south of the American continental ice cap and beyond southern margins of Eurasian Wisconsin ice. Resettlement of deglaciated lands was effected by old species, with only subspecific variation occurring. Quite valid subspecific taxonomic distinctions can be made, but we shall be hard put to define these variations by measurement as adaptive to arctic life.

Species residing in arctic refugia remained arctic, but Recent extinctions show that in the course of time their associations comprised different arrays of mammals. Certainly in this respect, they lived in an environment different from the present Arctic. Species that resided south of the ice sheets inhabited southern lands of widely differing nature that was alike over the northern hemisphere only in having annual seasonal cycles of temperate latitudes. In returning to post-glacial arctic lands they had to encounter new and changing environments. By the test of existence, these species are adapted to arctic life. During many years and generations they retained in southern land and seasons, unexercised by trial, their adaptability for arctic life. Evidence for life in the Pleistocene is only in long-dead relics. Their systematic relations, geographical locations, and position in geologically identifiable strata can be combined as evidence for species that persisted with very little change in form as they moved back and forth with the violent Pleistocene oscillations of climates and of the forms of lands and seas.

References

ARMSTRONG, T.E.: Russian Settlement in the North. Cambridge, England: University Press 1965.

BEE, J.W., HALL, E.R.: Mammals of Northern Alaska, Museum of Natural History, Univ. of Kansas, Lawrence, Kansas: The Allen Press 1956.

BURNS, J.J.: The Pacific Bearded Seal. Juneau Alaska Dep. of Fish and Game Report, 1967.

CATESBY, M.: The Natural History of Carolina, Florida and the Bahama Islands, Vol. 1. London 1731.

DARLINGTON, P.J.: Zoogeography. New York: John Wiley & Son 1957.

DUNBAR, M.J.: Ecological Development in Polar Regions; A Study in Evolution, Englewood Cliffs. New Jersey: Prentice Hall 1968.

FREUCHEN, P., SALOMONSEN, F.: The Arctic Year. New York: G.P. Putnam 1958.

HOPKINS, D.M. ED.: The Bering Land Bridge. Stanford, Calif.: Stanford University Press 1967.

IRVING, L.: Temperature regulation in marine mammals. In: The Biology of Marine Mammals. Ed. by H.T. ANDERSON. New York: Academic Press 1969.

MACPHERSON, A.H.: The origin of diversity in mammals of the Canadian arctic tundra. Systemtic Zool. 14, 153–173 (1965).

MACPHERSON, A.H.: The dynamics of Canadian arctic fox populations, Cand. Wildlife Service Report Series 8 (1969).

MARTIN, P.S.: Pleistocene niches for alien animals. Bioscience 20, 218–222 (1970).

McLAREN, I.A.: The biology of the ringed seal (Phoca hispida Schreber) in the eastern Canadian arctic. Ottawa, Canada: Bulletin 118 Fisheries Research Bord (1958).

PERRY, R.: The World of the Polar Bear. London: Cassell 1966.

RAUSCH, R.L.: A Review of the Distribution of Holartic Recent Mammals. Honolulu, Hawai: Bishop Museum Press 1963.

RICHARDSON, SIR JOHN: Arctic Searching Expedition. New York: Harper Brothers 1852.

ROGERS, G.: Alaska regional Population and Employment. University of Alaska, Institute of Social, Economic & Government Research Report 15 (1967).

SCHEFFER, V.B.: Seals, Sea Lions and Walrus: A Review of the Pinnipedia. Stanford, Calif.: Stanford University Press 1958.

SCHEFFER, V.B.: Marine Mammals and the history of Bering Strait. In: The Bering Land Bridge. Ed. by D.M. HOPKINS. Stanford, Calif.: Stanford University Press 1967.

SCLATER, P.L.: On the general geographic distribution of the members of the class Aves. J. of Proc. Linnean Soc. (Zoology) 2, 130–145 (1858).

STEJNEGER, L.H.: Georg Wilhelm Steller, the Pioneer of Alaskan Natural History. Cambridge, Mass.: Harvard University Press 1936.

WALLACE, A.R.: The Geographical Distribution of Animals (2 Vols.). London: MacMillan 1876.

Chapter 4

Arctic Land Birds and Their Migrations

Arctic bird life appears more complicated than that of the arctic mammals because there are more recognized species of birds that breed in the Arctic. A biologist knowledgeable about the American Arctic (DUNBAR, 1968) estimated 70 arctic-breeding species of birds out of a world list of 8600. Of 3200 listed mammals, he estimated that 23 lived on land north of forests, with five or six more occurring in arctic seas. Because birds are visible and audible in their activity by day, a great deal is known about their distribution and activities as they move and change in their annual programs. What we see and hear of birds seems understandable to us in terms that represent significant individual and social operations. The unconcealed and often noisy behavior of birds, much like our own, serves to characterize their populations better than we find possible for the usually secretive, obscure, and frequently nocturnal mammals, which are so strongly guided by the sense of smell that finds so little use by birds and men. Rather scant familiarity with birds in the Arctic, however, has led to some confusing generalizations upon the manner of their arctic life.

Birds Resident in High-arctic Latitudes

White fur or feathers characterizes some northern birds and mammals and some, like ptarmigan *(Lagopus)* and weasels *(Mustela)*, adopt white fur and feathers in winter. But whiteness is by no means a requirement for arctic life, as D'ARCY THOMPSON (1952) indicated: 'The ptarmigan and the snowy owl, the arctic fox and the polar bear are white among the snows; but go he north or go he south, the raven (like the jackdaw) is boldly and impudently black.'

I have added to FREUCHEN and SALOMONSEN's (1958) list of four birds wintering in high-arctic lands of Greenland and Canada their weights, occurrence on land or sea ice and southward nesting limits (Table 4.1). These species occur around

Table 4.1. Birds found in January in high-arctic regions of Greenland and Canadian islands

Species	Weight (kg)	Occurrence on land (L) or sea (S) ice	Latitude of southward nesting limit
Lagopus mutus (Rock ptarmigan)	0.5	L	45°
Nyctea scandiaca (Snowy owl)	1.5	L S	60°
Corvus corax (Raven)	1.5	L S	0°
Acanthis hornemanni hornemanni (Hornemann's redpoll)	0.015	L	70°

(From FREUCHEN and SALOMONSEN, 1958, p. 33)

37

the arctic world. It is surprising that some of the small (15 gram) Hornemann's redpolls (*Acanthis hornemanni hornemanni*) can exist through high-arctic winter in Greenland, certainly in small numbers, but nevertheless in small groups (SALO-MONSEN, 1950).

The other three high-arctic residents nest over larger ranges in much of the northern hemisphere. Races of the raven (*Corvus corax* of many subspecies) extend to equatorial Africa, black in all seasons and places. Rock ptarmigan *(Lagopus mutus)* of holarctic distribution occur far southward above tree line in mountain areas that are comparable to tundra. Both raven and snowy owl *(Nyctea scandiaca)* venture onto the sea ice in winter, the former seeking remains of seals killed by polar bears or any carrion on firm sea ice, the latter, so far as I know, attending congregations of sea birds near the southern margin of ice floes (IRVING et al., 1970).

In the years of cyclic decline in populations of American arctic lemmings, snowy owls appear far south of the Arctic. In these occasional late-winter ventures into temperate lands they demonstrate versatility in subsisting on prey strange to the Arctic. But since the owls are exposed to populous human attention and in strange circumstances, it does not appear that these irregular sothward irruptions can tend toward effective, regular migratory behavior. In some areas the strong-flying rock ptarmigan migrate to islands off shore or from the interior toward coasts. Generally their seasonal movements transport some parts of local populations over short distances to lower elevations in winter. In winter some of the little arctic redpolls appear in southern fjords of Greenland and even much farther south in North America, but reports are too infrequent to outline well-established programs of migratory behavior.

Winter Birds of the Alaskan Tundra and Adjacent Forests

Tundra

I have concentrated attention on the Alaskan birds that I know and believe to illustrate the ways of birds in arctic life (Tables 4.2 and 4.3). These are birds that nest on the tundra and in the adjacent margin of the forest in the interior of Alaska north of the arctic circle. Because these examples can often be identified as subspecies I have given names pertaining to the Alaskan locality. I have also shown in the last columns ranges of the species, many of which extend over the holarctic region.

The 11 birds found in winter on central Alaskan tundra (Table 4.2) include the four species earlier designated as high-arctic residents (IRVING, 1960). Among these, the little 11-gram hoary redpoll *(Acanthis hornemanni exilipes)* is a subspecies related to the redpoll wintering in Greenland. It is not often seen in arctic Alaska in winter and would be unlikely to persist on tundra without annual rein-forcement from the great influx of summer migrants. Of the remaining four winter-ing species that also nest there, the gray jay (*Perisoreus*) is of rare occurrence on the tundra. The dipper (*Cinclus mexicanus,* 50 grams) is a delightful surprise

Table 4.2. Winter birds of Alaskan tundra and adjacent forests

Species	Tundra		Forest			Range of the species	
Accipiter gentilis atricapillus (Goshawk)			P	N		Eu	Am
Falco rusticolus obsoletus (Gyrfalcon)	P	N	P	N		Eu	Am
Canachites canadensis canadensis (Spruce grouse)			P	N			Am
Lagopus lagopus alascensis (Willow ptarmigan)	P	N	P	N	M	Eu	Am
Lagopus mutus nelsoni (Rock ptarmigan)	P	N	P	N		Eu	Am
Bubo virginianus lagophonos (Great horned owl)	P		P	N			Am
Nyctea scandiaca (Snowy owl)	P	N	P			Eu	Am
Surnia ulula caparoch (Hawk owl)			P	N		Eu	Am
Strix nebulosa nebulosa (Great gray owl)			P	N		Eu	Am
Aegoleus funereus richardsoni (Boreal owl)			P	N		Eu	Am
Dendrocopus pubescens nelsoni (Downy woodpecker)	P		P	N			Am
Picoides arcticus (Black-backed threetoed woodpecker)			P	N			Am
Picoides tridactylus fasciatus (Northern three-toed woodpecker)			P	N		Eu	Am
Perisoreus canadensis pacificus (Gray jay)	P	N	P	N			Am
Corvus corax principalis (Raven)	P	N	P	N		Eu	Am
Parus atricapillus turneri (Black-capped chickadee)	P		P	N			Am
Parus cinctus (Gray-headed chickadee)			P	N		Eu	Am
Parus hudsonicus hudsonicus (Boreal chickadee)			P	N			Am
[a]*Cinclus mexicanus* (Dipper)	P	N	P	N			Am
Bombycilla garrula pallidiceps (Bohemian waxwing)			P	N	M	Eu	Am
Pinicola enucleator alascensis (Pine grosbeak)			P	N	M	Eu	Am
Acanthis hornemanni exilipes (Hoary redpoll)	P	N	P	N	M	Eu	Am
Acanthis flammea flammea (Common redpoll)			P	N	M	Eu	Am
Loxia leucoptera leucoptera (White-winged crossbill)			P	N	M	Eu	Am
	8 PN		6 PNM			8 Am	
	+3 P		+ 17 PN				

P = usually present – N = nesting – M = migratory
Eu = Eurasia; Am = America

[a] A similar species is found in Europe and Asia
(From IRVING, 1960)

Table 4.3. Birds nesting on interior Alaskan tundra
a) Species that migrate along Pacific American coasts

Species		Range of species		
Gavia immer (Common loon)				Am
Gavia adamsi (Yellow-billed loon)	A	Eu	As	Am
Gavia arctica pacifica (Arctic loon)		Eu	As	Am
Gavia stellata (Red-throated loon)		Eu	As	Am
Podiceps grisegena hollböllii (Red-necked grebe)		Eu	As	Am
Olor columbianus (Whistling swan)		Am		
Branta nigricans (Black brant)		Sib	Am	
Chen hyperborea hyperborea (Snow goose)	A	Sib	Am	
Anas acuta (Pintail)		Eu	As	Am
Anas platyrhynchos platyrhynchos (Mallard)		Eu	As	Am
Aythya marila nearctica (Greater scaup)		Eu	As	Am
Bucephala clangula americana (Common goldeneye)		Eu	As	Am
Bucephala islandica (Barrow's goldeneye)		Am		

Species		Eu/Sib	As	Am
Bucephala albeola (Buffle head)				Am
Histrionicus histrionicus (Harlequin duck)		Sib		Am
Clangula hyemalis (Oldsquaw)		Eu	As	Am
Melanitta deglandi (White-winged scoter)				Am
Melanitta perspicillata (Surf scoter)				Am
Mergus serrator serrator (Red-breasted merganser)		Eu	As	Am
Aquila chrysaëtos canadensis (Golden eagle)		Eu	As	Am
Haliaeetus leucocephalus alascanus (Bald eagle)				Am
Squatarola squatarola (Black-bellied plover)	A	Eu	As	Am
Numenius phaeopus hudsonicus (Whimbrel)	A	Eu	As	Am
Erolia alpina pacifica (Dunlin)		Eu	As	Am
Crocethia alba (Sanderling)	A	Eu	As	Am
Phalaropus fulicarius (Red phalarope)	A	Eu	As	Am
Lobipes lobatus (Northern phalarope)	A	Eu	As	Am
Stercorarius pomarinus (Pomarine jaeger)	A	Eu	As	Am
Stercorarius parasiticus (Parasitic jaeger)	A	Eu	As	Am
Stercoarius longicaudus (Long-tailed jaeger)	A	Eu	As	Am
Larus hyperboreus barrovianus (Glaucous gull)	A	Eu	As	Am
Larus canus brachyrhynchus (Mew gull)		Eu	As	Am
Larus philadelphia (Bonaparte's gull)				Am
Xema sabini (Sabine's gull)	A	Eu	As	Am
Sterna paradisaea (Arctic tern)	A	Eu	As	Am

Totals: 35 species   13 A

         8 Am
         3 Sib Am
        24 Eu As Am

b) Species that migrate overland through North America

Species		Range of species		
Branta canadensis taverneri (Canada goose)				Am
Anser albifrons frontalis (White-fronted goose)		Eu	As	Am
Anas carolinensis (Green-winged teal)				
Mareca americana (American widgeon)				Am
Aythya affinis (Lesser scaup)				Am
Buteo lagopus s. johannis (Rough-winged hawk)		Eu	As	Am
Falco peregrinus anatum (Peregrine)		Eu	As	Am
Falco columbarius benderi (Pigeon hawk)		Eu	As	Am
Grus canadensis canadensis (Sandhill crane)	A	Sib		Am
Pluvialis dominica dominica (Golden plover)	A	Sib		Am
Capella gallinago delicata (Common snipe)		Eu	As	Am
Bartramia longicauda (Upland plover)				Am
Tringa solitaria cinnamomea (Solitary sandpiper)				Am
Totanus flavipes (Lesser yellow legs)				Am
Erolia melanotos (Pectoral sandpiper)	A	Sib		Am
Erolia bairdii (Baird's sandpiper)	A	Sib		Am
Erolia minutilla (Least sandpiper)				Am
Limnodromus scolopaceus (Dowitcher)		Sib		Am
Micropalama himantopus (Stilt sandpiper)	A			Am
Ereunetes pusillus (Semipalmated sandpiper)				Am
Tringites subruficollis (Bay-breasted sandpiper)				Am
Sayornis saya yukonensis (Phoebe)				Am
Empidonax traillii traillii (Traill's flycatcher)				Am
Eremophila alpestris arcticola (Horned lark)		Eu	As	Am
Turdus migratorius migratorius (Robin)				Am
Hylocichla minima minima (Gray-cheeked thrush)		Sib		Am

Regulus calendula calendula (Ruby-crowned kinglet)		Am		
Anthus spinoletta rubescens (Water pipit)		Eu	As	Am
Lanius excubitor invictus (Northern shrike)		Am		
Dendroica petechia amnicola (Yellow warbler)		Am		
Wilsonia pusilla pileolata (Wilson's warbler)		Am		
Leucosticte tephrocotis irvingi (Gray-crowned rosy finch)		Am		
Passerculus sandwichensis anthinus (Savannah sparrow)		Am		
Spizella arborea ochracea (Tree sparrow)		Am		
Zonotrichia leucophrys gambellii (White-crowned sparrow)		Am		
Passerella iliaca zaboria (Fox sparrow)		Am		
Calcarius lapponicus alascensis (Lapland longspur)	A	Eu	As	Am
Calcarius pictus (Smith's longspur)		Am		
Totals: 38 species	6 A	24 Am		
		6 Sib	Am	
		8 Eu	As	Am

c) Species that winter in Asia

Species	Range of species		
Oenanthe oenanthe oenanthe (Wheatear)	Eu	As	Am
Luscinia svecica svecica (Bluethroat)	Eu	As	Ak
Phylloscopus borealis kennicotti (Willow warbler)	Eu	As	Ak
Motacilla flava tschutchensis (Yellow wagtail)	Eu	As	Ak

d) Species that migrate over the Pacific Ocean

Species	Range of species		
Limosa lapponica baueri (Bar-tailed godwit)	Eu	As	Am
Pluvialis dominica fulva (Golden plover)	Sib	Ak	
Arenaria interpres interpres (Ruddy turnstone)	Eu	As	Am
Heteroscelus incanum (Wandering tatler)	Sib	Ak	

e) Species that winter in Alaska

Species	Range of species		
Acanthis hornemanni exilipes (Hoary redpoll)	Eu	As	Am
Acanthis flammea flammea (Common redpoll)	Eu	As	Am
Plectrophenax nivalis nivalis (Snow bunting)	Eu	As	Am

A = species breeding largely in Arctic
Ranges: Eu = Europe; As = Asia; Sib = Siberia; Am = America; Ak = Alaska
(From IRVING, 1960)

to find in winter in the widely separated stretches of open water in arctic streams. A few old prospectors and trappers, who usually pay no attention to small birds, have remarked to me with pleasure about the little bird that sang sweetly in coldest midwinter on the ice ledges along the rare stretches of open water of frozen streams. The occurrence of one or two dippers in a few meters of open stream, isolated from nearest neighbors by some 80 kilometers of snow seems to make these arctic dippers about as widely dispersed as small birds can be and still exist as a coherent population.

The most numerous of tundra birds in winter is the willow ptarmigan *(Lagopus lagopus),* of holarctic distribution, with winter-resident adult males remaining on

Alaskan tundra near their nesting grounds (see p. 56). Large flocks of these gregarious birds form near the nesting grounds in autumn. Females and some young males migrate southward to forested land, to return north by May in a complexly organized migration that does not extend beyond a few hundred miles (IRVING et al., 1967). None of these species of arctic tundra birds is confined to the Arctic, although the snowy owl *(Nyctea scandiaca),* a tundra-nesting species, appears to forsake the tundra only erratically. Among the winter birds of the tundra only the gray jay *(Perisoreus canadensis)* is confined to America, if we consider that the western American dipper scarcely differs from a European counterpart of the same genus.

Margin of Arctic Forest

All of the tundra species enter the forests, if we include the irregular incursions by snowy owls (Table 4.2). In the interior of Alaska 23 species present in winter have nesting representatives just south of the tree line (IRVING, 1960). All but the gray-headed chickadee *(Parus cinctus)* also reside in lands far to the south. Only eight species are solely American in distribution, the remainder being holarctic and distributed over more or less considerable extents of latitude in Eurasia.

I have marked six species as migratory (M), but reservations should be added to this designation. Migration of willow ptarmigan is known to be orderly in some places, but it is short (IRVING et al., 1967). Individuals and flocks of the five others are seen in winter as much as 20° south of the arctic circle, but the movements of Bohemian waxwings *(Bombycilla garrula),* pine grosbeaks *(Pinicola enucleator)* and white-winged crossbills *(Loxia leucoptera)* can hardly be defined as regular. That leaves only the two redpolls as having a truly migratory component in the sense of showing a degree of regularity in their annual programs of prolonged movements through their northern range.

Survival in the Beringian Refuge

Unlike those of mammals, the bones of birds are so fragile that the array of identified fossils does not well define the occurrence of species in relation to the various events of the Pleistocene. Speculation on the ability of the forest-dwelling birds to have lived through the Wisconsin glacial maximum in the conditions attributed to the Beringian refuge shows my estimate of the firmness of their current arctic establishment rather than a conviction that the arctic birds of the present are derived from such relict populations. I believe that all but the last six species listed in Table 4.2 could have lived in the forested part of the Beringian refuge as its conditions during maximal Wisconsin glaciation are vaguely indicated. It seems doubtful to me that dippers, waxwings, grosbeaks, redpolls and crossbills could have existed without reinforcement of their ranks from populations south of the continental ice sheets, over which these small birds would not be likely to fly. The 17 other species seem now to be sufficiently established in arctic residence that they might have lived isolated in Beringia through the conditions that are ascribed to that refuge in the late Pleistocene.

It seems plausible to speculate that the eight presently American forest birds might have been restricted to that continent by addiction to dwelling in forests, which precluded their venture onto the probably forestless land bridge of Wisconsin time. But that argument weakens when we consider it in reverse. Goshawk, hawk owl, great gray owl, boreal owl, northern three-toed woodpecker, gray-headed chickadee, waxwing, grosbeak, common redpoll, and crossbill (10 species of Table 4.2), all of holarctic distribution, now only seldom venture onto tundra. In order for them to have maintained their apparent closeness to counterparts in Eurasia it would seem that they must have ventured over the broad tundra of a former land bridge. Speculative utilization of the land bridge to explain processes of distribution has logical difficulties for the biologist looking backward from the present.

Migrations of Birds

The advent of spring in the arctic brings migratory birds that make tundra, coasts and water lively with many summer species in numbers that far exceed the scant winter population. Migrants multiply the list of arctic winter species by more than ten and the numbers by many times tenfold. The major annual production of arctic birds results from the migrants that nest there in summer. Through their migrations to the Arctic for a few summer months, birds have exploited its resources for the reproductive support of their populations during many months in milder climates. The increase in bird life provides arctic residents with new food, but this supplement far exceeds the capacity of the few resident or migratory predators. Only with the recent increase in arctic people have arctic nesting places and populations of birds become endangered. The truly resident native people watched the arriving migrants with keen and knowledgeable pleasure and listened with delight to their calls and songs. Without written records, arctic Eskimos dated past events as occurring at the arrival of certain bird species and used migratory phenomena as calendars of progress of the seasons.

The springtime rise in arctic temperature and increase in daylight come suddenly and bring about the critical transition of ice to water. Pools, streams and marshes are essential sources of food for the birds that arrive with precision each year just at the dates when the climatic transition makes their existence possible. Vivid accounts by naturalists who have observed arctic migrations in many parts of the world show worldwide characteristics of migrations. The kinetic processes of migrations are based upon movement' of explicit populations to definite localities, which I shall illustrate in the birds that migrate to nest on tundra of interior Alaska (IRVING, 1960).

Migrations to Arctic Alaskan Tundra

The westerly extension of America in Alaska and its proximity to Siberia differentiate the kinds of birds migrating to nest in Alaska and their programs (IRVING, 1960). Early spring warming of northwestern America brings species to Alaska at dates when their eastern American counterparts are still 20° southward in Massachusetts (LINCOLN, 1939). Birds that have migrated over Panama pass 75° of longitude westward in attaining Alaska.

Birds arriving to nest on any arctic tundra are at the terminus of their migrations and form homogeneous breeding populations for which each individual is a fair representative. In a series of years the arrival of many species has occurred within a few days of the same date. We should recall, however, that a few days of arctic spring change length of day by more than a half-hour in comparison with a few minutes at medium latitudes, and that the average rate of warming in the arctic spring is correspondingly more rapid. A few days in arctic spring account for climatic progress equivalent to the change during weeks at lower latitude. The regular return of the birds occurs in spite of vagaries of arctic weather which, at a time near the critical transition from ice to water, can turn to conditions extremely inclement for small birds. On a morning after a not unusual snowfall early in June, sandpipers look miserable standing on projecting rocks, and their nests are covered. If the snow stands only a few hours the small birds can survive these climatic vicissitudes, but in some years there are many casualties. The regular return of species shows that they have on the average correctly estimated their physiological tolerance in relation to the duration of cold spells and have found advantages in encountering the risky arctic nesting conditions and the equally risky weather as they advanced in migration through northern lands as rapidly as melting made their sustenance possible.

Migrants arriving in the arctic are generally in good condition and fat enough to select and settle in their nesting places by the use of reserves adequate for some inclement weather. Though they are busily concerned with mating, nesting and attendant social activities, the food supply is evidently ample for their support without undue competitive struggle. No new land plants have matured at this date, and only a few early insects have emerged, but there appears to have been some early spring growth of aquatic algae and arthropods that starts even under covering of ice. On the tundra, the major food supply of early season birds is derived from berries, seeds, buds and sprouts of stems, and arthropods produced in the previous year and exposed in spring by melting snow.

Winter Residence Places of Arctic Migrants

Bird species migrating to nest in Alaska have wintered in parts of North and South America, on Pacific islands, coasts and oceans and even in the continent of Asia. A few populations can be assigned by taxonomic distinctions to localities of their winter residence. The progress of some species northward can be followed by dates of appearances along migratory routes consistent with the sharp programs of arctic arrival. Outlined migratory paths to Alaskan tundra show their impressive geographical extent and diversity.

Adults of a number of species of sandpipers and plovers leave the arctic tundra early in August, abandoning their fledged young to complete their growth to a size capable of long migratory flights southward. Numerous other migratory species depart from the arctic tundra by mid-August, although a few remain until imminent freezing endangers their feeding. My general impression is that avian populations of the tundra decline markedly during August at the time when annual production of food in the form of seeds, berries and invertebrates reaches its peak. Frost and snow then preserve a large part of the summer's increment of food until the following spring, when melting exposes an unharvested supply for the returning migrants.

On the tundra, still without new growth of vegetation in May and June, but with supply of buds, shoots from the last year's roots, berries, seeds, and still inactive insects preparing to emerge, the arriving migrants find a sufficient residue from the last year's production to sustain the early stages of reproductive activities. When the young are hatched, green new growth is abundant and insects have emerged. The fresh production of summer provides ample nourishment that fattens the birds before their departure on migrations southward. The unconsumed residue from summer's production evidently suffices to bring the birds back in the next spring while the tundra is still bleak and brown. It may well be that the northern part of migration in spring derives its power and northward inclination from the exposure of the previous summer's crop as the snow melts.

SIR JOHN RICHARDSON (1852) remarked that on the barren grounds of Canada the sudden freezing of grasses and lichens preserved their nutritive values for the caribou to use throughout the winter. He also noted that crowberries frozen at summer's end remained fresh to serve for the sustenance of migrating geese until mid-June.

Migrations Along Western American Coasts to Nest on Interior Alaskan Tundra

Some 90 species migrate to nest on the interior tundra of Alaska, numerically submerging the few species and numbers of local residents. Thirty-four of these species (Table 4.3 a) are found wintering or migrating along western American coasts. For nesting in the interior of Alaska they resort to tundra and fresh water. The transition to the inland nesting habitat is most marked in the case of six species that breed mainly in the Arctic: two phalaropes, (Phalaropus fulicarius, Lobipes lobatus), three jaegers (Stercorarius), and arctic tern (Sterna paradisaea). These six birds spend the nonbreeding season at sea and even over far southern oceans; or, in the case of the arctic tern, among Antarctic ice floes (SALOMONSEN, 1967). Arctic terns were one of five primary species of birds observed in a voyage through antarctic Weddell Sea (CLINE et al., 1969). Seven more of the species can be considered as largely arctic nesting birds. In fact sanderlings (Crocethia alba, 40 grams) and red phalaropes (Phalaropus fulicarius), of similar small size, proceed to nest in the highest latitudes attained by migratory birds. The remaining 22 species nest over wide latitudinal ranges in temperate North America.

Several of the Alaskan nesting populations are of subspecies recognized as nesting primarily in northwestern North America. A few returns of banded birds to arctic nesting grounds suggest that the habit of returning to nest in natal regions is maintained among many species of arctic breeding birds about as in other climates (WYNNE-EDWARDS, 1962). The evidence, however, is not statistically adequate. The appearance of bird species year after year, after long migrations, at arctic breeding places at regular dates just suitable for mating, nesting and rearing young involves accurate advance timing of physiological preparations in accord with the progress of spring on the long routes over which arctic migrants navigate. It does not seem possible that such tightly organized kinetic processes can be accomplished without basis upon prior experience in the courses and programs required for each local population to succeed in reaching its respective arctic destination. On the other hand, the habit of arctic nesting has not always so confined breeding as to establish visible local taxonomic differentiations, and the majority of species migrating to nest in Alaska are not distinguishable from the worldwide forms of the species.

Migrations Overland in North America

I have listed 38 species (Table 4.3b) that migrate over continental North America to nest on tundra of interior Alaska. Their winter resorts are widely dispersed through North, Central and South America. A surprising number of sandpipers make the long flight in spring from South America; Baird's sandpiper (*Erolia bairdii*, 40 grams), for example, winters far south in the Andes. The northernmost nesting of the species in eastern high-arctic Canadian islands and Greenland is over 100° of latitude from the southernmost occurrence of the species in Chile. Winter resorts are for some species well localized, and for others vaguely defined. For some species subspecific definitions serve to localize winter resorts and narrow the extent of nesting area attributable to a related population.

The majority (24) of the species listed in Table 4.3b are not found outside of America, and five of the remainder (marked SibAm) just enter eastern Siberia to nest. Large flocks of sandhill cranes (*Grus canadensis*) retain their organized formations as they circle high in air, as if to establish bearings, over Wales Mountain at the tip of Seward Peninsula before taking off purposively and in full melodious cry toward Siberia. Their westernmost nesting places require westward flights crossing one-fifth of the world's circumference from wintering places near the Gulf of Mexico. Some small Baird's sandpipers that attain high-arctic nesting grounds in the east also pass 100° of longitude westward from South America to nest in Siberia. The six American-wintering species that nest in Siberia pursue their migratory courses far westward from their American wintering places.

The northwesterly trend of American migrations is further shown by the Passeriformes (perching birds, beginning in Table 4.3b with Say's phoebe [*Sayornis saya*]). Thirteen of these passeriforms (designated American) are familar as woodland birds, which in fact just enter the tundra. In Alaska and Yukon Territory they approach but do not regularly reach arctic coasts. In eastern America their northern nesting lies to the southward in the proximity of the more southern tree line. The early and rapid spring warming of northwestern America that leads to the far northwestern nesting of the perching birds also permits their early spring northward migration at rapid rates of progress. This generalization is not quite true however, for three species of perching birds of holarctic range (EuAsAm in Table 4.3 b) manage to reach rather high-arctic nesting places by migration over the later-warming lands of eastern North America. Furthermore, species of American geese, ducks and sandpipers are not prevented from reaching arctic Canadian islands by the later spring warming of eastern American lands.

Oceanic and Asian Migrations to Alaska

Most impressive are the four small land birds that nest on tundra and winter in still undefined regions of Asia (Table 4.3 c). It is interesting that journals and reports of Captain Cook's expedition in late August and September 1778 through Bering Strait and along the coast of northwestern Alaska remarked upon flocks of small land birds flying southward over the broken sea ice. Three species wintering in Asia, the wheatear *(Oenanthe oenanthe)*, bluethroat *(Luscinia svecica)*, and yellow wagtail *(Motacilla flava)*, were described by the early exploring navigators and even depicted (THEED, 1968). The tiny arctic warbler of the old world *(Phylloscopus borealis*, 9 grams) nests in Alaska some 90° of longitude east of its suspected Asian wintering place, which in our experience with air travel would represent passage of six time zones, in addition to 25° of latitude northward. Alaska yellow wagtails *(Motacilla flava*, 16 grams) migrate for similar distances. Wheatears *(Oenanthe oenanthe*, 28 grams) and related bluethroats *(Luscinia svecica*, half as large as wheatears) probably fly at least 100° east and perhaps 30° north of their still obscure Asian winter resorts. Wheatears, frail-appearing small thrushes, are almost record-breakers among land birds for their eastward flights to arctic Alaska as well as for westward migratory flights from Europe to the tundra of Greenland and northeastern Canada. These four small landbirds that migrate from Asia barely extend their nesting eastward from Alaska into Yukon Territory. The Alaskan nesting wheatears are not distinguishable taxonomically from the nominate Eurasian form. The remaining three are distinguishable, within widespread Eurasian species, as races nesting in Alaska and probably in adjacent Siberia.

In addition to the oceanic-wintering phalaropes *(Phalaropus, Lobipes)*, jaegers *(Stercorarius)*, and arctic terns *(Sterna paradisaea)*, which also migrate along western American coasts (Table 4.3 a), Pacific golden plover *(Pluvialis dominica fulva)*, ruddy turnstones *(Arenaria interpres)*, bar-tailed godwits *(Limosa lapponica)* and wandering tatlers *(Heteroscelus incanum)* range in winter far over eastern Pacific Asian shores and south of the equator (Table 4.3 d).

Because many redpolls *(Acanthis)* and some snow buntings *(Plectrophenax)* spend the winter in Alaska I have listed these three separately, in Table 4.3 e, because some of them, at least, may migrate over only a few hundred kilometers within Alaska.

A summary view of routes of migrations to nesting-grounds on the tundra of Alaska (Table 4.4) shows that birds come from wintering in both continents of America, from over the waters and shores of the Pacific and from Asia. Their

Table 4.4. Routes traversed by birds migrating
to nest on interior Alaskan tundra

Route	Number of species
Pacific American Coasts	35
Over North America	38
Asia	4
Pacific Ocean	4
Alaska	4
Total:	84

(From IRVING, 1960)

various longitudinal ranges extend over more than half of the world. Many species winter far south of the equator and several oceanic species pass south of the Antarctic Convergence in the Pacific. If we were able to sort out the ranges of the great colonies of sea birds that nest on shores of the Bering Sea and the western Arctic Ocean we would find an even greater commingling of populations from over the oceanic waters and shores of the Pacific, mostly from the northern hemisphere, but with representatives from southeastern Pacific islands.

In any part of arctic Canada, Greenland and over arctic Eurasia there are similar illustrations of regular migrations converging on arctic nesting-grounds from lands and waters far southward and from the east and west. These migrations transport unbelievable numbers and masses of birds to produce and raise their young in the production of the arctic summer.

Migrations from Europe to Greenland

Migratory performances of similar order are seen in Greenland, where observant Danish officials, including high ranking administrators, have long kept careful records, with specimens and records of banding. Wheatears (*Oenanthe oenanthe leucorhoa*, 30 grams) that are subspecifically distinguished from the major population of the species in Eurasia and Alaska annually cross the North Atlantic to nest in Greenland and eastern arctic Canada. Wheatears banded in Greenland have been found in autumn in southwestern France before their winter resort to northwestern Afric (SALOMONSEN, 1950). The distance of their westward flights across meridians of longitude is like that of the wheatears flying eastward to Alaska. Another migrant from Europe that nests sparsely in east Greenland, the white wagtail (*Motacilla alba*), sends a related subspecies eastward from Asia to nest on St. Lawrence Island and increasingly in recent years on adjacent western shores of Alaska.

The ruddy turnstones (*Arenaria interpres*), knots (*Calidris canutus*) and ringed plovers (*Charadrius hiaticula*) nesting in Greenland and eastern Canadian arctic islands are considered to return to winter in Europe (SALOMONSEN, 1950). During a winter and spring in Cumberland Sound, Baffin Island, KUMLIEN (1879) found resident Eskimos who distinguished between the locally nesting ringed (European) and semipalmated plovers *(Charadrius semipalmatus,* American). On Disko Island, west Greenland, a Cumberland Sound Eskimo of the crew pointed out to Kumlien a ringed plover as one of the birds of his homeland.

Stability and Extent of Eskimo Knowledge of Birds

Eighty years after Kumlien's visit to Cumberland Sound I was able to satisfy myself in brief occasional conversations at Pangnirtung that resident Eskimos and I recognized and named 38 kinds of birds out of an avifauna that, according to the writings of several ornithologists who had studied the region, would present about 45 species. The time was late winter, when we saw only rock ptarmigan *(Lagopus mutus),* ravens *(Corvus corax),* snowy owls *(Nyctea scandiaca)* and one snow bunting *(Plectrophenax nivalis).* Our communication was aided by a wise interpreter, illustrations, imitative gestures and sounds and by Alaskan Eskimo names for birds.

Thinking it possible that the pintail *(Anas acuta)* had been seen around Cumberland Sound, I repeated my inquiry as I pointed to an illustration of the conspicuous pattern of the drake. Paulosee, one of the Eskimos, quickly remarked that he liked my duck and wished that it came to Pangnirtung but that it just was not one of their birds.

I found that 19 names given by the Eskimo Etwanga at Pangnirtung closely resembled those for the same species at Anaktuvuk Pass, Alaska, that I had earlier learned from Simon Paneak (IRVING, 1961). The similarity in naming at arctic localities 3000 kilometers separate indicates the stability in unwritten Eskimo designations over a wide expanse of their arctic range (IRVING, 1961). KUMLIEN (1879) published 24 Eskimo names for birds. Twenty-one of the names that I obtained in 1958 from Etwanga were like Kumlien's; only two were unlike. Considering probable errors in communication of this sort, the unwritten Eskimo names appear to have been remarkably stable, for close, resemblances of names cannot be fortuitous.

Indications for Changes in Range of Birds

There is also evidence in this stable Eskimo nomenclature for regularity in the habits of these birds, most of which make prolonged migrations to nest on southeastern Baffin Island. There are occasionally, nevertheless, documented changes in distribution. KUMLIEN (1879) wrote that Eskimos said that great cormorants *(Phalacrocorax carbo)* had become rare in Cumberland Sound. They are no longer reported from Baffin Island (American Ornithologists' Union, 1957) but are still common along shores of southwest Greenland (SALOMONSEN, 1950) and now known there to Greenlanders by the name obtained by Kumlien 70 years earlier in Cumberland Sound.

In contrast to the common regularity of migrations, individual birds stray from the courses of their respective populations. At Barrow, Alaska, where Eskimo residents and visiting naturalists have been recording observations of birds for nearly 100 years, I found listed 14 species of land birds, each represented by one or two specimens, that were more than 800 kilometers from their usual ranges (IRVING, 1960). These rare events did not result in settlement, for those species were totally unsuited for life on the arctic coast. Call them wanderers or explorers, as you wish, they demonstrate that individual birds far offbeat cannot effect settlement in a new range.

SIMON PANEAK of Anaktuvuk reported that in winter about 1908 he and some Eskimo boys found over 100 mud nests built against rock cliffs on the Kuparuk River (latitude 68° 35' N – longitude 149° 20' W) in tundra country 160 kilometers north of forest. The curious Eskimo boys knocked down some nests with poles and found them to contain well-feathered young birds judged to be about ready to fly when they were frozen (IRVING, 1960). Forty years later he showed me the nests on log houses at Bettles, within the forests, as those of the same cliff swallows (*Petrochelidon pyrrhonota*). This was an unsuccessful venture of a colony of swallows into the tundra.

An example of a well observed and apparently singular instance of nesting in strange territory is provided by the finding of ten curlew sandpipers *(Calidris ferruginea)* near Barrow, Alaska, in June 1962, which produced 2 nests with a clutch of four eggs in each (HOLMES and PITELKA, 1964). Only two specimens of the species had been taken earlier in this vicinity, where the watch for strange birds has been careful. The nearest previously recorded nesting place is about the delta of the Kolyma River, 1400 kilometers distant in Asia.

A striking example of new settlement by a European bird in west Greenland is provided by the meticulous observations of an incursion of rather small European thrushes, fieldfares (*Turdus pilaris*) (SALOMONSEN, 1950). Only twice had invidual specimens been taken in Greenland before 1939. Then in midwinter specimens of fieldfares were taken on Jan Mayen and on the same day on Ymer Island, east Greenland. They next appear to have made the improbable flight over the Greenland ice cap to afford specimen records in Godthab district, whence they moved southward to form within a few years a resident nesting population in the low birches and willows of the inner fjords of Julianehab district. SALOMONSEN (1950) remarked that their settlement was possible because of the recently warming climate that in southwest Greenland has made July 10° warmer and January 5° warmer than 50 years before. The fieldfares were initially blown in a violent storm far westward from their usual range in southern Norway. That they should have survived winter crossing of the Atlantic and Greenland ice cap seems miraculous. It will seem surprising to any but devoted watchers for birds that in those sparsely-manned arctic stations observers would be alert to record this new natural phenomenon.

The numbers of herring gulls *(Larus argentatus)* have greatly increased on both sides of the Atlantic in the last 50 years (WYNNE-EDWARDS, 1962). In addition to increases within the traditional ranges of gulls, during this century Iceland has become colonized by herring gulls, the black-headed gull *(L. ridibundus)*, lesser black-backed gull *(L. fuscus)* and mew gull *(L. canus)*, showing a considerable extension in their ranges. In the period of their expansion weather in the North

50

Atlantic appears to have warmed, but just how that might have affected the dispersal of gulls is a question.

WYNNE-EDWARDS (1962) also outlines the spread over the northeastern Atlantic of fulmars, which have established new and discrete colonies on the coasts of Scotland, England and Ireland. These colonists on new ground retain the dimensional characteristics of the subspecies *(Fulmarus glacialis glacialis)* of Iceland, whence they are presumably derived, and have established distant new colonies without visible modification in form. Fulmars are birds that nest in great aggregations over certain rocky cliffs to which they have returned faithfully for many centuries of recorded history. They have adhered to certain traditional nesting sites although others that appear to be as suitable are not utilized. Within a few centuries subcolonies derived from the subspecific population of Iceland have made their move southeasterly for a thousand miles in large, discrete jumps. For a high-arctic population of birds to emigrate far to milder temperate waters is contrary to the recent northward extension by birds in Greenland that is attributed to the secular trend of a warming arctic climate. Meanwhile there has been no reported new colonization from the colonies of fulmars *(F. g. minor)* of the western Arctic on sea cliffs of west Greenland and eastern Baffin Island. It seems that the traditions among fulmars that so firmly bring them back from wide oceanic ranges in winter to nest only on certain cliffs have broken down in a certain segment of the population during recent centuries.

Other examples of new settlement of birds remote from their usual habitats show that species are currently changing range by large jumps as well as by gradual extensions. The cattle egret *(Bubulcus ibis)* has recently established nesting populations in tropical and subtropical America, apparently originating in transatlantic flights from Mediterranean lands (American Ornithologists' Union, 1957). This widespread egret of warm Eurasia and Africa has been extending its range southward in Africa and eastward to Australia by what appears to be sudden development of an expansive inclination in the population. In recent years the redhead *(Aythya americana)*, and canvasback *(Aythya valisneria)* ducks and even bluewinged teal *(Anas discors)* have formed new large nesting populations on the Yukon Flats along the arctic circle in interior Alaska. It is my impression that small land birds wintering in Asia (p. 41) are becoming more commonly observed nesting in arctic Alaska because of their actually increasing prevalence in recent years.

Changes in Habits of Birds

For all that we are inclined to think that avian habits are maintained in stereotyped manner, birds have adapted their behavior with surprising versatility to utilize new conditions made by man. As human settlers have violently altered lands and vegetation they have usually paid little heed to the natural life that they disturbed, and such observations as were made were not regarded as significant for retention in the chronicles of history. As a result we have to extrapolate far backward in time from the present to reconstruct the effect of the distortion of natural conditions. Near arctic lands, however, the recent effects of invading settlement are still fresh and they are surrounded by relatively unchanged extents of lands and waters. Around Fairbanks, Alaska (65° N), violet-green swallows *(Tachycineta thalassina)* now familiarly nest in boxes and holes in old buildings, as do the tree swallows *(Iridoprocne bicolor)*, and both species of swallows perch and roost on power and telephone lines. At Old Crow, Yukon Territory (67° 40' N) a few tree swallows nest in boxes prepared by the Kutchin Athapaskans of the village. Along the valley of the Porcupine River in summer great numbers of these swallows hawk over the willows and nest in the natural crevices of soft, rotten dead stumps. I asked the ancient former chief, JOE KAY, why I had seen only one violet-green swallow in the village. He replied that, as its Kutchin name showed, it is a mountain swallow that naturally nests among crevices in cliffs, as I have often seen them nesting on high rocky cliffs of south central Alaska.

The barn swallow *(Hirundo rustica)* has been named for its practically complete assumption of the habit of nesting on beams and ledges in buildings. SIR JOHN RICHARDSON (SWAINSON and RICHARDSON, 1831) wrote that this swallow's original nesting places were in caves. Even in the recently settled areas of the lower Yukon and along coasts of Bering Sea old Eskimos knew that barn swallows nested on ledges and beams of the primitive houses, constructed of sod and drifted timbers, usually after they became unoccupied. For some reason barn swallows appear to be no longer common about the new buildings of that region. In 1825 RICHARDSON (SWAINSON and RICHARDSON, 1831) found that nests of barn swallows had been built in the ruins of Fort Franklin (67°), on Great Bear Lake. After openings in the building had been closed, for its use again in winter, a swallow that returned the next spring forsook the site.

Perhaps many observers of birds have not seen cliff swallows *(Petrochelidon pyrrhonota)* constructing their mud nests in colonies on the faces of hard rock cliffs, for they commonly apply their nests to our buildings of wood and stone to such an extent as to be often called eave swallows. SIR JOHN FRANKLIN had reported that in 1828 cliff swallows were nesting on log buildings at Fort Chipewyan, on Lake Athabaska. A few years later RICHARDSON (SWAINSON and RICHARDSON, 1831) remarked that FRANKLIN's record of nesting at Fort Chipewyan by cliff swallows 'was the first instance of this species placing itself under the protection of man within the widely extended lands north of the Great Lakes'. MACFARLANE (1891) reported that in 1836 there were 160 mud nests at (New) Fort Good Hope (66° 20'), the first use by cliff swallows of the buildings there. The new fort had been relocated southward from its former position, where FRANKLIN had earlier remarked upon nesting by barn swallows about the buildings.

In the course of their slow and arduous travels in American arctic lands the old explorers and officers of the Hudson's Bay Company observed and recorded the historic changes in the habits of birds as they suddenly adopted the first structures of the fur traders for use as nesting places. In the Arctic we can still observe the historic beginnings of modified habits of animals as they become affected by the powerful alterations caused by the sudden invasion of organized human power and machinery. In lands long settled the onset of these changes is so largely forgotten that the development of change is obscure.

Wisconsin and Post-glacial Migrations

Land Birds

Earlier speculation (p. 39) suggested that seventeen of the bird species now wintering on the interior tundra of Alaska seemed hardy enough to have lived through Wisconsin glacial conditions isolated in the refuge of Beringia. It does not seem likely, however, that any of the birds now migrating over continental America would have flown over a continental ice cap to nest in that arctic refuge. If this speculation is correct, the present patterns of migrations to nest in the Arctic have developed since the termination of the continental ice sheet, and, we should add, after the settlement of vegetation and animal life suitable for supporting the migrating birds. The sudden incursion of European fieldfares into a restricted area of southwestern Greenland after a winter crossing of the north Atlantic and Greenland ice cap shakes confidence in setting short limits on the capabilities of small land birds. But I think it warranted to point out that most of Canada and much of Alaska under the Wisconsin ice cover were then devoid not only of birds but also lacked plants, and that occupation of northern lands and the migrations that bring about their major annual production of bird life have been recent developments.

The land area of North America exploitable by birds has doubled in some 10 000 years. The continental migrations that currently appear so regular and stable have evolved with great rapidity in comparison with processes of evolution in form and the origins of new species. During many millenia species that were long confined to latitudes south of the continental ice must have retained unexercised their adaptability to northern arctic forest and tundra, ready to occupy and supposedly to reoccupy the northern lands from which life had been obliterated in four series of Pleistocene glaciations. Spread of the mobile land birds northward is impressive because we see that it recurs annually. Sedentary plants and animals must likewise have moved from limited glacial refuges or from the south to occupy northern lands set free from the cover of Pleistocene ice, but their progress is too obscure for speculation on the process.

Maritime and Oceanic Birds

Judging from their present migratory habits and abilities, most of the 34 species of maritime and oceanic birds now found nesting on interior arctic tundra (Table 4.3 a) might have migrated to Beringia under conditions then existing. The massive ice would certainly have caused restrictions in migration over southern Alaska, requiring detours to round the ice-covered western part of the Alaska Peninsula. The broad tundra of the then exposed continental shelf would have greatly altered routes of migration, and we can scarcely speculate upon summer habitability of arctic coasts. It is also to be considered that arctic coasts could only have been attained by long overland flights across the land bridge. Most conspicuous to our present view, there would have been but a narrow Bering Sea south of latitude 60°, with shores 100 meters below present sea level, for occupation by the spectacular colonies of fulmars, murres, auks, guillemots, puffins and gulls that now inhabit the cliffs about Bering Sea. It is difficult and still not very profitable to try to imagine the situation of life in the Arctic of those times (Table 4.5).

Residents in the south and over the Arctic agree in form, behavior and many habits with their congeners in the south and over the arctic world. A robin's (*Turdus migratorius migratorius*) nest is the same whether it is in New England or Alaska. The stable form of birds is ancient, for the present arctic species have existed throughout Pleistocene episodes of glaciation and milder intervals. A few species may have become differentiated in those long millenia of catastrophic climatic changes, and it is likely that many subspecies developed during the Pleistocene (JOHANSEN, 1956). It seems remarkable that the highly conservative structures

Table 4.5. Sea birds now nesting along shores of arctic Alaska that might have been capable of migrating to nest on coasts of Beringia

Gavia immer (Common loon)	*Falco peregrinus* (Peregrine)
Gavia adamsii (Yellow-billed loon)	*Pluvialis dominica fulva* (Pacific golden plover)
Gavia arctica (Arctic loon)	*Phalaropus fulicarius* (Red phalarope)
Gavia stellata (Red-throated loon)	*Lobipes lobatus* (Northern phalarope)
Fulmarus glacialis (Fulmar; no arctic counterpart of antarctic petrels)	*Stercorarius pomarinus* (Pomarine jaeger)
Phalacrocorax pelagicus (Pelagic cormorant)	*Stercorarius parasiticus* (Parasitic jaeger)
Phalacrocorax urile (Redfaced cormorant)	*Stercorarius longicaudus* (Long-tailed jaeger)
Branta nigricans (Brant)	*Larus hyperboreus* (Glaucous gull)
Philacte canagica (Emperor goose)	*Rissa brevirostris* (Red-legged kittiwake)
Anser albifrons (White-fronted goose)	*Rissa tridactyla* (Black-legged kittiwake)
Chen hyperborea (Snow goose)	*Xema sabini* (Sabine's gull)
Anas platyrhynchos (Mallard)	*Sterna paradisaea* (Arctic tern)
Anas acuta (Pintail)	*Uria aalge* (Common murre)
Clangula hyemalis (Old Squaw)	*Uria lomve* (Thick-billed murre)
Histrionicus histrionicus (Harlequin)	*Cepphus columba* (Pigeon guillemot)
Polysticta stelleri (Steller's eider)	*Fratercula corniculata* (Horned puffin)
Somateria mollissima (Common eider)	*Lunda cirrhata* (Tufted puffin)
Somateria spectabilis (King eider)	
Lampronetta fischeri (Spectacled eider)	

and behavior of avian species were still adaptable to the rapid evolution of the environment as it occurred in the Arctic. With scarcely visible evolution in form, or presumably in behavior, the avian species occupied the arctic world as it began developing in the late Tertiary. The adaptability of birds is obvious in the general success of their etablishment of resident and migratory arctic populations. Because the birds annually repeat migrations that each summer add many hundred-fold to the amount of avian arctic life, I have tried to illustrate the magnitude and nature of the seasonal change in birds nesting in the Arctic. The sedentary arctic mammals may increase in numbers only a few times in a single summer and only slowly extend or contract their ranges by movement of populations that we cannot see.

In Eurasia there are resemblances to American migratory distribution, with some complications added by the great breadth and diversity of its southern land mass, a babel of reporting languages and complexity of intellectual customs. The extent of our ignorance about current processes in distribution of birds is tantalizing because we can see some of the procedural elements in annual migrations. Until we can better know some recent steps in the history of distribution we will remain ignorant of its processes. Meanwhile we do know that complex migrations annually transport enormous numbers of birds in well organized populations to the Arctic and return them after a few months with increment sufficient to outlast most of the year's attrition in southern temperate and tropical climates. The Arctic has been exploited by men for the benefit of temperate societies for only one or two centuries. Exploitation of the Arctic by birds continued through millenia before history began.

Organization of Migrating Populations

Birds migrating to arctic lands are at the terminus of their migratory courses and settle in breeding populations that on their nesting grounds are homogeneous in reproductive state. Near northern continental limits no confusion is caused by the passage of birds destined for more distant and later breeding. In the majority but not in all species nesting on Alaskan tundra, the van of earliest-arriving birds precedes the bulk of arrivals by only a few days. In general, establishment of nesting territory separates nesting areas in each of which a female joins company with a male. Mates swiftly prepare nests and eggs, so that within a week or so reproduction is in progress with all birds in the same state. There is then apparent harmony in contrast with the brief period of early conflict over establishment of claims to space and mate. Orderliness is a feature of the program of each species, as birds that had been for many months more or less gregarious and sexless in behavior become settled in detached pairs.

Sex and Age Organization of Willow Ptarmigan

I do not think, however, that there is any peculiarity in the behavior of arctic breeding species except in the rapidity and synchrony of the transition from apparently sexless social to paired and located individuals. But sexual differences in aggregations are quite evident throughout winter in the large and conspicuous population of willow ptarmigan *(Lagopus lagopus alascensis)* in the central Alaskan tundra. In August females with well grown broods of chicks come together to form flocks of 50 to 100 ptarmigan near their northern nesting places. Family bonds seem to dissolve and flocks migrate southward from northern tundra through mountain passes of the Brooks Range that funnel their movement in the narrow strips of low willows about the streams.

Central Point in Migration of Willow Ptarmigan

At a central location in the mountains, Anaktuvuk Pass, we have continued observation of the ptarmigan for many years with effective assistance from the Eskimos resident in the little village. Flocks of willow ptarmigan begin to move through the Pass in a prevailing southward direction during October. The southward trend continues to be evident through November. In the dark and often stormy days of December and January flocks walk at rather orderly spaced intervals over the snow as they feed on the buds and twigtips of willows, or rise synchronously in rapid and concerted flight. In their midwinter period, when human observers are often weatherbound, no directional trend is apparent.

Late in January or early in February the ptarmigan begin to appear restless and 'talkative,' with evidence for beginning northward movements. These movements might subside during March but increase to a crescendo by the end of April, when several thousand birds have been counted daily in obvious progress northward, with uncounted numbers heard passing in flight. During four years we figured that from 21000 to 52000 birds were seen between January and May in prevailing northward movement over a 2-kilometer wide area of the stream flat in the Pass (IRVING et al., 1967).

Survey of Composition of Flocks

Surveys in adjacent country showed that many large flocks came in November to the Koyukuk Valley, 160 kilometers south of Anaktuvuk. By April these had departed in visible flights and along tracks in snow leading northward up the John River valley toward Anaktuvuk. One hundred sixty kilometers north of Anaktuvuk at Umiat, in the Colville valley, some winter flocks were present, but these consisted mainly of male birds over a year old (Figs. 4.1, 4.2 and 4.3). This principal nesting area lies on the Arctic Slope north of the Brooks Range, and many old male birds winter in the breeding areas, where they are joined in May by female birds. At the midpoint of this short migration, Anaktuvuk Pass, juvenile male birds predominate in early winter, to be joined by increasing numbers of adult males in March and April.

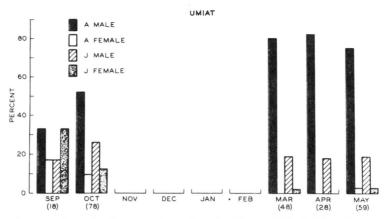

Fig. 4.1. Proportions by sex and age of willow ptarmigan collected at Umiat., 1963–65. (From IRVING et al., 1967)

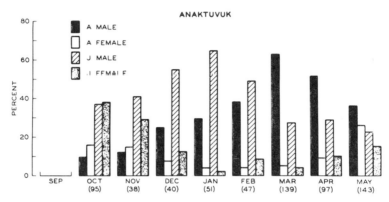

Fig. 4.2. Proportions by sex and age of willow ptarmigan collected at Anaktuvuk, 1961–65. (From IRVING et al., 1967)

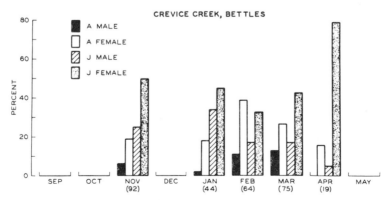

Fig. 4.3. Proportions by sex and age of willow ptarmigan collected at Crevice Creek and Bettles, 1963–65 (From IRVING et al., 1967)

The seasonally changing proportions of four distinguishable categories of this population at northern, southern and mid points on this migratory route showed that the age and sex composition of flocks changed at each place during winter months. We could not but conclude that each category of birds moved and changed the makeup of their social aggregations in flocks according to season and locality. In view of the coherent behavior of the winter flocks, which walked and roosted in snow in close order and synchrony, we were surprised at the evident impermanence of the membership of the flocks. Many ptarmigan captured and banded or colored at Anaktuvuk were seen to join a different flock when released. Rejection of strangers was not noticeable.

Migrations in Other Parts of Alaska

In other parts of Alaska it had been remarked that in winter, when willow ptarmigan were abundant, male birds remained at higher altitudes of alpine tundra, where they nested, while female birds often descended to the valley flats. The linear migration through Anaktuvuk Pass, free from significant human disturbance, afforded a model of organization of a population according to sex and age that in winter distributed the ptarmigan over a range far greater and more productive than the nesting area. The numerous population is evidently successfully supported by their references to locality and season.

Organization of Migrating Lapland Longspurs

We had noticed flocks of 50 to 100 Alaska longspurs *(Calcarius lapponicus alascensis)* in coherent daytime spring migratory flights parallel to the Alaska Highway in Yukon Territory and northern British Columbia. Organized flocks of longspurs arrived on tundra nesting grounds at Anaktuvuk, with early arrivals predominantly composed of flocks of 10 to 20 of the conspicuously distinguishable males. These flocks disintegrated as males chose nesting places. Females arriving in less coherent groups joined males later (IRVING, 1960). Records of early passage through subarctic approaches to tundra nesting places indicate that westward progress of the van of the population was more rapid than their northward progress (IRVING, 1961). HEMMINGSEN (1951) remarked that in northeastern China the eastward and westward progress of migrations was more rapid than their progress northward.

Migration Over Approaches to Arctic Alaska

Several routes of migration to Alaska have been indicated by directions of flights (Fig. 4.4). In 1966 the proportion of male longspurs in flocks along the Alaska Highway in British Columbia and Yukon Territory diminished from 100% to 20% between May 2 and 11, indicating that the temporal progress of the migration

58

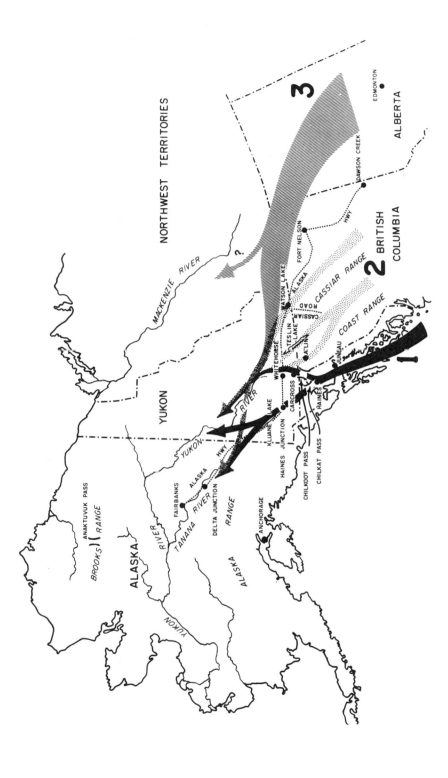

Fig. 4.4. Map of Alaska and western Canada showing the Alaska highway, locations of observations and collections of Lapland longspurs, and the suspected major migratory routes of longspurs mentioned in the text, 1. Coastal route; 2. intermountain route; 3. prairie route (From WEST, PEYTON and IRVING, 1968)

could be estimated by the proportion of males. In other years it became apparent that migratory components containing three different proportions of male birds could be distinguished as they converged in Yukon Territory from the prairies of Alberta, from intermontane routes, and from coastal routes through British Columbia. This discrimination was aided by the fact that in a year when heavy snow on the prairies was late in melting, passage of flights from the prairies was delayed until after the intermontane and coastal migrations.

At several locations flocks of feeding longspurs remained constant in numbers for several days (WEST et al., 1968). Captured longspurs were marked with attached colored feathers. Marked birds were observed in the same place during three to five days, but the marked numbers diminished gradually as if each individual departed from the feeding populations at the time of its choice. In an area near Watson Lake with stable numbers from May 5 to 9, 1967, the average weight of 11 captured longspurs on May 5 was 28.0 grams, and on May 9, 31.0 grams, with corresponding visible differences in fatness. We believed that this was evidence of replenishment of fat stores that would enable the migrants to reach their arctic nesting grounds with reserves of fat adequate for encountering inclement weather while selecting nesting sites and mates.

This view of the migratory approach to arctic nesting grounds shows well concerted operation of flocks of the gregarious longspurs. Individuals replenish fat stores by remaining in a feeding place long enough to suit their needs. Apparently the state of nourishment of an individual stirs it to join passing flocks in order to depart with others in like condition. Sex and nourishment are factors determining the time for joining in the movement of migrating flocks. Though extremely coherent, flocks of longspurs seem nevertheless to be, as in the migration of willow ptarmigan, composed of transients that elect to join the flocks that are going in their direction at a time that suits the individual's sex and condition.

Rugged mountains and narrow valleys in northwestern America constrain many species of migrating birds to flights through narrow valleys and passes in which food is obtainable. Large carnivorous birds, cranes and ducks possess reserves for long flights, but even these tend to pursue routes and schedules of migration that are repeated annually. In their approaches to arctic nesting grounds, cranes, geese and ducks congregate with some regularity at feeding stations along migratory routes. We cannot speculate upon the extent to which the flocks of species other than longspurs, which fly in such good order, are durable or transitory associations that disintegrate only at or near their arctic nesting grounds. Nor can we surmise whether the transient nature of longspur association in flocks exists over their earlier southern courses. It is evident, however, that considerable opportunities for viewing the organized operation of migrations exist as the birds approach their arctic nesting grounds.

References

AMERICAN ORNITHOLOGICAL UNION: Check-list of North American Birds. 5th Ed. Baltimore, Md.: Port City Press, Inc. 1957.
CLINE, D. R., SINIFF, D. B., ERICKSON, A. W.: Summer birds of the pack ice in the Weddell Sea, Antarctica. The Auk **86**, 701–716 (1969).

DUNBAR, M. J.: Ecological Development in Polar Regions; A Study in Evolution, Englewood Cliffs. New Jersey: Prentice Hall 1968.

FREUCHEN, P., SALOMONSEN, F.: The Arctic Year. New York: G. P. Putnam 1958.

HEMMINGSEN, A. M.: Observations on birds in northeastern China. Spolia zoologica Musei Haurriensis XI København (1951).

HOLMES, R. T., PITELKA, F. A.: Breeding behavior and taxonomic relationships of the curlew sandpiper. The Auk 81, 362–379 (1964).

IRVING, L.: Birds of Anaktuvuk Pass, Kobuk, and Old Crow – A Study in Arctic Adaptation, United States National Museum Bulletin. Washington, D. C.: Smithsonian Institution 1960.

IRVING, L.: Stability in Eskimo naming of birds on Cumberland Sound, Baffin Island. Anthro. Papers, Univ. of Alaska 10, 1–12 (1961).

IRVING, L., McROY, C. P., BURNS, J. J.: Birds observed during a cruise in the ice-covered Bering Sea in March 1968. The Condor 72, 110–112 (1970).

IRVING, L., WEST, G. C., PEYTON, L. J., PANEAK, S.: Migration of willow ptarmigan in arctic Alaska. Arctic 29, 77–85 (1967).

JOHANSEN, H.: Birds of the Arctic Regions: Review and Origin of Arctic Bird Fauna. Oslo, Norway: E. J. Hunksgaard 1956.

KUMLIEN, L.: Contribution to the Natural History of Arctic America, made in connection with the Howgate Polar Expedition, 1877–1878. Washington, D. C.: Gov't Printing Office 1879.

LINCOLN, F. C.: The Migration of American Birds. New York: Doubleday, Doran and Co. 1939.

MacFARLANE, R.: Notes on and list of birds and eggs collected in arctic America, 1861–66. Proc. US Natl. Mus. 14, 413–446 (1891).

RICHARDSON, J.: Arctic Expedition in Search of Sir John Franklin. New York: Harpers 1852.

SALOMONSEN, F.: The Birds of Greenland. Copenhagen: E. Munksgaar 1950.

SALOMONSEN, F.: Migratory movements of the arctic tern in the southern ocean. Danske Videnskab. Selskab, Biol. Medd. 24, 1–42 (1967).

SWAINSON, W., RICHARDSON, J.: Fauna Boreali-Americana-Part I. The Birds. London: John Murray 1831.

THEED, P.: Birds of the Early Explorers in the Northern Pacific. Comox, B. C. 1968.

THOMPSON, D'ARCY W.: On Growth and Form. Cambridge University Press. 1952

WEST, G. C., PEYTON, L. J., IRVING, L.: Analysis of spring migration of Lapland longspurs to Alaska. The Auk 85, 639–653 (1968).

WYNNE-EDWARDS, V. D.: Animal Dispersion in Relation to Social Behavior. New York: Hafner Pub. Co. 1962.

Chapter 5

Maintenance of Arctic Populations: Birds

The Influx of Birds to Breed on Arctic Lands

Most writings on the Arctic are by visitors. A visitor to arctic lands in winter is unlikely to see much life because resident birds are few and observation is difficult for a stranger. But even though few are seen, all of the resident populations of birds and mammals are present (Chapters 3 and 4). Hares and foxes remain above the snow; rodents forage in subnivean activity; poikilothermous animals in the soil and plants are quiescent; but to call the winter scene lifeless expresses the state of mind of the stranger, for indigenous people of the Arctic know that all of the arctic life is there except the migrants that will return in spring. These he knows will reappear for the very evident purpose of reproduction (Fig. 5.1).

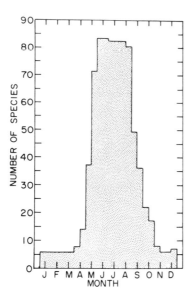

Fig. 5.1. The occurrence of species of birds at Ogoturuk Creek Alaska (lat. 69 °N) at two-week intervals throughout the year. Only species of regular occurrence are included. (From WILLIAMSON et al., 1966)

The arctic breeding season for birds is limited by the brevity of the period without snow and ice. The impression of its short duration is heightened by the formerly slow travel and hence late season of access to arctic lands by scientists. It is further emphasized by the preoccupation of visiting scientists with schedules that leave them time for only a short summer in the Arctic. Haste to utilize the short time available develops the impression that similar haste governs the summer programs of arctic life.

Some Common Limitations on Arctic Life

Certain conditions seem to be common determinants of the suitability of the Arctic for life. Progressing northward, the melting of snow-cover on land and ice-cover on the waters occurs increasingly later. On high-arctic lands and waters the beginning of growth by land and aquatic plants becomes deferred and its duration is shortened, requiring compression of the growing period and concentrating the production of vegetation in the short arctic summer. We have scant estimates of the quantity of food that is produced on land and of its distribution. We cannot evaluate periodic changes in food available for birds and mammals that show such a degree of depletion of nutrients as occurs when a fulminating bloom of marine algae almost totally consumes currently available phosphate from a region of the sea.

If we cannot demonstrate general limitations imposed upon mammalian and avian populations by the supply of food, we can nevertheless show operative limitations on their occurrence by studying their distribution in time (season) and location. Populations of birds and mammals are so conspicuously accustomed to occupy certain places for breeding at certain times that we will examine their observance of these programs. Dependence on time and place are more evident in the conspicuous avian populations than in the secretive mammals.

Birds of the Interior Tundra

Duration of Arrival

Migrating birds first arrived at Anaktuvuk Pass, Alaska, (lat 68° 10' N long. 151° 40' W) from early April to early June (Table 5.1). Only two species appeared in April, the small (30–35 gram) snow bunting (*Plectrophenax nivalis*) and the large, carnivorous golden eagle *(Aquila chrysaëtos)*. Birds that migrate farther northward may prolong their observed passage past localities south of their final destinations, but arctic land extends only 300 kilometers northward from Anaktuvuk to the arctic coast. Fluctuations in weather during the progress of migrations through southern courses may also affect arrival at final destinations. We know that in some years Lapland longspurs (*Calcarius lapponicus*) migrating toward Alaska are retarded during migration by heavy snow covering their distant routes of approach over the prairies of Alberta.

Near the terminus of northern lands one might expect that schedules would be more compact because the populations of species involved are homogeneous as they arrive on their common nesting ground. We can see the more closely scheduled uniformity in arrival of a few arctic species by comparing birds of Anaktuvuk with four species that URNER (URNER and STORER, 1949 observed in New Jersey during ten years.

	Inclusive dates of flights in New Jersey	Arrival period in days	
		New Jersey	Anaktuvuk
Charadrius semipalmatus	May 4 – June 4	31	20
Totanus flavipes	Apr 24 – June 13	50	8
Calidris minutilla	Apr 29 – May 30	31	12
Calidris pusillus	May 7 – June 7	31	9

The dates for arrival of species at Anaktuvuk showed concentration about May 20 (Fig. 5.2), which was the common median date in four of the six years of record. Earliest-arriving representatives of a species were often single birds or small flocks. After a few days the main members of the breeding populations had arrived and demonstrated preparation for settling on nesting areas.

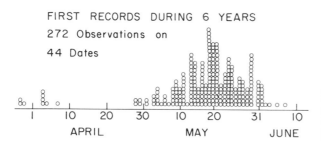

FIRST RECORDS DURING 6 YEARS
272 Observations on
44 Dates

Fig. 5.2. Dates of earliest recorded species arriving at Anaktuvuk, Alaska, 1948–1953. (From IRVING, 1960)

Interval from Arrival to Nesting

The usual interval between arrival of migrants at interior arctic lands and production of eggs (Table 5.1) appears short, considering that it must permit most species to select a territory for nesting, form the bond with a mate, and construct a nest in which to lay eggs. I had thought that the rate of progress of individuals toward nesting in the arctic was shortened and that the population was accordingly synchronized because exigencies of the short arctic summer would not permit most species to prolong stages in their breeding; but as WYNNE-EDWARDS (1962) points out, there are examples of regular seasonal synchronous breeding among tropical populations of birds, as well as some examples in which breeding is not well synchronized or even follows an irregular cycle with respect to the calendar.

Some of the hardy little snow buntings (*Plectrophenax nivalis*) can somehow obtain plant foods in April (and occasionally earlier) on hard frozen tundra, although they do not nest along the coast until June. Eagles *(Aquila chrysaëtos)* and rough-winged hawks *(Buteo lagopus)* can find prey or carrion of the resident mammals of the snow-covered tundra, and they have in their large size and carnivorous nature nutritional reserves to tide them over periods of scarcity. Most of the migrants to the tundra, like sandpipers (Scolopacidae), ducks and geese (Anatidae) and thrushes (Turdidae) must find the water and unfrozen ground that are essential for their feeding. Habits of feeding, as well as tolerance of cold, determine the limits of time in which populations can settle upon arctic nesting grounds.

Table 5.1. Duration of phases of migratory and reproductive cycles in 28 species of birds at Anaktuvuk Pass, Alaska (Latitude 68°10'N, Longitude 151°40'W).

Species	Arrival date		Duration of arrival period (days)	First egg date	Days from mid-arrival to mid-laying	Latest departure date	Duration of departure period (days)
	First migrant	Last migrant					
Plectrophenax nivalis nivalis	Apr. 1	June 1	60	June 1	34	Sept. 10	
Aquila chrysaëtos canadensis	Apr. 3	Apr. 18	15				
Lanius exubitor invictus	May 4	May 16	12	May 27	23	Oct. 15	
Calcarius lapponicus alascensis	May 6	June 7	32	May 31	14	Sept. 2	20
Buteo lagopus	May 8	May 23ᵃ	15				
Eremophila alpestris arcticola	May 10	June 1	20	May 29	13	Aug. 24	19
Anthus spinoletta rubescens	May 11	June 6	26	June 1	12	Sept. 3	30
Anas acuta	May 13	June 6	24	May 23	4	Sept. 10	10
Spizella arborea ochracea	May 13	May 30	17	June 3	17	Sept. 12	
Pluvialis dominica dominica	May 14	May 31	17	May 28	10	Aug. 15	15
Turdus migratorius migratorius	May 15	May 30	15	May 30	12	Sept. 18	13
Zonotrichia leucophrys gambelii	May 16	May 29	13	June 3	16	Sept. 12	12
Charadrius semipalmatus	May 16	June 5	20	June 12	21	Aug. 16	15
Anas carolinensis	May 18	June 5	14	May 27	6	Aug. 30	10
Totanus flavipes	May 19	May 27	8	June 1	13	Aug. 6	
Erolia bairdii	May 19	May 31	12	May 29	8	Aug. 10	
Aythya marila nearctica	May 20	May 26	6	June 5	17	Sept. 10	
Clangula hyemalis	May 20	May 28	8	June 4	15	Sept. 10	10
Lobipes lobatus	May 22	May 29	7	June 6	16	Aug. 25	10
Ereunetes pusillus	May 23	June 1	9				
Mergus serrator serrator	May 23	June 3	11	June 9	17	Sept. 10	11
Oenanthe oenanthe oenanthe	May 23	May 27	4	June 5	14	Sept. 1	20
Erolia minutilla	May 24	June 5	12	June 3	8		
Stercorarius parasiticus	May 24	June 5	12	June 8	13	Sept. 5	10
Melanitta deglandi	May 25	June 14	21	June 6	9	Aug. 30	10
Calcarius pictus	May 26	June 3	8	June 4	12	Aug. 24	10
Sterna paradisaea	May 28	June 6	9	May 31	4	Aug. 30	10
Motacilla flava tschutschensis	June 3	June 5	2	June 10	10		
Total (28)				(aver.) (14)			

ᵃEstimated from observations at Barrow.
ᵇEstimated form growth of young.

(From records made during several years of observation – IRVING, 1960)

Because they are not able to nest in the cold weather of arctic spring, some species that arrive early delay their schedules of breeding until the temperature moderates to within their capability. Others arrive from migration and proceed

65

to breed with surprising rapidity. White-crowned sparrows *(Zonotrichia leucophrys gambelii)* that nest in Alaska (Mountain Village, Alaska, lat. 62° 07' N) shortened the intervals between stages of breeding by about one-half in comparison with the subspecies *Z. l. pugetensis* that nests at Friday Harbor, Washington (lat. 40° N) (OAKESON, 1954; Table 5.2). At other localities of interior arctic Alaska and Yukon Territory similar short intervals between arrival and first egg were observed in *Z. l. gambelii* and in Fox sparrows *(Passerella iliaca zaboria)* (IRVING, 1960).

Table 5.2. Duration of intervals in breeding cycle of white-crowned sparrows

Interval	Z. l. pugetensis		Z. 1. gambelii	
	Median dates	Duration (days)	Median dates	Duration (days)
Arrival of males to arrival of females	April 10 (both sexes)	0	May 16–May 24	8
Arrival of female to first copulation	April 10–21	11	May 24–May 29	5
First copulation to first egg	April 21–29	8	May 28–June 2	5
Arrival of female to first egg laid	April 10–29	19	May 24–June 2	9

(From OAKESON, 1954)

It appears from studies in arctic Alaska that the time required for incubation is not appreciably different among populations of species that breed in temperate as well as in arctic localities. The time spent by nestlings in the nest before departure as fledglings does not appear with certainty to be shortened in arctic nesting portions of populations, although the period of growth of nestlings is not easily determined. Judging from observations in Alaska, and from the opinion that incubation and probably nestling growth are anciently established specific characteristics of individual birds, it seems unlikely that these periods can be readily modified as adaptations for populations that breed in the Arctic.

The fulminating onset of arctic spring, however, appears to synchronize behavioral expressions of local populations concerned with breeding so that breeding is effectively compressed within the time that is favorable in the arctic summer. The complex procedures of physiology and behavior are conspicuous in birds that migrate to nest in the Arctic, for prolonged physiological preparations for breeding must be initiated by the individual and must progress during migration from the wintering grounds according to schedules that will result in certain actions and conditions for breeding that become synchronous when the birds reach the nesting places that are their destination.

Number of Eggs Laid in a Clutch

I have not found that the number of eggs laid in a clutch is modified among species of birds that nest in both arctic and temperate regions. In a few arctic nests of western white-crowned sparrows *(Zonotrichia leucophrys gambelii)* the number of eggs laid slightly exceeded numbers reported from nesting places in localities further south. Among plovers (Charadriidae) and sandpipers (Scolopacidae) the usual numbers of eggs in a clutch is four in all climates. Arctic loons (Gaviidae) lay one or two eggs as elsewhere. Although some arctic species will replace a first clutch that is destroyed, the time available for renesting in the arctic is limited. Among passeriform species that repeat nesting and raise several broods during a summer in temperate lands I have not found that the short arctic summer allowed successful rearing of a second brood.

This climatic restriction is not an adaptation for arctic life, but the characteristic avian behavior is adaptable to arctic environmental signals. Simon Paneak of Anaktuvuk remarked that he had found dead nestlings of redpolls *(Acanthis flammea)*, well grown, fat and preserved by freezing in their nests. He surmised that the eggs had been laid too late and that when the parents saw other redpolls gathering in flocks the sight caused the parents to replace attachment to their young by desire to join flocks, which is the normal habit of redpolls as freezing weather sets in. The rapidly shortening days of late arctic summer evidently arrest breeding early, before its prospects of success become hopeless. It appears, however, that some arctic nesting populations are maintained with no more, or even less, expenditure of reproductive effort and time than in warmer climates. One might speculate that this economy makes it possible or even advantageous for birds to make their long migrations to nest in arctic lands.

Duration and Warmth of Incubation

CLAUDE BERNARD (1878) pointed out that incubation involves translation of regulated avian temperature beyond the body to eggs, a transfer regulated by parental behavior. He gave as illustration the mallee fowl (*Leipoa*) of the southwest Pacific, which A.R. WALLACE (1876) had described as assembling mounds of vegetation in which they laid their eggs, daily adding covering or effecting ventilation so that fermentation would maintain a temperature suitable for incubation. Many years later FRITH (1956) measured temperatures around 36° in these mounds built for incubation by fermentation.

Among the eggs in nine nests of seven arctic nesting species at Anaktuvuk, temperatures were warmer than 33° C in 74% of 49 occasional measurements and were not in any record colder than 25° (IRVING and KROG, 1956). Among the eggs of pintail ducks (*Anas acuta*), in a nest well insulated by downy feathers, recorded temperatures were no more steadily warm than among the eggs of pectoral sandpipers (*Erolia pusillus*) laid on a shallow scrape in the ground and surrounded by a very meager ring of grass and lichen. We can probably say that the periodically interrupted incubation by a single parent can succeed for ducks because of the insulation afforded by their nests of down. If incubation is shared by two parents, and consequently not interrupted, a meagerly insulated nest can suffice. The nests of other species differed widely in the amount of insulative protection afforded by their construction. The construction of nests of arctic species resembled nests of the same or similar species that one sees in temperate lands.

Among the eggs the temperature during incubation appeared to be maintained about as warm as is reported for nests in temperate regions. The duration from laying eggs to hatching in the Arctic also appeared to be like that reported for birds from other climates. We could not see evidence that the fashion of nests or the thermal or temporal regimes of incubation were modified as adaptations for reproduction in the Arctic. Specific thermal and temporal requirements for embryonic development in eggs are probably ancient establishments that birds brought with them when they became arctic nesters. In order to adapt their lives in the Arctic, parent birds can modify their behavior by paying closer attention to incubation.

In this particular nesting season at Anaktuvuk when temperatures were measured the weather was mild, with only 2% of recorded air temperatures close to the nests below freezing and air warming above 20° in 5% of records. The climatic stress was not severe. Near the arctic coast at Barrow (latitude 71°), in weather frequently as cold as -5°, NORTON (1970) recorded continuously for long periods that temperatures in dummy eggs introduced into the nests of dunlins *(Erolia alpina)* were held from 35.6° to 40.5° during incubation by the presence of a brooding parent during 97.7% of the time. Eggs that were removed and cooled for a time hatched when returned to the incubating parent. Eggs that had been kept in air at -5° for several hours were found to hatch successfully after return for incubation in the nest.

MATTHEWS (1954) found that in eggs removed from incubating Manx shearwaters *(Procellaria puffinus)* after about 3/4 of normal incubation and cooled to 15°, one embryo remained sensitive to mechanical stimulation after 10 cool days and none became insensitive to stimulation before seven days. He points out that an incubating shearwater faithfully awaits return of its mate from feeding at sea before leaving the eggs in their burrow, one bird having been recorded as continuing its brooding when unrelieved for 16 days. The eggs of seven other species of Procellariiformes are also reported to be tolerant of prolonged cooling, but in view of the common attentiveness of brooding behavior that is shared by both sexes, tolerance of cold by these embryos did not appear to Matthews to be important for survival of populations of the species.

Eggs of pheasants *(Phasianus colchicus)* in Michigan were found to be surprisingly tolerant of cooling (MACMULLEN and EBERHARDT, 1953). Eggs of northern loons, grebes and some gulls are often wet in their floating nests, which the parents abandon for long periods when an approaching man is still far distant. We shall later remark that the eggs of some, but not all, species of colonial sea birds in the Arctic are laid in contact with ice or frozen ground. But there are not enough thermal measurements in studies of habits of incubation to compare the tolerance of cooling by embryos or to show to what extent it is now useful in the maintenance of populations.

Birds are notable for adherence to custom and I have remarked that they, and all animals, must adapt their present operations to suit characteristics that were fixed in a remote past and in circumstances altogether different from those in which they now nest. In many respects species have been more stable in form and ways than their changing environments have been. As will be discussed later, each individual regulates certain internal conditions, without regard for circumstances, within narrow ranges suitable for itself and such as permit its continuous operation as an individual detached from its fluctuating environment. As CLAUDE BERNARD (1878) remarked, a certain amount of internal homeostasis, which means detachment from the immediate environment, is essential for free existence.

Newly-hatched Young

Eggs from which young birds are hatched in condition ready to leave the nest (precocial) are large enough to sustain development to a degree of capability for locomotion allowing the chicks to forage for themselves. Newly hatched ptarmigan *(Lagopus)* forage for themselves, and ducklings *(Anatidae)* soon enter the water, though for a few days they are brooded by the mother according to the weather. Newly hatched sandpipers *(Scolopacidae)*, though active, are thinly feathered, and depend upon frequent brooding to retain their warmth. As has been shown in the newborn of many birds and mammals, they tolerate deeper and longer hypothermia than do adults. It is likely that this tolerance of cooling is more useful in a cold than in a warm climate, but parental attention is so effective that it would be hard to demonstrate to what extent tolerance of cold by nestlings is usefully invoked.

The growth of altricial nestlings can be observed as they are nourished in nests from a very immature stage until ready to begin flying. Among 144 single records of temperature among nestlings in ten inland arctic nests, only 15% were lower than 34° (IRVING and KROG, 1956). We believed that the measurement did not much disturb brooding, but we cannot say whether it affected development of the nestlings. Long days of arctic summer prolong the daily periods during which nestling birds can be fed as well as producing effects that long photoperiods might have upon their growth. We did not find good evidence that the interval from hatching to departure from nests was shortened in the interior Arctic in the species that have populations nesting in both arctic and temperate climates. The duration of a short life as nestling birds is complicated by the intervals between hatching of several eggs and intervals between departure of several nestlings. Departure is a further complicating process because it may be accelerated by disturbance caused by the observer, and after the fledglings have left the nest it is difficult to observe whether their free life is successful. Weak and inexperienced fledglings are vulnerable to predation.

Success in Arctic Breeding

In arctic interior lands a number of nests that I have watched released young birds without losses. To be sure these were in areas with apparently abundant food, few wild predators and no disturbance by people or domestic animals. Unseasonable cold, rain and snow are special arctic hazards. Near their northern limits in Alaska late cold weather in summer has been observed to delay or even prevent the usual dispersion of flocks of geese into pairs, so that in bad seasons some sections of the migratory species did not breed. Close observations of breeding sandpipers near Barrow, Alaska, during several years indicated that in the cyclic years when lemmings were scarce the attention of predators was concentrated upon the vulnerable young sandpipers. Narrative accounts indicate that unfavorable arctic seasons for breeding occur, but the evidence for particular circumstances, their extent and consequent reduction of successful breeding does not clearly show how often or how much the annual fluctuations of arctic seasons reduce the yields from reproduction in the arctic.

Of eight broods of white-crowned sparrows *(Zonotrichia leucophrys gambelii)* that were carefully watched at Mountain Village, Alaska (lat. 62 ° N), 6 were successfully fledged, a better rate of success than was observed in nests of southern subspecies (OAKESON, 1954). I remarked upon a similar degree of success in fledging of arctic Alaskan white-crowned sparrows and fox sparrows *(Passerella iliaca zaboria)*.

Instead of being impressed by the hardships encountered by birds breeding in the arctic interior I have thought that food and space were sufficient so that competition was not conspicuous, that predation appeared to have only a marginal influence, and that climatic vicissitudes were commonly bearable. Over the high ground where arctic rock ptarmigan *(Lagopus mutus)* nest, the cock bird in white plumage stands conspicuously on an eminence, proclaiming the territory of his nest. Attention drawn to the male by his conspicuous color and exposed position is evidently important for signalling his territory to other ptarmigan, and exposure to predators is of less concern for the population. Rock ptarmigan are to be sure alert, swift-flying birds, but they are captured in winter by gyrfalcons *(Falco rusticolus)* and snowy owls *(Nyctea scandiaca)*. I believe, however, that in the usual arctic summer, easily-captured prey so saturates the needs of predators that only a small proportion of capable adult birds are taken.

My bias in viewing conditions for arctic breeding favorably comes from seeing them while in the company of cheerful native residents who like their country and enjoy their arctic way of life. They have not yet become accustomed to complain about their hard times because relief from a disastrous season could come only from their own efforts. Eskimos have found arctic life adequate to maintain their population during several millenia of residence in arctic lands. From year to year some populations of migratory birds in a few months of summer derive the sole reproductive increment that maintains their populations during eight or nine months in the milder climates of their winter resorts. Over past millennia species have extended their breeding ranges into the Arctic as it became suitable for their ways and have withdrawn before changing conditions caused their extinction. I can think of no common reason for wild animals or people in primitive states of organization to keep moving into lands for which they are not suited and in which their populations cannot be maintained with satisfactory biological economy. In this respect some modern human populations seem to be different.

Nesting in the High Arctic

I will now consider the nesting of birds in arctic situations differing from interior Alaska. Even in the relatively uniform Arctic it will be evident that local variations in conditions profoundly affect reproductive programs. Generalization on arctic breeding will be replaced by illustrations of the variety of ways in which species meet special arctic conditions and even by the modifiability of habits within species that determines their adaptability for breeding in the Arctic. As·a caution, it can be remarked that each biologist sees arctic birds through his own observational methods, from his known area and its species, and not least with desire to generalize from his limited experience that leads to a variety of personalized opinions on the adaptation of populations for arctic life.

Birds of High-arctic Lands

A few snow buntings (*Plectrophenax nivalis,* 30 grams) migrate to nest in Peary Land of northern Greenland, where rock ptarmigan *(Lagopus mutus)* and rare snowy owls *(Nyctea scandiaca)* reside. There the knot *(Calidris canutus),* sanderling *(Crocethia alba,* 50 grams) and ruddy turnstone *(Arenaria interpres)* migrate to nest. The most northerly specimen of this turnstone was prepared at 83° 7' N in Peary Land by T. WULFF and preserved after he perished on the expedition (FREUCHEN and SALOMONSEN, 1958). Breeding in high-arctic Greenland are Sabine's gull *(Xema sabini),* the ivory gull *(Pagophila eburnea),* arctic tern *(Sterna paradisaea)* and phalarope *(Phalaropus fulicarius),* "red" in its arctic nuptial plumage, but "grey" as named when it migrates through Britain.

At the station of the Canadian Defence Research Board on Lake Hazen in north Ellesmere Island (lat. 81° 49' N, long. 71° 18' W), 18 species of birds have been found, 14 of which were observed nesting (N) (SAVILE and OLIVER, 1964):

Gavia stellata
  (Red-throated loon) N
Chen hyperborea
  (Snow goose) N
Clangula hiemalis
  (Old squaw N
Somateria spectabilis
  (King eider) N
Lagopus mutus
  (Rock ptarmigan)
Grus canadensis
  (Sandhill crane)
Arenaria interpres
  (Ruddy turnstone) N
Capella gallinago
  (Common snipe)
Calidris canutus
  (Knot) N

Calidris bairdii
  (Baird's Sandpiper) N
Crocethia alba
  (Sanderling) N
Stercorarius longicauda
  (Long-tailed jaeger) N
Larus hyperboreus
  (Glaucous gull) N
Sterna paradisaea
  (Arctic tern)
Nyctea scandiaca
  (Snowy owl) N
Acanthis h. hornemanni
  (Hoary redpoll) N
Calcarius lapponicus
  (Lapland longspur) N
Plectrophenax nivalis
  (Snow bunting) N

Rock ptarmigan and Hornemann's redpoll are probably resident birds; the others are migratory.

In the rather mild but dry desert land at Hazen the local density of birds was nearly three times that found in the cold moist desert at Isaachsen (latitude 73°). Birds were some 20 times as numerous on the low arctic tundra of southwestern Baffin Island (SAVILE and OLIVER, 1964). The sparse condition of vegetation at Hazen supported only a few species of mammals in small numbers:

Alopex lagopus
  (Arctic fox)
Canis lupus
  (Wolf)
Mustela erminea
  (Ermine)
Ovibos moschatus
  (Musk ox)
Lepus arcticus
  (Arctic hare)
Discrostonyx groenlandicus
  (Collared lemming)
Rangifer tarandus
  (Caribou)

An impressive number of 14 adults and six calves of musk oxen were near the camp.

In those years in the high Arctic when warming is delayed and land remains late covered with snow and ice persists in covering the waters, king eiders *(Somateria spectabilis)* and red-throated loons *(Gavia stellata)* may never settle down to nesting and consequently depart without breeding (FREUCHEN and SALOMONSEN, 1958). Observations on progress of gonadal development and regression in these circumstances of day length and temperature are too sparse for speculation upon the course of environmental influences in their reproductive cycles in high arctic lands. But FREUCHEN and SALOMONSEN (1958) remark that seasons without breeding are not seen among the colonial sea birds that nest on arctic cliffs.

Colonial Maritime Birds

Sea Birds that Nest in Arctic Colonies

Great numbers of birds assemble in localized colonies on certain cliffs, mountain slopes and shores of arctic seas. These aggregations form at sites appropriate for the nesting habits of each species, to which the populations return annually according to a tradition that is rather faithful to given localities and on a seasonal schedule that is likewise currently regular and which pursues a temporal tradition. In the southern oceans, annual migratory courses that resort to traditional nesting places of component populations of oceanic bird species have been related to the annual cycles of winds and oceanic currents (MURPHY, 1936). Recent extensions to new breeding areas by Atlantic fulmars *(Fulmarus glacialis)* and several species of gulls of the North Atlantic (see p. 51) show that the traditions binding a population to a locality and a seasonal schedule, although durable, can nevertheless be changed. Changes in the traditions of spatial and temporal distribution of sea birds would seem to be necessities as climates, oceanic currents and extent and amount of sea ice change in mean periodicity over the years.

Birds of the North Atlantic resort to nest in large colonies at local sites along the western and eastern shores of Davis Strait and Baffin Bay, on the shores of east Greenland, Iceland, Jan Mayen, on continental shores of Barents Sea, and on the islands of Svalbard, Novaya Zemlya and Franz Josef Land. Nesting on shores of Bering Sea and Chukchi Sea are maritime populations of the North Pacific. Between the maritime populations of the North Pacific and North Atlantic, the arctic coasts of North America and Asia sustain smaller and often geographically separated populations. Taxonomic differences distinguish those of the Atlantic from their Pacific relatives. For example only one species, the dovekie *(Plautus alle)*, constitutes a numerous North Atlantic and high-arctic population of small auks. In Bering Sea there are several species of small auks, which together with maritime subspecies distinguishable from North Atlantic forms indicate a special avifauna, called Aleutican by FAY and CADE (1959), to suggest its separate development during the Pleistocene and through the subsequent climatic and geographical changes that have so profoundly affected the waters and lands about Bering Sea.

Nesting on Arctic Atlantic Shores

BELOPOL'SKII'S (1961) comments on the seasonal dates of breeding of sea birds in colonies about Barents Sea (Murmansk coast, Novaya Zemlya, Franz Josef Land and Svalbard) illustrate oceanic conditions that govern their programs of breeding. Breeding progresses northward and eastward approximately when warm currents from the Atlantic break the margin of sea ice (Fig. 5.3) and moderate the cold on adjacent shores (Fig. 5.4). The turbulent encounter of warm oceanic

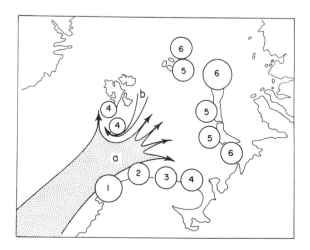

Fig. 5.3. Currents of the Barents Sea and distribution of nesting regions of birds which begin their egg-laying period at different times (according to BELOPOL'SKII, 1961, p. 175). a) direction of warm streams; b) direction of cold streams; (numbers in circles show the consecutive order of the beginning of the egg-laying period)

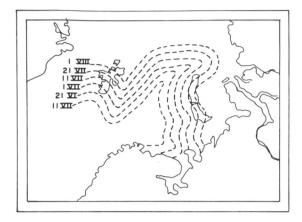

Fig. 5.4. The distribution of the isophenes of the beginning of hatching of the common murre *(Uria aalge)* in the Barents Sea region. Dashed lines are isophenes of the beginning of hatching; Arabic and Roman numerals give the date (day and month) of the beginning of each 10-day period. (From BELOPOL'SKII, 1961, Fig. 93, p. 210)

water with cold arctic water newly released from ice prepares a medium productive of marine organisms on which the birds can feed. Evidently the traditional location and timing of colonial nesting in the Arctic makes for an assured reproductive program, for both BELOPOL'SKII (1961) and FREUCHEN and SALOMONSEN (1958) remarked that colonial breeding of the arctic North Atlantic maritime birds was not interrupted by unsuccessful years, as occurs occasionally on arctic lands. It may be that moderation by the sea regularly tempers their environment, but the considerable annual fluctuations in the northward retreat of margins of the arctic sea ice suggest that highly variable annual regimes in local marine environments are not recognized as influences upon breeding.

Because significant records of dimensions of birds are not common I have compiled some from BELOPOL'SKII's (1961) extensive studies of colonial nesting maritime birds of Barents Sea (Table 5.3). They appear to be close to the few and occasional records of related species and subspecies breeding on arctic shores of the western Atlantic Ocean and Bering Sea. In this compilation, however, I have taken average weight of the species without regard for the often considerable difference between males and females.

In order to characterize these birds with some reality I interject some descriptions of their activities. The cliff- and mountain-nesting sea birds are essentially carnivorous. Eiders *(Somateria mollissima)* that nest on flat coastal lands feed largely on mussels; gulls (Laridae) and jaegers (Stercoraridae) are omnivorous in taking almost any living or dead prey; the fierce big glaucous gull *(Larus hyperboreus)*, is a predator on eggs and on young and crippled birds, as well as on any dead animal matter; in addition to their predatory capture of small birds, swift parasitic jaegers have marked skill at harrying other birds as they return from successful fishing until the victim drops or disgorges the food that it was transporting to its nestlings, which the swift jaeger then seizes. So impressive is this behavior, in which several jaegers often act in effective concert, that Alaskan Eskimos name the parasitic jaeger Mirgiaksyook, which, as it sounds, means vomit (IRVING, 1953). I find this name more apt than the implication of sportsmanship in our designation of the jaeger as hunter.

It is most pleasing to watch Arctic terns *(Sterna paradisaea, 100 g)* intently

Table 5.3. Incubation period, weight of new chicks and adult weight of some sea birds of Murman Coast of Barent Sea (Arranged in order of adult weight)

Species	Depth of feeding	Period from 1st egg to hatching (days)	Weight of adult (kg)	Weight at hatching (g)
Somateria mollissima (Common eider)	shallow	24	2.0	68
Larus marinus (Great black-backed gull)	surface	31	1.65	80
Larus hyperboreus (Glaucous gull)	surface	28	1.6	84
Larus argentatus (Herring gull)	surface	28	1.1	58
Uria aalge (Common murre)	diving	32	1.05	73
Uria lomvia (Thick-billed murre)	diving	32	1.00	71
Alca torda (Razor-bill)	shallow	33	0.71	63
Fratercula arctica (Common puffin)	shallow	35	0.49	46
Stercorarius parasiticus (Parasitic jaeger)	surface	25	0.44	33
Cepphus grylle (Black guillemot)	diving	29	0.43	34
Larus tridactyla (Kittiwake)	surface	24	0.40	36
Larus canus (Mew gull)	surface	25	0.40	36
Sterna paradisaea (Arctic tern)	surface	21	0.10	13

surveying the water over which they fly and making their sudden dives, in which they swiftly sideslip to correct their initial estimates of their target, and emerge from a shallow depth with their prey of small fish or crustacean. At places where terns congregate for nesting they combine so effectively in defensive action as to repel invaders many times their size. It is even said that the less pugnacious eiders seem to take advantage of the protection to be gained by nesting near a colony of terns.

Fulmars (Fulmarus g. glacialis) arrive at high rocky cliffs in west Greenland a month before laying a single egg per pair in late May or early June in their colonies situated from 600 to 1500 meters above the sea. At this time firm sea ice may extend far out from shore, requiring flights for several hundred kilometers to their supply of food in open water. A long interval follows between arrival and nesting. The young birds are fed so well that they approach adult weight by the beginning of August. The large, fat chicks then remain for three weeks without further feeding while their feathers develop until they take off from the ledges for the sea. Numbers in populations are so rarely given that I quote SALO-MONSEN's (1959) estimate that 200000 pairs of fulmars nest in west Greenland.

The small dovekies *(Plautus alle,* 165 g) nest in great aggregations under stones on mountainsides of the high arctic Atlantic regions. FREUCHEN and SALOMONSEN (1958) estimate the population of dovekies to be 30x10⁶ in northwest Greenland and as many more in Svalbard, with another 10x10⁶ in Jan Mayen, Franz Josef Land and Novaya Zemlya. The total of some 70x10⁶ for this species of the north Atlantic sounds large until we reflect that it equals the numbers in the human population of a small country of Europe. At places and times along arctic shores where sea birds congregate their numbers and densities appear vast. For a brief part of the year in selected places, birds appear to exist in limitless supply for the sustenance of the avian predators, arctic foxes and resident people. Within the margin of the pack ice in central Bering Sea 12 species of birds were observed during a cruise in March. Among them the murres *(Uria)* were in such conspicuous numbers as to lead to the impression that their ultimate consumption of marine productivity might, even in winter, exceed that of the seals and walrus breeding in the late winter ice (IRVING et al., 1970). The marine nourishment of these birds is evidently present in copious amounts. It would only be a poor guess, however, to say that the productivity of birds in their limited arctic season and restricted localities is probably not great in comparison with such biomasses about southern shores as have produced the beds of guano on the islands off the shores of Peru.

Diversity in Schedules of Breeding

Fulmars in west Greenland, remain at their colonies during three months. The duration of incubation and the length of stay in the nest until fledging of 14 species of colonial birds of Barents Sea show wide diversity (Fig. 5.5). Green cormorants *(Phalacrocorax aristotelis),* common eiders *(Somateria spectabilis)* and arctic terns *(Sterna paradisaea)* also nest southward along boreal coasts of Europe,

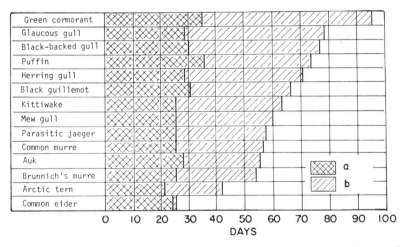

Fig. 5.5. Average duration of incubation and stay in the nest of nestlings of a pair of various Barents Sea birds. a) brooding period; b) period of the stay in the nest or on the nesting site. (From BELOPOL'SKII, 1961, Fig. 114, p. 246)

76

so that their breeding programs are adaptable to an extended range of climate. BELOPOL'SKII (1961) remarked that on warmer European coasts green cormorants expend many days more at nesting than on the colder coast of east Murmansk (Fig. 5.6). In contrast kittiwakes *(Rissa tridactyla)*, puffins *(Fratercula arctica)* and black guillemots *(Cepphus grylla)* spend progressively shorter periods in nesting on more northern coasts. He commented that prolonged nesting of the cormorant on cold coasts east of Murmansk was related to its being near the coldest limit of this cormorant's range and suggested that the species had not yet become adapted to the arctic regime of cold like the three others (in Fig. 5.6) that have become adapted during a long time to breeding on high-arctic coasts.

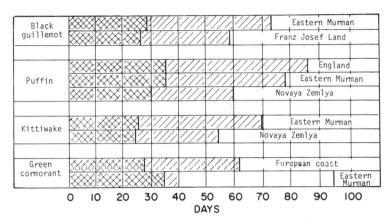

Fig. 5.6. Average (approximate) duration of the nesting period of one pair of birds of some species in relation to the nesting region. (From BELOPOL'SKII, 1961, Fig. 115, p. 247)

Kittiwakes *(Rissa tridactyla)* that breed about Barents Sea also breed on the temperate coast of Britain and Channel Islands and about the Arctic Circle in Bering Sea. Over wide ranges of longitude and latitude, the reported duration of incubation in colonies of black legged kittiwakes *(Rissa tridactyla)* did not differ (Table 5.4). As I observed earlier in relation to an interior Alaskan situation (p. 67), the duration of incubation appeared to show little adaptation to locality and climate, being a relatively unmodifiable characteristic of the species. The prepa-

Table 5.4. Duration of incubation of black-legged kittiwakes *Rissa tridactyla* as observed at several locations

Location	Latitude	Number of eggs	Average incubation (days)	Range (days)
Northumberland England	55°	119	27.3	25–32
Novaya Zemlya USSR	72°	6	25	24–26
Cape Thompson Alaska	69°	15	28	25–31

(From SWARTZ, 1966)

ratory stay on the nesting site and the subsequent duration of parental care until the time of departure from the nest (fledging) appears to be modifiable by adjusting the duration of some behavioral sequences to suit local circumstances. It is dubious speculation to ascribe modification of timing of the sequences in a portion of a bird's breeding program to adaptation by natural selection when it is known that the periodicity of physiological phases of the program of breeding is evoked by signals from the environment that predict the progress of seasons.

References

BELOPOL'SKII, L.O.: Ekologiya Morskikh Kolonial'nykh Ptits Barentscva Moryova Izdatelstvo Akademii Nauk SSSR. Moscow and Leningrad. (Ecology of the sea colony birds of the Barents Sea. By Israel Program for Scientific Translations, Jerusalem, 1961).

BERNARD, C.: Leçons sur les Phénomènes de la Vie communes aux Animaux et aux Vegetaux. Paris: Bailliere 1878.

FAY, F.H., CADE, T.J.: An ecological analysis of the avifauna of St. Lawrence Island, Alaska. University of California Pub. in Zoology, Vol. 63, No. 2, 73–150 (1959).

FREUCHEN, P., SALOMONSEN, F.: The Arctic Year. New York: Putnam 1958.

FRITH, H. J.: Temperature regulation in the nesting mounds of the mallee fowl, *Leipora ocellata* Gould. CSIRO Wildlife Research 1, 79–95 (1956).

IRVING, L.: The naming of birds by Nunamiut eskimos. Arctic 6, 35–43 (1953).

IRVING, L.: The birds of Anaktuvuk Pass, Kobuk and Old Crow. United States National Museum Bulletin 217. Washington, D.C.: Smithsonian Institution 1960.

IRVING, L., KROG, J.: Temperature during the development of birds in arctic nests. Physiol. Zool. 29, 195–205 (1956).

IRVING, L., McROY, C.P., BURNS, J.J.: Birds observed during a cruise in the ice-covered Bering Sea in March 1968. The Condor 72, 110–112 (1970).

MacMULLEN, R.A., EBERHARDT, L.L.: Tolerance of incubating pheasants to exposure. J. Wildlife Mgt. 17, 322–330 (1953).

MATTHEWS, G.V.T.: Some aspects of incubation in the Manx shearwater. Ibis 96, 432–440 (1954).

MURPHY, R.C.: Oceanic Birds of South America. 2 Vols. New York: Amer. Mus. Nat. History 1936.

NORTON, D.W.: Thermal regime of nests and bioenergetics of chick growth in the Dunlin *(Calidris alpina)* at Barrow, Alaska. Univ. of Alaska, Thesis (1970).

OAKESON, B.B.: The Gambel's Sparrow at Mountain Village, Alaska. The Auk 71, 351–365 (1954).

WALLACE, A.R.: The geographical Distribution of Animals. London: MacMillan 1876.

WILLIAMSON, F.S.L., THOMPSON, M.C., HINES, J.O.: Avifaunal investigations. In: Environment of the Cape Thompson Region, Alaska. Ed. by N.J. Willimovsky and J.N. Wolfe. Oak Ridge, Tenn.: USAEC Div. of Techn. Information Ext. 1966.

WYNNE-EDWARDS, V.C.: Animal Dispersion in Relation to Social Behavior. New York: Hafner Pub. Co. 1962.

Chapter 6

Maintenance of Arctic Populations of Mammals

Marine Mammals that Breed on Ice

Seals roaming freely over the oceans are difficult to observe and are obscure in their ways. At the season of breeding, however, they resort to firm ice or shores and for periods explicit for each population they become attached to specific breeding localities until the pups acquire sufficient capability for independent aquatic life. In these temporarily fixed situations the populations are visible. Exposure at time of breeding, particularly by populations that congregate in numbers, has favored human exploitation leading to near-extinction of some populations. The tenacity of traditional attachments to breeding localities is shown in their persistent exploitation. On the Pribilof Islands the hauling out of fur seals (*Callorhinus ursinus*) in their established rookeries has worn the hard rock smooth. On some southern coasts the smoothly worn rocks attest that ancient breeding places were long utilized by populations that are now extinct. Erosion of the rocky breeding places demonstrates the persistence of their seasonal use. Northern elephant seals (*Mirounga angustirostris*) and a northern outpost of southern fur seals (*Arctocephalus phillippii townsendi*) have reconstituted populations from at most only a few survivors of slaughter to occupy again rocks or beaches used by their predecessors off western coasts of Mexico and California.

Obscure in their maritime life but exposed at traditional breeding places, the populations of seals can be referred to place, date and numbers more accurately than the populations of mammals that breed scattered over land. Seal pups require both time and maternal care to develop capability for swimming and diving. Pups born on cold arctic or antarctic ice must at first encounter cold air and then develop quite different insulation to cope with the cooling effect of cold water that is the environment of adults (see p. 29). In the exacting conditions of arctic and antarctic seas the seals meet the most severe cold encountered by mammals. Yet of 30 populations of Phocidae named by SCHEFFER (1958), 17 breed on ice, and his minimum estimates of breeders on ice amount to near 11 000 000 in comparison with fewer than 600 000 that breed on shore (IRVING, 1969) (see p. 29).

Seals and Walrus of Bering Sea

None of the fur seals or sea lions of the family Otariidae breed on ice and they are not referrable to the Arctic. Seven of the species of hair seals (Phocidae) breed on arctic ice. Four of these species and the Pacific walrus (*Odobenus rosmarus*) breed on the ice of Bering Sea (Table 6.1). The physical data for mothers and pups represent characteristics of populations of each species that breed within the margin of ice in late winter in central and eastern Bering Sea (Table 6.2). All but ribbon seals also range widely over arctic waters, but the sizes and timing reported for those of Bering Sea represent individuals of populations that can properly be regarded as coherent and perhaps distinct from distant congeners.

Table 6.1. Pinnipeds breeding in Bering Sea

	Birth Date	Place	Time to weaning	Lanugo Color	Time to molting
Odobenus rosmarus (Walrus)	Apr–June	Ice	12–24 mos.	white	prenatal
Phoca vitulina (Harbor seal)	Mar–Apr	Ice	2–4 wks	white	2–4 wks
Phoca hispida (Ringed seal)	Mar–Apr	Ice Lair	4–6 wks	white	4–6 wks
Histriophoca fasciata (Ribbon seal)	Mar–Apr	Ice	4–6 wks	white	3–6 wks
Erignathus barbatus (Bearded seal)	Mar–Apr	Ice	2–3 wks	gray-brown	prenatal to 1–2 wks

(Data provided by JOHN J. BURNS, Alaska Department of Fish and Game)

Table 6.2. Weight at birth, when weaned, and as adults, duration of nursing, and growth for several pinnipeds

Species	Weight at birth (kg)	Weight when weaned (kg)	Adult weight of female (kg)	Weight of pup as percentage of mother' weight At birth	When weaned	Period of nursing	Increase during nursing period
Odobenus rosmarus (Walrus)	38.5	338	800	4.3.–5.3.	41.9	18 mos.	8.8×
Phoca vitulina (Harbor seal)	10.0	25.5	89	11.2	28.6	3–4 wks	2.6×
Phoca hispida (Ringed seal)	4.5	12	68	6.7	18.0	4–6 wks	2.7×
Histriophoca Fasciata (Ribbon seal)	11.0	26.3	81	13.6	32.4	3–4 wks	2.4×
Erignathus barbatus (Bearded seal)	33.0	85	270	12.3–12.9	31.2	12–18 days	2.5×

(From compilation by JOHN J. BURNS, 1967)

Seasonal Conditions and Exposure of Pups

I am indebted for most of my information about seals and walrus of Bering Sea to many conversations with my colleagues F. H. FAY and JOHN J. BURNS. At the season of birth of the four species of seals (March–April) the margin of ice has only started to retract northward from its southern limit in Bering Sea and the snow covering the ice is thick, cold and dry. Only ringed seals are born in lairs covered with snow, well concealed, sheltered from wind, and in air moderated by the entrance to the water that is used by the mother. The sheltered pups of ringed seals in their lairs are said to be inactive and inoffensive. Pups of three other species lie on snow exposed to cold wind; they are not deliberately shielded by the mother except by contact while nursing. These exposed pups are active and react to a stranger by biting effectively. The conditions in which pups of these four species develop are commonly dry and cold, so that their infantile fur, lanugo, is not wetted. The large pups of the bearded seal soon enter the water, which the pups of the other three species avoid until near the time of weaning. Pups of walrus, on the other hand, are born later in the season (April–June) after the sea ice has moved northward and when snow covering the ice floes is melting and wet. In fact walrus pups may be born in water and they take to the water readily, with solicitous maternal care. For many months the mother nurses them and carefully enfolds them with her flippers for deliberate protection from cold (FAY and RAY, 1968). Similarities and variations in the environment and exposure of pups are met by differing programs of development and care.

Condition of Pups at Birth

Pups of harbor, ringed and ribbon seals are born with thick, white infantile fur (lanugo). This fur is wettable but suited for insulation in cold air as is the fur of northern land mammals. At this early stage these pups do not take to the water for escape, and if wetted they are likely to perish from cold. The large pups of bearded seals are born with or without brownish-gray lanugo and enter the water early in their rapid growth (BURNS, 1967). Pups of walrus have already shed lanugo *in utero*. About as bare as adults, they are born on wet ice and readily enter water, although not able to maintain body temperature without maternal care.

Development through Weaning

The rapid growth of pups (see Table 6.2) is sustained by milk that contains up to 50% fat (COOK and BAKER, 1969). With 6% or 7% protein, the small proportion of water makes it appear that if evaporative cooling were important, as it may be in strong arctic insolation in spring, the supply of water could be critical.

Pups of seals are slender at birth but as they suck the rich milk they expand rapidly in girth without much early increase in length. The mothers shrink visibly during these rapid early stages of growth of the pups. Measurements by AMOROSO and MATTHEWS (1952) on growth of captive gray seal *(Halichoeros)* pups (in Britain) illustrate the process of growth. The mother, which fasts during nursing, lost 43 kg while nursing her pup from the 3rd to the 18th day, while the pup gained 27 kg. In the transfer 16 kg were lost, but the conversion of maternal substance seems large in comparison with rates reported for domesticated mammals. Seal milk is unique in its large content of fat and data are not yet available for evaluation of the energetics of growth in the interesting situation of the marine mammals.

During growth, while nursing, pups of seals progress to molting of their infantile fur and become rather uniformly enclosed in a capsule of blubber through which the head and appendages protrude, only thinly covered. This sheath of

81

blubber affords passive insulation, but through the blubber there develops a rich and reactive vascularity that permits variation in loss or retention of heat to meet the extreme conditions of life on and in arctic seas. The operation of the insulation provided by the coat of blubber will be considered later (Chapter 9). For lack of information we cannot consider the development of capability for swimming and diving, which makes such rapid progress that by the time of weaning the pups have been converted from land animals to animals capable of independent life in the sea.

Special Condition of Walrus Pups

In their amiable social behavior walrus present a contrast to the social behavior of seals. The species of seals vary from solitary in habit to various degrees of specific gregarious association. None of the arctic seals associate to make bodily contact as do breeding fur seals and some species of hair seals in southern rookeries or hauling places. But even where gregariousness leads to crowding and contact, relations among individual seals appear restless and marked by unamiable sounds and gestures that imply that their social aggregations, while doubtless serving the population usefully are not those of friendly sociability. According to accounts and illustrations, walrus in their usual aggregations enjoy close contact in truly "friendly" behavior (FAY and RAY, 1968).

Physical contact of aggregations of walrus on ice to some degree pools bodily heat and shields individuals from weather. In addition there are advantages to a social group from utilizing the experience and memory of the elders for preserving a traditional program that will lead the groups to areas appropriate for feeding and breeding. We humans, who so largely surrender individual choice of action to the dictation of our societies, should appreciate values of social life in other animals, but it is difficult to make scientific identification of values in an association.

As noted above pups of walrus have shed lanugo prenatally. Born on ice, or even in water, their skin is as little protected by hair as in the adults. Nursing continues until the pups approach half of the mother's weight, while the mother solicitously assists the young in water and on ice enfolds it with her flippers for ptotection from cold (see p. 81).

Geographical Variation in Development of Pups of Harbor Seals

The northernmost pups of harbor seals (*Phoca vitulina*) are born on the dry snow of the ice of Bering Sea, covered with white infantile fur (lanugo). In the dry cold their condition can be compared with that of the fur-covered land mammals until they develop capability for aquatic life. By contrast, the pups born on wet rookeries south of the ice have shed lanugo before birth and are early tolerant of wetness that would be fatal to the white-coated pups born on ice. Southward in their range, which extends to Baja California, the season of birth becomes later until birth occurs in late summer. Thus in the harbor seals of the American Pacific the condition of newborn pups and the circumstances and season of birth are quite various. Taxonomic distinction of these populations is still unclear in spite of the pronounced differences in condition and circumstances of the pups

82

at birth. In contrast, disjunct populations of the ringed seals of Lake Baikal *(P. hispida sibirica)* and the Caspian Sea *(P. hispida caspica)* retain the habit of breeding on ice in winter and in their present ranges show no disposition toward breeding on shore in the temperate conditions of summer.

The harbor seals of the American Pacific that show these large variations in condition, circumstance and season of birth make corresponding geographical differentiations in their annual programs. We assume that the differences are adaptive and suspect that the plasticity of the species has been drawn upon by genetic selection that develops through coherence of the differentiated populations that maintain sufficient degrees of isolation in the various localities.

Mammals that Breed on Land

At the time when young are born, mammalian mothers are more or less immobilized and can be definitely assigned to given situations (Table 6.3). During the remainder of the year they may move, according to their natures, over wider ranges. Their movements are constrained by limitations other than power of locomotion. In varying specific degrees there are inclinations for social aggregation, and tendencies to repeat the same paths in each recurrent season are conspicuous in annual programs of mammalian societies. Geographical and seasonal order of seals is conspicuous on their breeding grounds. Mammals that breed on land are usually secretive and dispersed over sparsely inhabited arctic lands. It is so difficult to observe natural populations of arctic animals that biologists are understandably inclined to extrapolate from small collections of data to construct plausible descriptions of populations. I also am biased by seeking for evidence of regularity in the relation of each mammalian population to a place and time of reproduction. The evidence for orderliness in the reproduction of arctic mammals on land is not comprehensive, but there are a few illustrations that point in that direction.

Table 6.3. Situation at birth on land of some arctic mammals

Burrows underground	Nests at interface of snow and ground	Exposed on snow
Citellus (Ground squirrel)	*Microtus, Clethrionomys* (Vole)	*Lepus* (Hares)
Marmota (Marmot)	*Lemmus, Dicrostonyx* (Lemming)	*Rangifer tarandus* sp. Caribou
Mustela (Weasel)	Soricidae (Shrew)	*Ovibos moschata* sp. Muskox
Gulo gulo (Wolverine)		
Canis lupus (Wolf)		
Alopex, Vulpes (Fox)		
Ursus maritimus (Polar bear – (burrow in snow)		

Musk Oxen

Over arctic Canada west of Hudson Bay, on the Canadian arctic islands, in East Greenland and formerly in arctic Alaska a unique ruminant, the musk ox (*Ovibos moschata*), ranged in small herds on the tundra. TENER (1965) estimated its numbers at 1500 on the mainland of Canada, with 8400 on several arctic islands, in addition to the population of east Greenland. Before 1917, when legal protection effected their survival and subsequent gradual increase, musk oxen had been much reduced by explorers and native hunters. With thick wool and long hair, the stocky animals (weight 360 kg) withstood any arctic cold where their food in form of willows, grasses, sedges, forbs and some other woody plants was available without thick cover by snow. Part of their success is attributable to their habit of slowly wandering to feed without remaining to eradicate the plant cover. Their usual paths did not exceed 80 kilometers in a year. Herds were often settled enough to be considered in local residence, but wanderers have recently resettled in distant areas from which they had been eliminated, even by crossing the ice between arctic islands.

Another important factor is their social habit of forming closely coherent herds, in which the experience of older members doubtless guides the young to areas formerly found suitable according to the season. The defensive action of the small herds is well known, in which the adults form a compact group about the calves to present their formidable horns in charges to repel attacking wolves. This habit made them easy prey of man.

Closely attended captive musk oxen become gentle and apparently even affectionate toward their keepers. I cannot forego the story told to me on separate occasions by two highly respected elder scientists, who as young men had cared for captive musk oxen at the University of Alaska. They claimed to have watched their senior and admired director of the operation as he climbed the fence enclosing a large bull. The bull showed his intent to charge and swiftly consummated the act, but stopped short an arm's length from the director, who rewarded the bull by rubbing its nose. The narrators of this story both separately explained that training had eliminated the hostility of the beast, but that his inclination to charge was more deeply seated and ineradicable. I found this analysis of animal behavior too interesting to question the facts and I have not found further evidence for such heroic behavior in a trainer.

Reindeer and Caribou

Reindeer and caribou (both frequently designated alike as *Rangifer tarandus*, with debatable separation of some taxa as species and a number of accepted local subspecies) are one of the several kinds of large land mammals that invaded America in the Pleistocene and have survived until modern times while many ancient kinds of large American mammals (mammoths, horses, camels, several bisons, and some carnivores) became extinct. Since the disappearance of the Wisconsin ice caps boreal and arctic people have subsisted largely on caribou or reindeer. Because of hunting and domestication the wild habits of Eurasian reindeer have become much obscured.

Caribou of Canada

In boreal and arctic Canada great herds of caribou roamed over tundra in numbers of legendary magnitude. As did the reindeer of the tundra and adjacent taiga of Asia and Europe, American caribou sustained prehistoric men with meat, fat, skins useful for clothing because of their warmth and lightness and suitable for kayaks and tents, sinew for thread and cords, and bone and antlers for many implements. Early explorers of North America found the Indians of the margins of forest and tundra principally dependent on caribou. Even then, when the prehistoric caribou of the Barren Grounds westward from Hudson Bay nearly to the Mackenzie Valley might have numbered 3 000 000 (KELSALL, 1968), they were unevenly distributed in time and locality. Annual migrations proceeded into the northern forest in winter and northward in summer to areas of tundra rather conventionally used for calving. The main bands of some migrating herds appear to have travelled as much as 600 linear kilometers in each annual movement, probably the longest migratory traverse of mammals on land.

Until 1900 the population of caribou of the Barren Grounds may not have been depleted in spite of their support of a few thousand resident Indians and Eskimos. In addition, they sustained the highly organized northern Canadian fur trade and its elaborate system for supply and export. Economy in use of natural resources existed neither in the fur trade nor among the Indians and Eskimos when impelled by desire for trade goods to collect fur for export. Exploiting the occasional concentrations that occurred as herds of caribou traveled over traditional migratory routes simplified the opportunistic and wasteful slaughter by both native people and traders. Alarmed by the declining numbers of caribou and the consequent want and even starvation of native residents, the Government in 1950 banned killing by non-residents of the area. Surveys then estimated that only some 200 000 caribou remained of the once great herds. Subsequently numbers have recovered in a slow but encouraging manner.

On the tundra the apparently leisurely movement of feeding caribou often transports them faster than human pursuit can overtake. When a team of dogs perceived caribou the dogs became uncontrollable and so often upset the sled that the method of pursuit was pointless. Now the increasingly prevalent snow machines do not so alarm the caribou, and heedless drivers can harass the animals and disorganize the orderly movements upon which they naturally depend. Domesticated reindeer are trained, by continuous attention of their herders with aid from their clever herd dogs, to remain in selected feeding areas. With proper attention the herders can then assemble the deer before the pasture is depleted and move them to a fresh area. When they are herded into a compact mass by their accustomed herders it is remarkable how rapidly the crowded deer can move without injuring each other.

By their natural dispersion the moving herds do not eradicate their diversified food, in which lichens, grasses, and sedges, and willows are important components. From recorded weights of wild caribou (KELSALL, 1968) it appears that growth in bulk occurs mainly in a few summer months, while the longer winter finds them just maintaining weight and apparently economizing by diminished activity. There is no indication that winter cold exacts special metabolic expenditure.

85

My early ideas about wild herbivores had been derived from the few that I had seen restlessly alert or fleeing from danger. When I first saw a herd of caribou on Alaskan tundra in September, I was impressed by the leisurely manner of their movements and their dainty, occasional feeding. Adults might stop to lie down and ruminate, and calves with little horns might pretend to spar as if in playful emulation of a later stage in adult life. Never had I seen hundreds of large wild animals slowly passing near me. It occurred to me that just before winter life should not be taken so casually. Then I thought that my impression of the necessity for herbivores to feed avidly was derived from watching domesticated cattle busily feeding to prepare the milk and meat which they were driven to produce by dispositions selected for the profit of man.

This drive was not felt by the wild caribou and, in general, I suppose that wild animals on the natural ranges to which they are adapted pass most of their lives at a leisurely pace. Likewise, simple societies of people living in the ways and places of their ancestors are not distracted to artificial tasks by competitive industry, either for survival or for the aggrandizement of their unpretentious societies. The economy of well adapted life seems strange to urban man. Arctic living is not all effortless, but to observe it well requires avoidance of wasteful haste and, at times, withdrawal from concern for the affairs that are designed to keep man busy.

On a day in late summer SIMON PANEAK and I sat on a low mountain overlooking the Etivluk Valley, near Howard Pass, Alaska. Many caribou were moving in small and large bands over the valley, leaving to enter small valleys into the mountains, or entering the larger valley from mountain passes. Their movements were usually unhurried as they fed in leisurely manner or lay down to rest and ruminate; but on one occasion a wolf that had been resting, surrounded by the unconcerned caribou at a distance of 200 meters, made a sudden sally. The caribou that it approached ran swiftly ahead. After a brief run the wolf resumed its rest and the caribou returned to feeding. Simon remarked that it must be a young and foolish wolf. In a few hours we estimated that some 10000 caribou were within our view.

On another day we watched from a long distance as a wolf slowly pursued a band of caribou cows up the shoulder of a mountain. As they reached the summit of the shoulder another wolf suddenly appeared from the opposite direction and seemed to collide with one of the startled oncoming caribou. The animal was immediately dispatched and the two wolves ate briefly from the carcass. When we visited the place a day later a bear had removed the remains.

In northwestern America several herds of caribou persist in distinguishable coherent annual migrations that appear to be focused upon restricted calving areas. North of the Brooks Range in Alaska, pregnant cows of a herd recently estimated to number altogether around 140000 resort for calving to the tundra south of the northeastern arctic coast and east of the Colville River. After calving in late May and early June, the cows with their calves move southward and eastward late in summer to mingle with the more dispersed males and barren females as they pass through the Brooks Range into its forested southern wathershed in northeastern Alaska and arctic Yukon Territory. Rut and breeding occur in October. In their continual movement during the winter, the bands and their composition are rather variable in course and date from year to year, except for the concentration of calving cows, which is relatively regular in date and region. Archaeological remains indicate the antiquity of use of the calving area, which seems to be the geographical reference of this particular group.

There is another calving area, serving a population now estimated at 260 000 caribou, in northwestern Alaska, west of the Colville River and about the upper Meade and Utokuk rivers. After calving there, cows move southward through the central and western Brooks Range, joining with males and barren cows in wandering bands that pass into its southern watershed. Moving groups may lead bands of many thousands of caribou through valleys over routes and on schedules that are expected by resident Eskimos to be used, but in which there is much variation from year to year. Limits of the extent of southward movement have been especially variable in recent years, but the calving area appears to have been prehistorically in regular use.

Other Alaskan caribou are ascribed to several separate calving centers in regular use, about which each herd circulates during the year. The rather vaguely defined margins of movement of these herds, when not involved in calving, at times approach within easy walking range of other herds of the fast-travelling caribou, and it is suspected that individuals or bands occasionally cross over. In fact, massive detachments have been observed to move to join another territorial group.

The southern domains of caribou herds have met reduction and extinctions over considerable parts of Alaska, as well as contamination of the wild stock by periodic escapes from domesticated reindeer introduced from Asia. It is in fact remarkable that the native caribou have maintained territorial coherence in the face of so much disturbance. Surprisingly, the numbers of caribou in the arctic Alaskan herds and in some herds of the interior have been sustained in recent years. Their utilization of extensive range and subsistence on slow-growing vegetation of tundra and their desirability as game seem to place the last survivors of the once large herds of North American herbivores in danger, but at least there is a partial record of their natural annual cycle.

Lemmings

Distribution of Taxa

Many taxonomically distinguishable populations of two genera of lemmings extend over the tundra in rather well defined geographical areas. Brown lemmings (several species and subspecies of *Lemmus*) extend across western and central arctic America, but not so far north in the arctic islands of America as varying lemmings (several species and subspecies of *Dicrostonyx*); nor do brown lemmings occur east of Hudson Bay. In arctic Asia populations of both genera *(Lemmus,* and the varying lemming, *Dicrostonyx)* extend from eastern Siberia to the River Ob, while only brown lemmings (*Lemmus*) occupy tundra westward through the European Arctic.

Delineations of geographical distribution and taxonomic relations among populations indicate that present distribution of varying lemmings in America is the result of orderly extension from ranges in which ancient populations were restricted and isolated (Fig. 6.1). These ancestral populations were apparently confined during Wisconsin Glaciation within refuge areas not covered by the prevalent northern ice caps. Occasional fossil remains and good inferences from present

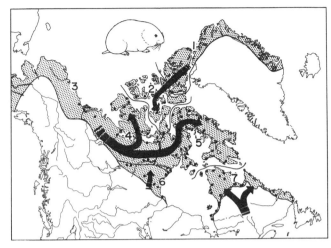

Fig. 6.1. Varying lemming (*Dicrostonyx* spp.). Canadian localities and approximate North American distribution. 1: *D. torquatus groenlandicus*, 2: *D. t. clarus*, 3: *D. t. rubricatus*, 4: *D. t. kilangmiutak*, 5: *D. t. lentus*, 6: *D. t. richardsoni*, 7: *D. hudsonicus*. (From MACPHERSON, 1965)

characteristics indicate that after survival isolated in refuges during Wisconsin Glaciation, lemmings of discrete populations expanded their ranges as the ice caps became ablated. During extensions of postglacial geographical populations numbers have multiplied, but morphological traces of their ancestry have remained in the enlarged and expanded populations. Thus recognizable forms have persisted in discrete regions through such extraordinary variations of their environments during glaciation and deglaciation as would seem to have required major variations in adaptive behavior and physiology.

Fecundity and Cyclic Variations in Numbers

The decline in numbers and extent of arctic populations during Wisconsin Glaciation and their subsequent expansion appear also in the records of other small and large mammals of the North American Arctic (MACPHERSON, 1965). The view into the changing past of lemmings brings out the fecundity for which their populations are now renowned. Periodic multiplication of lemmings to great numbers, and their ensuing migrations, have led to extravagant popular stories about these animals, which are unimpressive as individuals. We must recognize, however, that many stories about arctic life are narrated for social entertainment in circumstances in which it would be inappropriate to question numerical or factual precision, for sociable conversation exists only upon the merit of the interest and pleasure that it evokes. Often obscure in these stories are traces of real events observed during long residence that can supplement the brief studies of the scientist in an arctic locality.

A considerable diversity in accounts of the fluctuation in numbers of lemmings also arises from the hasty inclination of scientists to generalize on populations from brief or occasional observations and to seek for causes of the cyclic variation in numbers. The brown lemmings *(Lemmus)* of Scandinavia have attracted most attention because of the long tradition of Scandinavian biologists for studies in natural history (MARSDEN, 1964). During two or three years between the "lemming years" these little mammals are inconspicuous denizens of grassy and sedgy tundra that extends marginally into suitable adjacent wooded lands. In the third or fourth winter and spring of the cycle numbers in local populations multiply enormously. For reasons that remain obscure, and as if nature had recognized that reproduction had erred to excess, they erupt in crowds that roam away from their usual confines. Valleys may assemble the moving lemmings along easiest paths. Streams and margins of lakes or sea may obstruct progress and cause convergence at promontories. Reports do not indicate that judgment or leadership chooses practical crossings to favorable destinations but rather that blind impetuosity leads to the death of most of the small and weak swimmers.

Wanderings on land seem to be likewise undirected and to result mainly in destruction. The lack of observed organization and the near or total destruction of the wandering lemmings gives rise to the impression that their migrations are naturally designed to bring about reduction in excessive populations. That is certainly a result, for after a "lemming year" the residual survivors have more space for living and overgrazed vegetation recovers. In fact, overpopulation by herbivores periodically accelerates massive conversion of vegetation to animals and their droppings, thus tending to develop cyclic variation in the flow of energy and substance from plants to animals and in return. But data are lacking that would establish net results of the conversion and their cumulative effects upon the environment.

Explanation of Cyclic Variations in Numbers

The cycles of abundance of lemmings have not been connected with near or remote terrestrial or cosmic cyclic phenomena. They are not synchronous over large regions nor are the visible numbers of lemmings alike in successive cycles or over wide distances. The biologist seeking to find in their consistency and apparent effects an explanation of causes and adaptive usefulness of the cycles must resort to rather hopeless speculation. We are not inclined to believe that the ways of nature are capricious and suspect that failure to agree upon an explanation of cyclic fluctuations is likely the result of lack of information and understanding.

American Lemmings

Regarding the lemmings in America we must recall that their arctic haunts are sparsely occupied by man and only occasionally visited by a scientist. West of Hudson Bay the brown and varying lemmings both occupy the tundra, *Lemmus* preferring damper and *Dicrostonyx* drier areas. Local variations in soil and vegetation of tundra are great, and in the prevalent winds the prolonged snow cover in winter changes and differs from place to place. Small northern mammals cannot survive cold or winter without protection from cold by the cover of snow, which confines them to runways at the margin between snow and the vegetation on which they feed (see p. 14).

Lemmings at Baker Lake

At Baker Lake in Keewatin, brown and varying lemmings, laboriously observed from 1959–62, increased from low numbers in 1959 to effect a 25– to 50-fold increase in the winter of 1959-60, with but little decline in numbers in the summer of 1960 (KREBS, 1964). The main decline in numbers occurred in the winter of 1960-61 and continued through the summer of 1961. In summer of 1962, numbers in the area of study were again increasing. In the spring of the peak year considerable traffic of lemmings was visible, but it was not orderly or massive. Avian and mammalian predation did not increase conspicuously, nor did visible signs of disease fluctuate. Their forage was not reduced by more than 30% in wet habitat and the lemmings did not visibly fluctuate in fatness.

Surprisingly, the male lemmings of both species were heavier in the summer of the peak year, attaining 90 grams *(Lemmus)*, although seldom reaching 70 grams in other years. Krebs considered that increase in size was truly a property of the population in that year and not a result of statistically relative conditions. He referred to an interesting theory proposed by CHITTY (1960, further reviewed in 1967) that was based upon cyclic fluctuations in voles. It was suggested that cyclic crowding of the combative little lemmings could bring about, in a polymorphic population, selective survival of large (and mean) males that were intolerant of other males, dangerous to those next to mature, and so wasteful of their own energy as to impair their reproduction. I cannot make critical comments on this idea beyond that it does suggest that in an enormously fecund population rapid qualitative changes might occur which could in turn be cyclically reversed. Conventional causal and mechanistic ideas about populations appear to be inadequate for explanation of the cyclic fluctuations in numbers.

Lemmings at Barrow – 1949

At Barrow, Alaska, cyclic fluctuations in populations have been under observation since 1949. In March of that year there was evidence of many brown lemmings under the snow (RAUSCH, 1950). As the season progressed we saw individuals emerge and run over the surface of the snow toward no obvious goal or to no explainable purpose. As snow began to melt it was evident that lemmings had been concentrated under snow that covered suitable vegetation. As the snow diminished late in May, lemmings in areas of their winter concentration became exposed and were scattered by human and animal predators as well as by their own natural dispersal. Many were consumed by an influx of snowy owls *(Nyctea scandiaca)*, pomarine jaegers *(Stercorarius pomarinus)* and arctic foxes *(Alopex lagopus)*. Many more perished without obvious reason – unless we assume that members of the erupting population simply and aimlessly fled from appropriate cover and food to die from exhausiton or cold, for grossly visible signs of morbidity were not noticeable. By late summer there were few lemmings and the predators had scattered, but the supply of lemmings had produced more than usual numbers of young owls and pomarine jaegers.

Lemmings at Barrow and Their Predators

PITELKA and colleagues (PITELKA et al., 1955) and THOMPSON (1955) observed predation in the cyclic increases of 1953 and in subsequent years at Barrow, when again brown lemmings erupted and scattered widely from their winter covering of snow. Most of the wandering lemmings perished from exhaustion or because their exposure attracted predation by pomarine jaegers, snowy owls and short-eared owls (*Asio flammeus*). In spite of the influx of predators they were so easily supplied by the excess of lemmings that apparently young birds were spared and achieved better production than usual. By late summer lemmings were again scarce. A local cyclic increase in predatory birds had occurred at the expense of the lemmings and then left the opportunistic production of predators to make its own subsequent existence by deployment to other areas and prey.

Periodic Southward Invasion by Snowy Owls

In connection with a recorded invasion by snowy owls *(Nyctea scandiaca)* of southern Canada and northern states in 1945-46, GROSS (1947) remarked that the preceding year had been an arctic "lemming year," favoring development of many young owls. In the year marked by the large influx of owls into southern territory, arctic lemmings were scarce. This logical view of relation of numbers of prey and predators developed through the deployment of the supposedly hungry owls over a wider and, for the displaced individuals, probably unfamiliar range.

Population Cycles and the Northern Catch of Furs

In 1911 SETON observed scarcity and starvation in the lynx *(Lynx canadensis)* of northern Manitoba (boreal Canada) in a summer when varying hares *(Lepus americanus)* had suffered an extreme decline in their cyclically changing numbers. Examining annual catches of fur in the records of the Hudson's Bay Company, he remarked upon large cyclic variations, reaching peak numbers of pelts of lynx at intervals of 10 or 11 years, and of pelts of varying hares at similar intervals but preceding the abundance of lynx by about a year.

Exhaustive studies of reported appearance of obviously excessive numbers of several species of small rodents showed that over much of their northern range cyclic peaks of numbers in populations occurred at intervals of three or four years (ELTON, 1942). Whether these fluctuations, which are often so gross as to appear excessive and wasteful in a natural economy, result from factors intrinsic in the populations or extrinsic in their environment remains, to my mind, undetermined.

Arctic Foxes

In a population of arctic foxes *(Alopex lagopus)* of the interior of Keewatin, west of Hudson Bay, a cycle of fluctuation in numbers showed no change in the annual (and numerous, averaging 10.6) placental scars showing implantation of embryos (MACPHERSON, 1969). Successfully weaned litters of whelps, however, varied from an average of 9.7 in 1960 to 4.6 in 1961 and to none observed in 1962. In all years remains of lemmings (brown and varying) in fox droppings, as great as 90% and always more than 50%, showed their importance in nutrition of the growing whelps. Dependence upon lemmings kept the population of foxes in relation and was apparently at the base of annual variations in the catch of pelts of white foxes, which move cyclically to maximal numbers in the winter after a maximum in numbers of lemmings.

Traditional Use of Dens and Distinction of Taxa

In five years 203 dens were watched. Many were extensive burrows that had been prepared in an earlier summer when ground was unfrozen. Some den systems may have been in use for several hundred years (MACPHERSON, 1969). Accordingly the sites are traditional breeding resorts of local populations, but I have seen no report on the adherence of individuals to dens or areas. Nor is there information about whether foxes that have been seen far from shore on polar ice return to regular denning areas. White foxes are reputed to be produced mainly from populations feeding on lemmings, blue pelaged foxes from some coastal and island situations in which food is largely derived from the beaches. Colored populations of arctic foxes on some islands of Bering Sea are ascribed to taxonomically distinguishable isolates comprised of residents. Well differentiated populations of arctic foxes are also found in mountainous areas of Scandinavia, their distinctness indicating that they are breeding isolates. Over much of arctic America, Eurasia, Greenland and their islands, the degree of localized differentiation appears debatable and recovery of marked foxes has been insufficient to demonstrate regularity in their return to natal or formerly used places of denning. It is apparent that many biologists feel that continous use of certain breeding areas implies order in the geographical reference of individual animals, but frequent lack of good geographical taxonomic distinctions suggests interchange for breeding over wide areas. There is need for records of the actual movements of individual foxes before we can conclude what are the actual factors of coherence in this species, from which individuals appear at times far out on the ice, remote from breeding places.

The foxes that cover so much of the Arctic and which are capable of long travels over the sea ice are examples of animals that, like birds, can seasonally forget or disregard association with a natal area, and in conjunction with physiological progress toward readiness for reproduction, revive impulses leading them toward suitable places for breeding. Attraction to denning places is rather prolonged, for it brings the pair together to mate some two months before the young are born in May or June, and the pair remain associated in caring for the whelps until late July. After this time the bond between parent and young dissolves, the latter scatter, and it is unclear what the foxes are up to until pairs are again found about the dens in mid-winter.

Polar Bears

Polar bears *(Ursus maritimus)*, sometimes reputed to be the largest of the carnivores, are to be found in all national sectors of the Arctic. Valued by the old Eskimos for thick, durable fur that does not mat when wet with sea water, and for food, they were killed with the flint-tipped spear by certain expert bear hunters among those brave old ancients. Long famed and feared by early arctic explorers, they have latterly been vigorously hunted for exhibition of their skins. Cubs can be transported and raised in captivity, where they attract popular interest in zoos. Captives have thrived and reproduced during many years, even in warm temperate climates. Recently, hunting for trophies has caused alarm for the survival of the species that has brought about international conferences on the state of the population (U. S. Department of the Interior, 1965).

Dens and Cubs

Over the arctic circumference the population of polar bears is estimated to be around 20000. Local populations, have not been clearly distinguished and individuals have been found even in the vicinity of the pole. For production of young, however, females resort in autumn to certain coasts, where they prepare dens in snow in which to bear one or two very small cubs in November or December. Cubs are nursed by the mother until, attaining weights around 10 kg in March or April, they are led out to the sea ice. At this time she resumes the capture of seals and the cubs remain in her company into the winter after their birth.

Scope of Wandering by Bears

Except for the restriction of females and cubs to dens on land, movement by the enduring bears over the ice can undoubtedly extend for great distances. Some distribution is, in a sense, due to chance drifting on the seasonally changing margin of arctic ice, but bears are numerous on some arctic coasts and rare on others. Wrangell Island is reported to be a favored denning site in the Soviet Arctic. In Alaska a considerable capture of bears occurs on the ice within a few hundred kilometers of the northwestern coast of Chukchi Sea and off the western arctic coast. Bears of various ages and of both sexes are found there. Few dens on land have been reported in Alaska, but some young cubs captured there appear to have been born in dens on the sea ice along the northeastern coast.

In Canada the northeastern coast of Southampton Island has numerous dens (HARINGTON, 1968). For reproduction, then, polar bears resort to coastal lands in shelters and conditions not unlike those in the northern dens on land of their close relatives, the brown bears *(Ursus arctos)*. In the remainder of their life individual polar bears range over distances on ice that may exceed the scope of any other land mammal, unless perhaps the little arctic fox, which sometimes follows bears far onto the polar ice to feed upon remnants of their captured seals. Marking or following bears has not yet defined their annual courses. But from the repeated utilization of certain coasts for denning it seems likely that, as in other species, individuals maintain some reference to localities and that the population is to a degree geographically organized.

References

AMOROSO, E. C., MATTHEWS, L. H.: Reproduction and lactation in the seal. Report to 2nd Int. Congr. Physiol. Pathol. Animal Reprod. Artificial Insemination, Copenhagen (1952).

BURNS, J. J.: The Pacific Bearded Seal. Alaska Dept. of Fish and Game Report., Juneau, Alaska.

CHITTY, D.: Population processes in the vole and their relevance to general theory. Canad. J. Zool. **38**, 99–113 (1960).

CHITTY, D.: The natural selection of self-regulatory behavior in animal populations. Proc. Ecol Soc. Aust. **2**, 51–78 (1967).

COOK, H. W., BAKER, B. E.: Seal milk. I. Harp seal *(Pagophilus groenlandicus)* milk: Composition and pesticide content. Canad. J. Zool. **47**, 1129–1132 (1969).

ELTON, C.: Voles, Mice and Lemmings. Oxford: The Clarendon Press 1942.

FAY, F. H., RAY, C.: Influence of climate on the distribution of walruses, *Odobenus rosmarus* (Linnaeus). I. Evidence from thermoregulatory behavior. Zoologica 53, 1–18 (1968).

GROSS, A. O.: Cyclic invasions of the snowy owl and the migration of 1945–46. The Auk **64**, 584–601 (1947).

HARINGTON, R. C.: Denning habits of the polar bear. Canad. Wildlife Soc. Report Series 5 (1968).

IRVING, L.: Temperature regulation in marine mammals. In: The Biology of Marine Mammals. Ed. by H. T. ANDERSEN. New York and London: Academic Press 1969.

KELSALL, G. P.: The migratory barren-ground caribou of Canada. Dept. of Indian Affairs & Northern Development. Canad. Wildlife Service Bulletin (1968).

KREBS, C. J.: The lemming cycle at Baker Lake, Northwest Territories, during 1959–62. Arctic Inst. of North America Tech. Paper 15 (1964).

MACPHERSON, A. H.: The origin of diversity in mammals of the Canadian arctic tundra. System. Zool. **14**, 153–173 (1965).

MACPHERSON, A. H.: The dynamics of Canadian arctic fox populations. Canad. Wildlife Service Report Series 8 (1969).

MARSDEN, W.: The Lemming Year. London: Chatto & Windus 1964.

PITELKA, F. A., TOMICH, P. Q., TREICHEL, G. W.: Ecological relations of jaegers and owls as lemming predators near Barrow, Alaska. Ecol. Monographs **25**, 85–117 (1955).

RAUSCH, R. L.: Observations on a cyclic decline of lemmings *(Lemmus)* on the arctic coast of Alaska during spring of 1949. Arctic **3**, 166–177 (1950).

SCHEFFER, V. B.: Seals, Sea Lions, and Walruses: A Review of the Pinnipedia. Stanford, Calif.: Stanford University Press 1958.

SETON, E. T.: The Arctic Prairies. New York: Charles Scribner's Sons 1911.

TENER, J. S.: Muskoxen in Canada. Ottawa: Queens Printer 1965.

THOMPSON, D. Q.: The 1953 lemming emigration at Point Barrow, Alaska. Arctic **8**, 37–45 (1955).

U. S. DEPARTMENT OF THE INTERIOR: Polar Bear. Proc. of 1st Int. Sci. Meet. on the polar bear. Fairbanks, Alaska, Sept. 6–10, 1965.

Chapter 7

Warm Temperature of Birds and Mammals

Velocities of reactions in tissues and the rates of application of power to the operation of vital machinery are in general increased by warmth and depressed by cold. So the cold-blooded organisms act only as rapidly as their temperature permits, at levels imposed by their surroundings. Some poikilotherms can adapt their essential metabolism to some extent to the climate in their geographical range, and some adjustments for optimal activity can suit them for operation in the changing temperatures of the seasons. These adjustments are limited, slow and inflexible in relation to the daily and seasonal fluctuations that are so marked in arctic climates. Freezing arrests productive metabolism in all organisms.

Birds and mammals have developed metabolic systems for rapid and varying activity at their relatively even warm temperature. By becoming warm homeotherms they carry on their lives at their own specific rates independent of the fluctuating temperature caused by the weather in their environment. Homeostasis of body temperature is the condition of their continous free existence at their own rates. This independence permits their operation in tropical, temperate and arctic conditions in specific biological activities that are recognizably alike in all climates and seasons. Their high-powered warm activity and fine senses enable the warm-blooded kinds to overtake cold-blooded prey. By virtue of their homeothermic processes tropical deer and arctic reindeer run at similar speeds, as do their respective carnivorous predators. Air in the tropics is unchangingly close to 30°; in the Arctic it may be 20° in summer, 70° colder in winter.

Early Reports from Arctic Explorers

The warmth of arctic animals attracted attention from arctic explorers who, confined by inexperience and ill-suited clothing to their poorly conditioned ships, themselves encountered difficulties in keeping warm. In narratives of the American arctic voyages of Parry between 1819 and 1825 the body temperatures of foxes, a wolf, polar bears and ptarmigan were mentioned as being as warm as those of animals from temperate regions. Parry was led to communicate these arctic measurements to French scientific journals (PARRY, 1824), for in France philosophical scientists were inquiring imaginatively and by clever experimentation into the physical and chemical nature of animal heat.

Warmth of Arctic and Other Animals

The interior of birds and mammals is kept rather evenly warm by distribution of heat through the circulation among the internal organs. Since not all organs are equally active or regular in producing metabolic heat, temperatures differ a little among the viscera and in the varying activity of muscles, as is to be expected in a composite machine producing heat, but effective vascular convection evens the temperature in what is represented as an internal core. When the animal is comfortable and at rest, the temperature of the core is remarkably steady and characteristic of an individual and a species, as is recognized by the physician's use of a thermometer for diagnosis of normal and febrile conditions. Following our inclination to generalize we can regard the temperature of the interior of a few individuals as a useful index of the thermal state of the species.

Arctic Mammals

In the core of examples of 19 species of wild arctic and boreal mammals, all were warmer than 37° and two that seemed dubiously high reached 40°. That the animals were relatively inactive was determined by observation before they were killed by shooting. The average temperature of the northern species was 38.3°, which was 0.5° warmer than the average of records of 53 species compiled by Morrison and Ryser (1952) from temperate and tropical regions (Fig. 7.1).

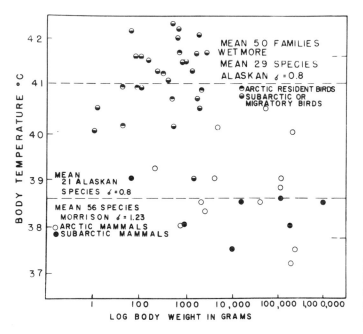

Fig. 7.1. Mean body temperature of arctic and subarctic birds and mammals. (From Irving and Krog, 1954)

Birds

Among many species in 50 families of birds of temperate and tropical regions Wetmore (1921) found the average of their temperatures to be 41.6°, which was 0.5° warmer than the average of our 29 Alaskan boreal and arctic species (see Fig. 7.1). Two species of Antarctic penguins are as warm as penguins from milder regions. In subarctic and arctic Scandinavia Udvardy (1955) found the bodies of small tits (Paridae, 10 to 20 g) about as warm as he had found other northern birds (see also HISSA and PALOKAREGAS, 1970).

Physiologists are constantly at work to formulate facts of life in general terms, and the temperatures of avian species can be ordered with relation to size within statistical limits, except, perhaps for humming birds (Apodiformes) (McNAB, 1966).

Among the arctic examples birds are warmer than mammals, as in warmer climates. The generally warmer condition of birds may reflect the separate evolution of the classes from different reptilian ancestry, such that the warm blooded habit evolved along two lines and possibly even originated twice. The state of arctic animals does not further that speculation, but it reveals that warm bodies are doubtless far older in evolution than the age of the comparatively modern ice capped poles (see p. 17). The temperature of mammals is, of course, a product of metabolic heat production and insulation, or its reciprocal, conductance. Of the three terms in the equation for heat, body temperature appears to be prescribed by nature for species and probably some larger systematic groups. I would therefore agree with the statement that body temperature is not modifiable in adaptation to climate (see SCHOLANDER, HOCK, WALTERS, JOHNSON and IRVING, 1950; SCHOLANDER, HOCK, WALTERS and IRVING, 1950).

Contrast of Environmental and Animal Warmth

Comparison of climates throughout the world reveals the extreme seasonal variation in temperature of the Arctic in comparison with the lesser variation in temperate seasons and least variation in the tropics. Over their geographical ranges resi-

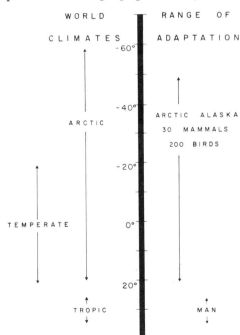

Fig. 7.2. The range of temperature encountered in the climates of the world and the range of adaptation of warmbloodes animals. (From IRVING, 1965)

dent birds and mammals maintain their characteristic even warm body temperature without evident modification for present geographical differences in climate (Fig. 7.2). As in many other physiological und behavioral ways the level of temperature of a species is adapted to its anciently prescribed central temperature.

Variations in Temperature of the Body

Birds

During the day the temperature measured in the cloaca of a few captive small boreal birds in small cages fluctuates within a range of 1°, as is illustrated by the record of the gray jay *(Perisoreus canadensis fumifrons,* 80 g) at Fairbanks (lat. 65° N) (Fig. 7.3). The temperature declined about noon, at the time when we are accustomed to see northern land birds taking a quiet siesta, both in winter and summer. The level of temperature by day was not different from summer to winter, but the duration of warm daytime temperature was extended in summer and shortened in winter within the span of sunlight at that latitude. The birds cooled rather promptly at sunset and rewarmed toward dawn. The evident anticipation of sunrise in winter and deferment of cooling after sunset conforms with our observation of the regime of activity of northern birds in winter during twilight that could extend the arctic day's activity a little beyond the visibility of the sun.

During midwinter months at Barrow, GESSAMAN (1968) continuously recorded temperatures in snowy owls through a transmitter from a sensor implanted in the abdominal cavity. The owls were outdoors and exposed to temperatures falling below −30° and the prevalent considerable winds. Except for some surprising depressions, temperatures fluctuated only between 40.8° and 41.1° but did not show the decline seen in the sleeping and resting periods of many birds. During 10-day periods one owl showed from one to nine arrythmic depressions of temperature from 0.5° to 8.4° during a 24 h period. Most of these depressions lasted from 26 min to 188 min. The rather sudden, irregular and often marked cooling of the owls was not referrable to time, weather or other observed circumstances. I do not know of records of such transients in temperature of other birds. Smaller and rather frequent rhythmic rise and fall of body temperature was reported in arctic ground squirrels *(Citellus)* by continuous monitoring from an internally placed sensor (FOLK, 1966). It is likely that we have missed many points in the operation of animals by occasional or intermittent observation.

In winter at Anchorage (lat. 60° N) seven species of captive birds living outdoors, differing in weight between 100 g and 1.5 kg, showed nocturnal cooling of the same order as is reported for birds in warmer climates (IRVING, 1955). Elevation of temperature of the bird's body during exercise has also been observed in arctic birds shot during flight. All in all there appears no peculiarity in body temperature among arctic birds to suggest significant adaptive modification to their climate.

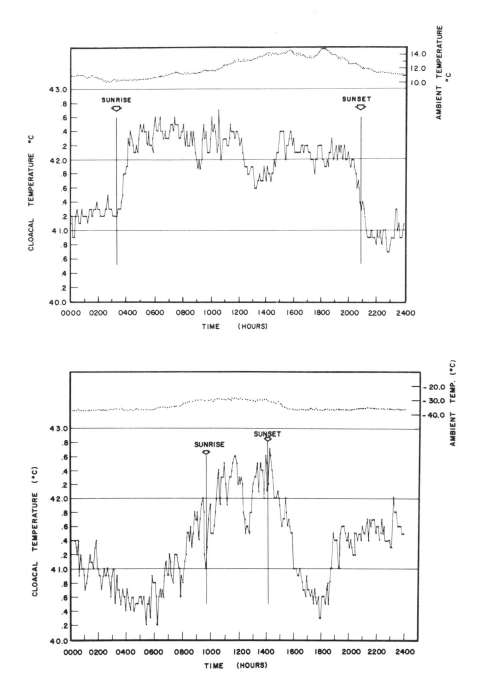

Fig. 7.3. Average summer (July 30, 1961) and winter (January 6, 1962) diurnal cloacal temperatures of the gray jay at Fairbanks, Alaska. (From VEGHTE, 1964)

Mammals

Many measurements of temperatures in the bodies of mammals have been reported. I shall remark upon only a few that I think illustrate common views. The ground squirrel *(Citellus,* 700–1300 g) of arctic Alaska in summer, exposed for several hours to air at temperatures between +30° and –30°, maintained rectal temperatures between 36.5° and 39.0° (ERIKSON, 1956). Part of the extent of fluctuations in temperature can be attributed to short cyclic changes between sleep and activity that occur in these squirrels during a summer's day (FOLK, 1966). Mammals smaller than squirrels periodically vary their activity and temperature during 24 h in cycles of rest and activity that are probably related to the requirement imposed by their small size and related small metabolic reserves for frequent periods of feeding and rest.

When an arctic white fox *(Alopex lagopus)* was thrust into a cold chamber at –80° for an hour it shivered but showed no decline in rectal temperature after being removed from the exposure to cold (SCHOLANDER, HOCK, WALTERS, JOHNSON and IRVING, 1950). The sturdy little fox (4 kg) had undergone transportation from Barrow, Alaska, to Washington, D. C., for exposure in a facility for providing low temperature, and still retained its arctic capability.

A large (40 kg) and especially gentle arctic sled dog, with long hair, was enclosed in a cold chamber for three hours at –50°. When it was removed there was no change in its rectal remperature, nor had the temperature at the surface of the skin or the subcutaneous temperature under thick fur over the femur changed appreciably. Under the somewhat thinner fur over the tibia the subcutaneous

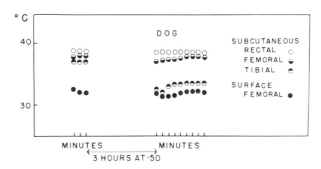

Fig. 7.4. Comparison of measurements of rectal, subcutaneous and skin temperatures of a quiet arctic sled dog before and immediately after experimental exposure to cold. Legends show location of measurement. (From IRVING and KROG, 1955)

temperature had declined about 3° (IRVING and KROG, 1955) (Fig. 7.4). Under the thick fur of arctic mammals larger than the fox, the warmth of the body extends nearly to the skin without much decrement even in coldest weather. The same extent of bodily warmth is likely under the thick contour feathers of arctic birds of the size of ptarmigan *(Lagopus)*, but measurement on their skin may be made uncertain by disarrangement of the feathers.

Temperature of Sleeping Men

I am not aware that the internal temperature of people has been found significantly different in the Arctic. A few (11) young Indian men in arctic Yukon Territory and 10 young Eskimo men of Baffin Island cooled about a degree toward morning while sleeping comfortably warm, not differing from young white men with whom they were compared. When sleeping in cold with insufficient covers, restless and shivering, the Indians and Eskimos cooled on the average 0.5° more than the whites. The samples are not sufficient to represent a population and the amount of cooling did not represent significant metabolic change (HART et al., 1962). Although we cannot ascribe thermal significance to the daily changes in temperature of arctic animals, they do represent circadian rhythms that reveal waxing and waning of controlled metabolism.

Elevation of Temperature in Exercise

In sustained strenuous exercise a man may warm by several degrees, and the warming has been considered to be proportional to the effort (metabolic use of oxygen) in a modest range of warm to cool air. These observations have been made in warm climates on lightly clothed athletes in air temperatures tolerable to nearly naked men. In cold arctic air, man's requirement for clothing imposes an extrinsic insulation that constrains his freedom of heat regulation and complicates the physiological picture to an uncertain degree. It is certainly the impression from experience and observation that hard work in arctic cold increases the feeling of warmth to an uncomfortable degree unless clothing can be discarded or ventilated.

Grueling exercise of Alaska sled dogs in a 50 kilometers championship race resulted in elevations of rectal temperatures that were seldom over one degree (EAGAN et. al., 1963). In this particular race the air was near freezing, which is warmer than is considered desirable for racing dogs. During exercise at about four times resting metabolic rate, pulling a sled in Lappland, a reindeer commonly warmed about half a degree (HAMMEL et al., 1962). These few measurements point to effective regulation of temperature in working arctic mammals. In fact the changes are less than human long distance runners sustain in warm weather without the apparent impairment that accompanies elevation of temperature in fever. The elevation of body temperature in human athletes is related to the rate of their performed work. Athletes and trained dogs can both expand their rate of production of metabolic heat over 15 times, but the elevation of human body temperature during exercise may be ascribed to the relatively poor insulation of man and his high rate of sweating, for man is rather peculiar in his methods of regulating heat.

Arctic birds and mammals that have been shot while actively flying or running have commonly been found warmer than at rest, but the observations are not well enough controlled to show the relation between elevation of temperature and rate of working. The insulation of arctic mammals is so effective in preserving interior warmth that our problem later will be in seeing how the heat of intense activity can be dissipated without undue elevation of temperature of the body.

General Observations on Temperature in the Body

The interiors of mammalian and avian bodies are maintained at levels of temperature fixed for each species and perhaps for their operational state and not subject to alteration by the climates in which they live. Having made that sweeping generalization I shall have to make several reservations. Egg-laying mammals (Monotremata), marsupials (Marsupiala), sloths, armadillos and anteaters (Edentata) are reputedly lax about regulating their temperature, as if as representatives of primitive orders in the system of mammalian classification they had not perfected homeostasis. They are also commonly inhabitants of warm countries. Some, however, dwell at chilly high elevations and opossums (Didelphidae) extend in America to cold Patagonia and southern Canada. None now occur in or near the Arctic.

The interior of birds and mammals at rest but awake is held at even warmth characteristic of each species. In sleep the temperature declines, perhaps more in birds than in mammals, and the decline and recovery of warmth pursues, in various species, different courses which we cannot suspect of identity in detail. Furthermore, in exercise the temperature of the core may rise by several degrees. All of these fluctuations in temperature appear to be common conditions of warm-blooded existence. They are adjustments to which the animals are constrained by their specific nature or inheritance and by some common relation as homeotherms. Arctic or tropic surroundings seem to have little effect on internal temperature and none that appears to be really adaptive to the external environment.

If internal temperature does not specially adapt animals to suit arctic life, why waste time on its discussion? Homeostasis of internal temperature is one of the conditions that allows birds and mammals to operate independent of their environment. Levels of homeothermism were, I suspect, established by evolution before an arctic climate existed on earth. Next we will consider the means by which warmth is maintained in the Arctic.

References

EAGAN, C. J., DURRER, J. L., MILLARD, W. M.: Rectal temperature of the working sled dog. Tech. Doc. Report AAL-TDR-63–40, Arctic Aeromedical Laboratory, Ft. Wainwright, Alaska (1963).

ERIKSON, H.: Observations of the body temperature of arctic ground squirrels *(citellus parryi)* during hibernation. Acta Physiol. Scand. **36**, 1–2 (1956).

FOLK, G. E., JR.: Environmental Physiology. Ed. by G. E. FOLK, JR. Philadelphia: Lea & Febiger 1966.

GESSAMAN, J. A.: Metabolism and thermoregulation of the snowy owl. Ph. D. Thesis, Univ. of Illinois, Dep. of Zool. (1968).

HAMMEL, H. T., HOUPT, T. R., LANGE-ANDERSEN, K., SKJENNEBERG, S.: Thermal and metabolic measurements on a reindeer at rest and in exercise. Techn. Doc. Report AAL-TDR-61-54. Arctic Aeromedical Laboratory, Ft. Wainwright, Alaska (1962).

HART, J. S., SABEAN, H. B., HILDES, J. A., DEPOCAS, F., HAMMEL, H. T., ANDERSEN, K. L., IRVING, L., FOY, G.: Thermal and metabolic responses of coastal Eskimos during a cold night. J. Appl. Physiol. **17**, 953–959 (1962).

HISSA, R., PALOKAREGAS, R.: Thermoregulation in the tit mouse *(Parus major)*. Comp. Biochem. Physiol. **33**, 942–953 (1970).

IRVING, L.: Nocturnal decline in the temperature of birds in cold weather. The Condor **57**, 362–365 (1955).

IRVING, L.: Animal adaptation to cold. In: Conference on cold Injury. Josiah Macy, Jr., Foundation 5th series 1957, 11, 60.

IRVING, L.: Ecology and thermoregulation. Proc. of Claude Bernard Symp. Paris 381–391 (1965).

IRVING, L., KROG, J.: Body temperature of arctic and subarctic birds and mammals. J. Appl. Physiol. **6**, 667–680 (1954).

IRVING, L., KROG, J.: Temperature of skin in the arctic as a regulator of heat. J. Appl. Physiol. **7**, 355–364 (1955).

KING, J.R., FARNER, D.S.: Energy Metabolism. In: Biology and Comparative Physiology of Birds, Vol. II. Ed. by A. J. MARSHALL. New York: Academic Press 1961.

McNAB, B.K.: An analysis of the body temperature of birds. The Condor **68**, 47–55 (1966).

MORRISON, P.R., RYSER, F.A.: Weight and body temperatures in mammals Science **116**, 231–232 (1952).

PARRY, W.E.: Journal of a Second Voyage for the discovery of a Northwest Passage from Atlantic to the Pacific in his Majesty's Ships Fury and Hecla. London: John Murray 1842.

SCHOLANDER, P.F., HOCK, R., WALTERS, V., IRVING, L.: Adaptation to cold in arctic and tropical mammals and birds in realtion to body temperature, insulation, and basal metabolic rate. Biol. Bull. **99**, 259–269 (1950).

SCHOLANDER, P.F., HOCK, R., WALTERS, V., JOHNSON, F., IRVING, L.: Heat regulation in some arctic and tropical mammals and birds. Biol. Bull. **99**, 237–258 (1950).

UDVARDY, M.D.F.: Body temperature of parids in the arctic winter. Ornis Fennica **32**, 101–107 (1955).

VEGHTE, J.H.: Thermal and metabolic response of the gray jay to cold stress. Physiol. Zool. **3**, 316–328 (1964).

WETMORE, A.: A study of the body temperature of birds. Smithsonian Misc. Coll. **72**, 1–52 (1921).

Chapter 8

Maintenance of Warmth by Variable Insulation

Caribou *(Rangifer)*, foxes *(Alopex)* and arctic sled dogs seem undisturbed by winters' cold as they proceed about the usual affairs of animals. Ravens (*Corvus corax*), conspicuous against the snow, pursue their deliberate individual flights in any degree of arctic cold, or congregate to feed on carrion or sometimes to perform aerial manoeuvers that we call social play. The unconcern with which animals encounter arctic cold impresses the arctic man laboring in thick clothing and always mindful that at the day's end he must find shelter from cold and stormy winds. Before this century most of the arctic explorers in winter were confined to their ships or cabins and only rarely and with elaborate preparations did they attempt travel. Eskimos, on the other hand, hunted in winter, and groups with women and children travelled over land and ice to move their bases of operations nearer to seasonal concentrations of the moving animals upon which they lived. Indigenous people of the Arctic possessed excellent clothing, which they prepared according to their traditional patterns with extraordinary skill.

In temperate climates, winter at places and at times approaches arctic cold, and numerous experiments have been performed to examine reactions to cold. In relation to natural animals in arctic cold the temperate-climate animals utilized were not particularly relevant and scientists confined to urban living were not in a position to see the dominance of cold in arctic circumstances. With a roster of arctic Alaskan birds and mammals to examine at Barrow, factors measured in their economy of heat began to indicate the manner of their adaptation to arctic cold. To verify adaptation to arctic cold realistically, Scholander proceeded to tropical Panama in order to compare the reactions to cold in animals of an even, warm climate. The comparison provided extremes of difference in natural economy of heat in animals, facilitating empirical determination of some general conditions for maintenance of the warmth that is necessary for birds and mammals (SCHOLANDER et al., 1950a, b, c).

Insulation of Arctic Animals by Fur and Feathers

Common experience tells us that bodily warmth can be preserved by clothing made from thick winter fur of mammals. Measurement of insulation of pelts (Fig. 8.1) showed that in fact the winter fur of large arctic mammals affords insulation in proportion to its thickness and about like materials considered to be especially effective as thermal insulators.

Small arctic mammals bear only thin fur and correspondingly small insulation. Those of the size of arctic ground squirrels *(Citellus undulatus,* 500 to 1000 g) and lemmings *(Dicrostonyx, Lemmus,* 50–80 g) seek sheltered burrows or nests in winter. The next-larger marten *(Martes)* and varying hare *(Lepus americana,*

1.5 kg) obtain some shelter in their forms in winter. Had nature endowed the small short-legged kinds with fur as long as that of fox and caribou, they would have been immobilized.

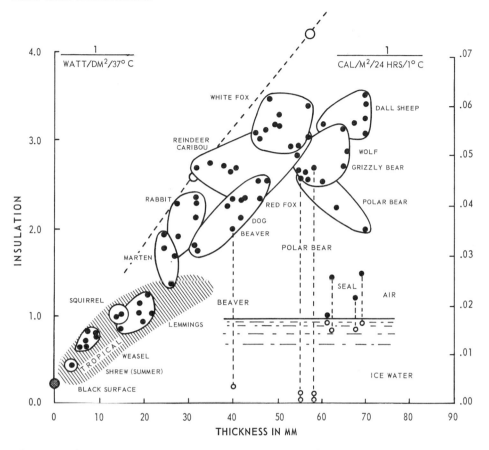

Fig. 8.1. Insulation in relation to winter fur thickness in a series of arctic mammals. The insulation in tropical mammals is indicated by the shaded area. In the aquatic mammals (seal, beaver, polar bear) the measurements in 0° C. air are connected by vertical broken lines with the same measurements taken in ice water. In all cases the hot plate guard ring unit was kept at 37° C. and the outside air or water at 0° C. The two upper points of the lemmings are from *Dicrostonyx*, the orthers from *Lemmus*. (From SCHOLANDER, WALTERS, HOCK, and IRVING, 1950)

Insulation of Tropical Mammals

A series of 16 tropical mammals from Panama, ranging in size from a small marmoset *(Leontocebus geoffroyi)* to a deer *(Mazama sartorii)*, 50 times as large as an arctic lemming and with correspondingly longer legs, possessed short fur and insulation as small as the small arctic mammals. In tropical Panama at sea level, temperatures in shade vary only a few degrees about 28° during the year in contrast with temperatures reaching –50° in arctic winter.

105

Size and Insulation

A further examination of the relation of size to insulation (Fig. 8.2) showed that in a series of arctic mammals insulation of fur increased with weight to about 5 kg, and was not more in animals of much greater size. These large animals could easily carry thicker insulation.

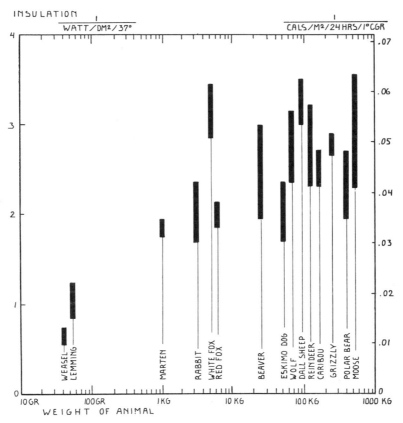

Fig. 8.2. Insulation of the winter fur in relation to the body weight in a series of arctic mammals. From a 5 kg fox to a 500 kg moose the insulation does not vary much in most of the animals. (From SCHOLANDER, WALTERS, HOCK, and IRVING, 1950)

Insulation of Birds

When skins are removed from birds the feathers are disturbed, so that the conventional method of direct measurement of insulation cannot be utilized. The use of feathers in protecting the living birds from cold must be inferred from other thermal measurements. The covering of feathers is unevenly distributed and its protection varies with the posture of the bird and particularly with wing position. In very cold weather Alaskan gray jays *(Perisoreus canadensis)* and chickadees *(Parus atricapillus),* when perched, erect their contour feathers so as to appear

106

nearly spherical. The fine structure of their feathers is such that the barbules cohere effectively and doubtless increase their insulating value. Feathers are not kept in this position during flight, when it would seem that the thin cover of feathers under the wings would expose the birds to severe cooling. Ravens *(Corvus corax)*, willow ptarmigan *(Lagopus lagopus)*, and even domesticated pigeons seem not averse to flying even in very cold air. It can also be suggested that although the fur of mammals shows in general an insulative function, aerodynamic use of feathers in flight and hydrodynamic functions in aquatic birds are not related to temperature. In visual comparison with arctic birds, tropical birds do not appear to have plumage as different in thickness as is the fur of arctic and tropical mammals.

Aquatic Birds and Mammals

The aquatic mammals present a special case of insulation provided by fur, in the case of beaver *(Castor fiber* and *canadensis)* and polar bear *(Ursus maritimus)*, and by thick blubber surrounding the bodies of seals. In water the fur of beaver is compressed to small insulative value, but water penetrates practically to the skin of polar bears (see Fig. 8.1), reducing their insulation; but it is worth remarking that, although its heat capacity is so much greater, water is never as cold as arctic air. The insulation provided by blubber of hair seals (Phocidae) is noteworthy for not being much reduced in water because the blubber is incompressible. In addition to its aerodynamic function in flight the plumage of aquatic birds must meet hydrodynamic requirements for swimming and the hydrostatic compression encountered in deep diving by ducks and loons. It is commonly considered that aquatic insulation by fur and feathers depends in part upon air trapped in fur and feathers above the skin. If that is true, diving loons *(Gavia)* and some ducks *(Clangula hyemalis)* at a depth of 100 meters might lose some 90% of this insulation during a brief period of submergence by compression of trapped air. The insulation of aquatic animals will be treated in Chapters 10 and 11.

Formulation of Thermal Balance with Environmental Temperature

Continuing our restriction to a series of arctic and tropical land animals, we measured the metabolism of some examples by determining their consumption of oxygen and production of carbon dioxide while confined in boxes regulated at a variety of temperatures. From the oxygen consumption and respiratory quotient (RQ) the heat production of the animals could be calculated by conventional methods of indirect calorimetry. It was an agreeable result to find that the captive wild animals would settle down in enclosed chambers to operate consistently at the temperatures to which they were exposed. Taking the mean low metabolic rates of each species as 100 allows comparison of the effects of temperature upon animals of different size.

Two pups of Eskimo sled dogs (9 and 15 kg) showed metabolism persisting steadily at the resting rate until they were cooled below $-20°$. Three arctic lemmings *(Dicrostonyx,* 45–56 g) began to elevate production of heat at about $+15°$. The

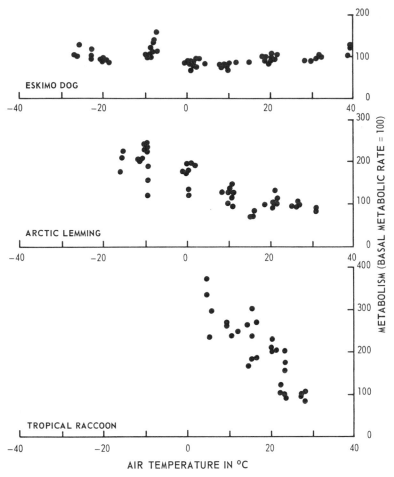

Fig. 8.3. Effect of environmental temperature on the metabolic rate in Eskimo dog, arctic lemming, and tropical raccoon expressed in terms of basal metabolic rate = 100. The steepness of the curves describes the relative temperature sensitivity of the animal but does not correlate with the weight of the animals or with their body insulation. (From SCHOLANDER, HOCK, WALTERS, JOHNSON, and IRVING, 1950)

considerably larger tropical raccoon (*Procyon cancrivorus*, 1.16 kg) began to increase its production of heat at 25° (Fig. 8.3). The small pups did not elevate metabolic heat until the air cooled to about the temperatures of arctic spring and autumn, and their big confreres, with their thick winter fur, could doubtless meet −40° without increased metabolic effort. Little arctic lemmings which normally find shelter in their runways and nests, in their poorly insulating short fur could not encounter winter air without greatly expanded metabolic production of heat. The much larger tropical raccoon, with its relatively thin fur and meager insulation, was constrained to extend its metabolism at a temperature just below prevalent temperature of its habitat in lowland Panama.

Model of Heat Production by Regulated Warmth

As an attempt to resolve thermal conditions in a series of animals, imagine a system in which an electrically powered fan maintains 40° within an insulated compartment as the air surrounding it is cooled (Fig. 8.4). Assume that as the surrounding air cools, the fan is set to produce heat at steady rate 100 while the insulation surrounding the compartment is increased to a maximum value = 1. As increasing

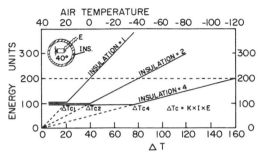

Fig. 8.4. Diagram of a thermoregulated system consisting of an electric fan inside a rigid insulator (insert). The full drawn lines represent the relative energy input necessary to maintain the „body temperature" of 10° for different air temperatures, assuming a minimum (basal) energy level of 100 and a maximum insulation of 1, 2, and 4 units. The thermoregulation is assumed to proceed in two steps: first an increase in insulation until it reaches maximum at the critical temperature, then an increase in the metabolic rate. At the critical temperature the body-to-air gradient is called the critical gradient ΔTC. At constant insulation the system cools proportionally to the gradient and it will be seen from the figure that the critical gradient is proportional to both insulation and metabolic rate according to the equation given. (From SCHOLANDER, HOCK, WALTERS, JOHNSON, and IRVING 1950)

insulation approaches the assigned maximum, the internal temperature is maintained with constant application of heat until the change in external temperature develops a gradient ΔTc between internal and external temperature, with conditions as given,

ΔTc = K x I x E, in which
Tc = 'critical' temperature
ΔTc = gradient from body to air at critical temperature
K = a constant of dimensions
I = 'overall' insulation value = 1
E = energy, as heat, applied to the motor

While cooling down to Tc_1, increasing insulation maintains the temperature at 40° around the motor with constant input of energy. If at Tc_1 insulation can be no further increased, and thereafter remains constant, a temperature of 40° can be maintained around the motor only by increasing input of energy (E).

Maximum of Variable Insulation

If the insulation were enlarged to value 2, constant input to the motor would maintain 40° within the motor chamber until Tc_2, with the result that ΔTc_2 would be twice ΔTc_1. After attainment of maximal insulation, maintenance of internal

109

temperature as the external air cooled would be effected by increasing application of heat (E). But with insulation maximum = 2 the increments of heat required beyond Tc_2 progress along a less steep line. Likewise, increasing the maximum of variable insulation (I) to 4 increases $\triangle Tc$ four times, and the further application of heat (E) required to maintain 40° around the motor proceeds along a still less steep line.

As this model for preservation of even warmth was developed it was referred to as an example of Newton's law of cooling, as had frequently been proposed for a physical formulation to describe regulation of temperature in animals. In fact, animals regulate temperature without cooling, and Fourier's law might better have been applied (KLEIBER, 1961). The formulation used can also be compared with Ohm's law or Fick's law of diffusion. This is no place for debate on physical laws, and the formulation presented, which is empirically based, summarizes the situation for production of heat within an insulated covering.

Many observers had described regulation of warmth by animals in the only ways that are known to derive flow of heat, and usually by reference to Newton's law. In the broad comparison of production of heat and maintenance of warmth in arctic and tropical animals the usefulness of the formulation became conspicuous.

Formulation of Economy of Animal Heat

Thirteen mammals (seven arctic, six tropical) were compared in respect of lower critical temperatures (Tc) and slope of further elevation of metabolism by cold, presenting the array shown in Fig. 8.5. In similar fashion comparison of three tropical and three arctic birds showed correspondence with mammals in the position of curves for arctic and tropical species (Fig. 8.6). If this formulation from

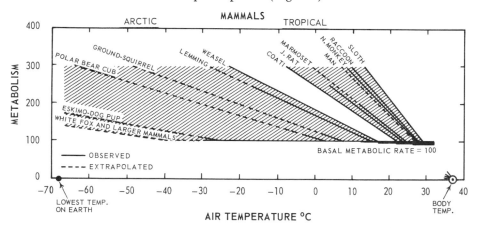

Fig. 8.5. Heat regulation and temperature sensitivity in arctic and tropical mammals based on plots in Figs. 8.3 and 8.4. The fox needs only slight increase in metabolic rate to stand the coldest temperature on earth. The critical gradients (tp sensitivity) and the slope of the curves depend on the product of the basal metabolic rate and the overall body insulation. (From SCHOLANDER, HOCK, WALTERS, JOHNSON, and IRVING, 1950)

110

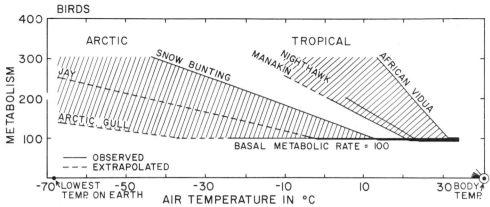

Fig. 8.6. Heat regulation and temperature sensitivity in arctic and tropical birds, based on plots in Fig. 8.4 (From Scholander, Hock, Walters, Johnson and Irving, 1950b)

a few examples of arctic and tropical animals truly describes a common characteristic of heat regulation, it should appear in the numerous measurements of effects of cooling on animals of temperate climates. Plotted in these terms, results of 19 reports on 15 species of mammals and seven reports on six species of birds could be represented by the same scheme. Many subsequent studies have been usefully described in this manner.

Some investigators have welcomed the simplicity of these procedures for comparing birds and mammals while others have found objections to regarding animals in such restricted terms. There are some inadequacies in the data on which conditions are assumed that will be mentioned later in more detail. The temperature within the insulation of the animals is assumed to be maintained over the body. This steadiness is common at rest (Chapter 7), but differs appreciably with states of activity. Resting metabolism, or as it is often called, basal or standard metabolism, changes with stage and state of nutrition and with sleep or wakefulness. Muscular activity increases metabolic rates. In view of these likely perturbations, it seems remarkable that many investigators examining animals of different size and disposition should arrive at comparable characterizations of their economy of heat. On the other hand, measurements of metabolism are made under conditions established by strict conventions upon experience and theory.

In a recent survey Pohl (1969) remarked that data reported for 67% of 125 species (68 mammals, 57 birds) fit Scholander's model. Later we shall attempt (rather ineffectively) to consider changes in heat production related to the states of activity, for a state of rest does not suffice to maintain an animal in any climate.

Formulation of the economy of animal heat in general terms discards behavior variable and deviant from the basic assumptions but that may nevertheless be real and significant for animals that live by adjusting activity to differing circumstances in a changing environment. We can see, however, that the insulation of large arctic animals is such that at a resting rate of heat production they can maintain essential warmth without increased metabolic effort in arctic cold. Birds and mammals with insufficient insulation are constrained to exert their capability for metabolic production of heat in cold. Even below its critical temperature (about -40°)

the arctic fox would need to increase heat production only slightly to meet the lowest temperature reported in the Arctic, around -70°. With the insulation of tropical animals a 3-fold increase of heat production would be invoked around 10°, and even at this temperature the metabolic expense would be severe.

Above critical low temperature insulation increases with declining temperature. Insulation cannot be regarded as a fixture but it is a variable. Obviously, insulation is a composite of all resistances to loss of heat, such as the fur, which cannot be quickly shed like clothing but which can be made more effective if the animal coils in a compact form that diminishes exposed surface and covers thinly protected extremities and belly. The arctic dog's bushy tail covers the legs and shields the nose. The warmth of skin, particularly on extremities, can vary to reduce or increase outward flow of heat. Although they cannot much change loss of heat by evaporation from the skin, working arctic dogs pant when running even at −40°. So the overall or composite insulation is variable over a long range in the arctic animals.

In a popular lecture in Washington, D.C. I described the ability of arctic animals to utilize their variable insulation so that they could carry on the necessary activities of their kind without being driven to obtain food for maintenance of heat in quantities beyond the requirements of animals in a milder climate. Afterward a very kindly-appearing lady thanked me for relieving her of the deep concern that she had felt for the cold and harried lives of arctic animals in their struggle to keep warm. Seldom have I received so much satisfaction from interpreting the uses of science.

In Fig. 8.5 unclothed man, with low critical temperature around 28°, falls among the tropical mammals. Among several races of man that have been examined and among people supposedly adapted to life in cold climates there is little evidence for much difference in unclothed critical temperature, and we can see that a doubling of the overall insulation of a naked man would be required to lower his critical temperature to the 18° of a temperate summer's day.

At some early stage of evolution in warm climates the primitive hominid developed cultural skill at providing shelter, clothing and fire to preserve warmth. Only a few aboriginal human populations visible in historic times lived even in cool climates without well developed insulative protection by means extrinsic to their bodies. Traces of ancient arctic people are associated with shelter, fire and clothing that were apparently obtained by skills prerequisite for entering the arctic world. This is not to deny that man can become physiologically adapted to life in a cold climate (see Chapter 12), but the measurable differences are obscure and are certainly small in comparison with the conspicuously adaptive insulation of large arctic mammals.

References

KLEIBER, M.: The Fire of Life: An Introduction to Animal Energetics. New York: John Wiley & Sons, Inc. 1961.
POHL, H.: Some factors influencing the metabolic response to cold in birds. Fed. Proc. **28**, 1059–1064 (1969).

Scholander, P.F., Hock, R., Walters, V., Irving, L.: Adaptation to cold in arctic and tropical mammals and birds in relation to body temperature, insulation, and basal metabolic rate. Biol. Bull. **99**, 259–269 (1950).

Scholander, P.F., Hock, R., Walters, V., Johnson, F., Irving, L.: Heat regulation in some arctic and tropical mammals and birds. Biol. Bull. **99**, 237–258 (1950).

Scholander, P.F., Walters, V., Hock, R., Irving, L.: Body insulation of some arctic and tropical mammals and birds. Biol. Bull. **99**, 225–236 (1950).

Chapter 9

Metabolic Supply of Heat

For birds and mammals heat is of obvious importance in arctic life. The preservation of warmth, however, is a requirement in all climates. As air warms in desert and tropical situations toward the temperatures of birds and mammals, their problem of existence becomes one of losing heat. In the arctic climate the conspicuous problem of warmblooded life appears to be the retention of heat. In cold, this problem can be regarded in somewhat simplified physiological terms that allow some general views understandable through common experience. Large differences between internal warmth and environmental cold provide correspondingly large scales for viewing the essential processes of production of animal heat and its adequate retention.

Comparison of Specific Metabolic Rates

In developing a theoretical view of the preservation of warmth by variable insulation, the metabolic production of heat was set at a figure empirically characteristic of each species (Chapter 8). This figure has no dimensions, and it is clear that by differing in size, nature and condition, species differ also in the essential ability to produce heat. Size of birds and mammals is easily definable as weight, and we shall defer discussion of how the animal's surface is involved in its economy of heat. Many measurements of basal metabolism, mainly by indirect calorimetry, have been made on many species. F. G. BENEDICT (1938) compared the heat production of a number of species of mammals and found that when the data were plotted on log-log coordinates, the basal metabolic production of heat related to weight fell upon a straight line, referred to by SAMUEL BRODY (1964) as the "mouse to elephant curve".

Discussion, both profound and trivial, toward explaining this interspecific regularity has not altered the empirical usefulness of this common relation. The most satisfactory recent formulation for mammals (mainly domesticated) is given by KLEIBER (1961 as $M = 70 x W^{3/4}$ in which $M = kcal/24$ h and $W =$ weight in kg). There is a certain fallacy in this formula because measurements are accepted that were made during periods of a few hours and then extrapolated to the day of 24 h. Furthermore, it is commonly the resting metabolism that is measured, which changes over the day and night and in relation to activity, for the basal condition is difficult to determine. In spite of questions about the relation of variations in metabolic rate to the idealized notion of basal metabolism, we find great value in comparing species and individuals in respect to their resting or basal metabolic rates at the rate calculated for 24 h.

Metabolic Rates of Northern and Tropical Mammals

There are not many reported measurements of metabolism of arctic and northern mammals. Under circumstances in the field and outlying laboratories there are questions of technique and, still more, of whether the wild animals of varying sizes had rested without food long enough to avoid the calorigenic effects of food. I have selected examples that appear to represent metabolism that, if not strictly basal, has been measured during steady conditions at rest.

The high metabolic rate of least weasels is probably attributable to the restlessness of the excitable little animals. As young animals, polar bear cubs and young pups of sled dogs would be expected to exceed basal rates of adults. Tropical two-

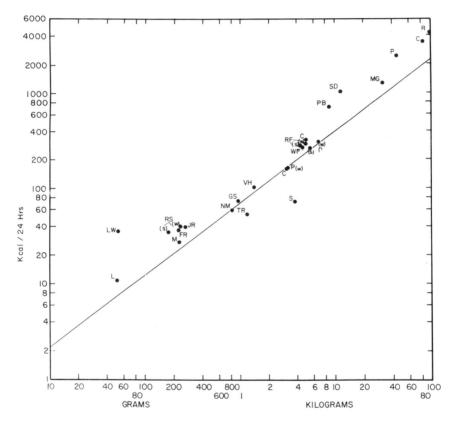

Fig. 9.1. Metabolism of some northern and tropical mammals

Symbol	Number	Species	Weight	Location	Reference
L	3	*Dicrostonyx* (Lemming)	52 g	Barrow (71 °N)	SCHOLANDER, HOCK, WALTERS and IRVING, 1950
LW	3	*Mustela rixosa* (Least weasel)	53 g	Barrow (71 °N)	SCHOLANDER, HOCK, WALTERS and IRVING, 1950

115

Symbol	Number	Species	Weight	Location	Reference
RS	1	*Tamiasciurus hudsonicus* (Red squirrel)	(w) 235 g (winter) (s) 175 g (summer)	Anchorage (60 °N)	IRVING et al., 1955
FR	4	*Rattus norvegicus* (Feral brown rat)	220 g not fasted	Fairbanks (61 °N)	KROG et al., 1955
JR	1	*Proechimys semispinosus* (Jungle rat)	260 g	Panama (9 °N)	SCHOLANDER, HOCK, WALTERS and IRVING, 1950
M	1	*Leontocebus geoffroyi* (Marmoset)	225 g	Panama (9 °N)	SCHOLANDER, HOCK, WALTERS and IRVING, 1950
NM	1	*Aotus trivergatus* (Night monkey)	810 g	Panama (9 °N)	SCHOLANDER, HOCK, WALTERS and IRVING, 1950
GS	4	*Citellus undulatus* (Ground squirrel)	930 g	Barrow (71 °N)	ERIKSON, 1956
TR	1	*Procyon cancrivorus* (Tropical raccoon)	1.18 kg	Panama (9 °N)	SCHOLANDER, HOCK, WALTERS and IRVING, 1950
VH	1	*Lepus americanus* (Varying hare)	1.40 kg	Anchorage (60 °N)	IRVING et al., 1957
C	2	*Nasua marica* (Coati)	3.2 and 5.1 kg	Panama (9 °N)	SCHOLANDER, HOCK, WALTERS and IRVING, 1950
S	1	*Choloepus hoffmanni* (2-toed sloth)	3.8 kg	Panama (9 °N)	SCHOLANDER, HOCK, WALTERS and IRVING, 1950
RF	2	*Vulpus fulva* (Red fox)	(w) 5.0 kg (winter) (s) 4.4 kg (summer)	Anchorage (60 °N)	IRVING et al., 1955
P	3	*Erethizon dorsatum* (Porcupine)	(w) 6.8 kg (winter) (s) 5.6 kg (summer)	Anchorage (60 °N)	IRVING et al., 1955
WF	4	*Alopex lagopus* (White fox)	3.8–5.5 kg	Barrow (71 °N)	SCHOLANDER, HOCK, WALTERS and IRVING, 1950
PB	2	*Ursus maritimus* (Polar bear cubs)	8.9 kg	Barrow (71 °N)	SCHOLANDER, HOCK, WALTERS and IRVING 1950
SD	2	*Canis familiaris* (Sled dog pups)	12 kg	Barrow (71 °N)	SCHOLANDER, HOCK, WALTERS and IRVING, 1950
MG	1	*Oreamnus americanus* (Mountain goat)	32 kg	Anchorage (60 °N)	KROG and MONSON, 1964
P	2	*Sus scrofa* (Pig)	45 kg	Anchorage (60 °N)	IRVING et al., 1956
C	2	*Rangifer tarandus* (Barren ground caribou)	85 kg	Vancouver (49 °N)	McEWAN, 1970
R	1	*Rangifer tarandus* (Reindeer – domesticated)	99 kg	Finland (70 °N)	HAMMEL et al., 1962

toed sloths are notoriously sluggish and usually several degrees colder than most mammals. Most of the mammals, both northern and tropical, fall within twice the conventional rate for their size (Fig. 9.1). With most biologists, I find it not evident that basal metabolism varies in relation to climate (SCHOLANDER, et. al. 1950). I suspect, however, that variations within and among species are greater than is commonly granted. Statistical definition of variation conceals differences that are real.

Populations of wild animals living in the natural temperatures of their climate have met the conditions with success. Animals in the laboratory that are experimentally thrust into controlled cold do not meet a condition for which they are prepared nor have they passed the test of existing as natural populations. White rats (*Rattus norvegicus*-domesticated) removed from 30° air and held for some weeks in 5° air increased, basal metabolism about 40% (KROG et al., 1955). Wild brown rats of the same species captured in winter on the dumps of Fairbanks (lat. 65° N) had basal metabolism only slightly elevated above that of white rats kept warm. As HEROUX (1961) pointed out, wild brown rats from dumps at Kingston, Ontario (January average –7°), showed none of the morphological changes produced in white rats exposed experimentally to steady cold. The wild rats did not show the physiological signs of stress that accompanied experimental exposure of white rats to cold.

Metabolic Rates of Marine Mammals

The resting metabolic rates of a few marine mammals (Fig. 9.2) have consistently been found to be higher than those of land mammals. Metabolic rates of four species of seals, all of the hair seal type, Phocidae, possessing sparse wettable hair affording little insulation, were consistently alike in air or water and higher than in most land mammals. These seals range into cold arctic Atlantic waters. In warm water (23°) in summer the metabolic rate of harbor seals (*Phoca vitulina*)

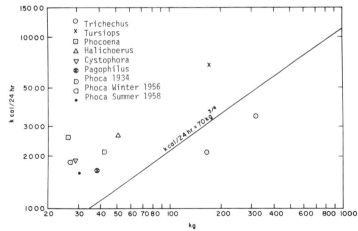

Fig. 9.2. Metabolic heat production of some marine mammals

Species	Location	Reference
Trichechus manatus (Florida manatee)	Florida	SCHOLANDER and IRVING, 1941
Tursiops truncatus (Bottle-nosed porpoise)	Florida	IRVING et al., 1941
Phocoena phocoena (Common porpoise)	Oslo	KANWISHER and SUNDNES, 1968
Halichoerus grypus (Gray seal)	Oslo	SCHOLANDER, 1940
Cystophora cristata (Bladder-nosed seal)	Oslo	SCHOLANDER, 1940
Pagophilus (Phoca) groenlandicus (Harp seal)	St. Andrews, N. B.	IRVING and HART, 1957
	White Sea	DAVIDOV and MAKAROVA, 1964
Phoca vitulina (Harbor seal)	St. Andrews, N. B. summer	IRVING et al., 1935
	St. Andrews, N. B. winter 1956	IRVING and HART, 1957
	Woods Hole, Mass. summer 1958	HART and IRVING, 1959

was little less than in winter. For reasons of management the seals (30 kg) were only about half of their adult weight, which may well mean that their metabolic rates were greater than those of fully grown animals.

In regard to the metabolic rate of the harbor porpoise (*Phocoena phocoena*) in water (8°) at Oslo, KANWISHER and SUNDNESS (1966) commented upon the high metabolic rate within a body surrounded by 40% of its weight in fatty blubber. Fully grown bottle-nosed porpoises (*Tursiops truncatus*) from warm water off Florida were likewise at a high metabolic level. The quite unrelated Florida manatee (*Trichechus manatus*), a creature as passive as seals and porpoises are active, was at a low metabolic level. Specific differences in metabolism appear among these aquatic mammals, but not in obvious relation to climate.

Basal Metabolism of Birds

Basal metabolic production of heat measured in many species of birds can be described for the slightly differing passerine and non-passerine species of birds by the expression $M = 86.4W^{0.668}$ (LASIEWSKI and DAWSON, 1967) in which M = kcal/24 h and W = weight in Kilograms. Some measurements on a few northern and a few arctic birds (Fig. 9.3) show deviations from the average for all birds. Measurement of one arctic glaucous gull (*Larus hyperboreus*) at almost three times the average rate appears out of line. VEGTHE'S (1964) numerous measurements on gray jays (*Perisoreus canadensis*) represent that species better than our measurements. WEST'S (personal report) good series of measurements on small redpolls (*Acanthis flammea*) show their higher basal production of heat in winter, as did the measurement on a single northwestern crow (*Corvus caurinus*) and black brant (*Branta nigricans*). Since willow ptarmigan (*Lagopus lagopus*) produced somewhat less heat in winter than in summer, the influence of season is not general. It is significant that a species truly resident in the arctic, a raven (*Corvus corax*), and a southern raven of similar size were similar in heat production. Snowy owls (*Nyctea scandiaca*) kept captive outdoors at Barrow during arctic winter were

118

below average in production of heat. Antarctic Adelie (*Pygoscelis adeliae*) and
African (*Speniscus demersus*) penguins of quite different climates did not differ
from expectation in basal production of heat.

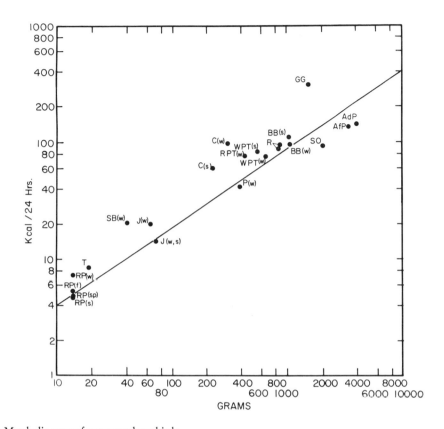

Fig. 9.3. Metabolic rates of some northern birds

Symbol	Number	Species	Average Weight	Location	Reference
CR	24 (spring) 15 (summer) 24 (fall) 24 (winter)	*Acanthis flammea* (Common redpoll)	13.9 g	Fairbanks (65 °N)	WEST, unpublished
T		*Parus major* (Great tit)	18 g	Turku	HISSA and PALOKAREGAS, 1970
SB	7	*Plectrophenax nivalis* (Snow bunting)	41 g	Barrow (71 °N) (winter)	SCHOLANDER, HOCK, WALTERS and IRVING, 1950

119

Symbol	Number	Species	Average Weight	Location	Reference
J (W)	2	*Perisoreus canadensis* (Jays)	64 g	Barrow (71 °N) (winter)	SCHOLANDER, HOCK, WALTERS and IRVING, 1950
J	several	*Perisoreus canadensis* (Jays)	71 g	freshly captured at Fairbanks (65 °N)	VEGHTE, 1964
C	1	*Corvus caurinus* (Northwestern crow)	282 g (summer) 306 g (winter)	Anchorage (60 °N)	IRVING et al., 1955
P	5	Domestic pigeons	390 g	Barrow (71 °N) (winter)	SCHOLANDER, HOCK, WALTERS and IRVING, 1950
RPT	6	*Lagopus mutus* (Rock ptarmigan)	425 g (winter)	Fairbanks (65 °N)	WEST, unpublished
WPT	19	*Lagopus lagopus* (Willow ptarmigan)	550 g (summer)	Fairbanks (65 °N)	WEST, unpublished
WPT	19	*Lagopus lagopus* (Willow ptarmigan)	650 g (winter)	Fairbanks (65 °N)	WEST, unpublished
R	1	*Corvus corax* (Raven)	850 g (winter)	Barrow (71 °N)	SCHOLANDER, HOCK, WALTERS and IRVING, 1950
R	1	*Corvus corax* (Raven)	866 g		LASIEWSKI and DAWSON, 1967
BB	1	*Branta bernicla* (Black brant)	1.12 kg (winter) 1.13 kg (summer)	Anchorage (60 °N)	IRVING et al., 1955
GG	1	*Larus hyperboreus* (Glaucous gull)	1600 g (winter)	Barrow (71 °N)	SCHOLANDER, HOCK, WALTERS and IRVING, 1950
SO		*Nyctea scandiaca* (Snowy owl)	2026 g (winter)	Barrow (71 °N)	GESSAMAN, 1968
AP	2	*Spheniscus demersus* (African penguins)	300 g	long captive at Baltimore	LERESCHE and WEST, 1967
AdP	4	*Pygoscelis adeliae* (Adelie penguins)	4100 g	long captive at Baltimore	LERESCHE and WEST, 1967

kcal = 86.4 W $^{.668}$ (LASIEWSKI and DAWSON, 1967)

Human Basal Metabolic Production of Heat

The number of measurements of human basal metabolic rates far exceeds measurements on animals. Many concern patients of uncertain normality in hospitals and many are referred to size in terms of area of body surface estimated from linear dimensions and differentiated by sex and age. Reviewers have not agreed whether race or climate of residence differentiate people. I am inclined to accept that in rather small numbers of examples the basal metabolic production of heat has often been found to be 20 to 30% above usual in arctic resident Eskimos and American Indians, but there is no statistical verification that these samples represent racial populations. Variations reported among races of man are small in comparison with over twofold specific differences among species of other animals.

Adaptive Value of Basal Metabolic Production of Heat

It does not appear that arctic birds and mammals are distinguishable from others in respect of basal production of heat (SCHOLANDER, HOCK, WALTERS and IRVING, 1950). The designation "basal metabolism" implies that it is the minimum metabolic rate for maintenance of an individual at comfortable warm temperature. As the mouse to elephant curve shows, it is characteristic of a species in standard condition, although, as is shown by variations among domesticated races of animals and perhaps among races of man, etablishment of variant strains within a species is possible. The isolation necessary for differentiating basal metabolism among the races or subspecies of species of wild animals may not have often occurred, but it seems not to have been examined in wild populations.

Within its definition, which is rather arbitrary since we do not know the true meaning of the term, basal metabolic production of heat appears not to be modified to meet climatic conditions. In this sense it is like temperature of the body. We shall later discuss the utilization of metabolic heat above the basal rate for preservation of warmth in small arctic birds and mammals. Now we will conclude that the basal metabolic production of heat is a specific character empirically related to weight. It is a source of the heat that maintains bodily warmth, but it is not readily modifiable, in contrast with the quickly modifiable and large insulation with flexibility so well demonstrated in arctic forms. The use of metabolic heat above the basal rate for preservation of warmth is restricted by the availability of food, by the time and capability for obtaining nourishment and by the not unlimited capacity of the organism for metabolic production of heat. Variable insulation is conservative while metabolic production of heat is expensive.

Lower Critical Temperatures of Mammals

Measurements of basal metabolic rates have engaged the attention of physiologists seeking and commonly finding rates of heat production characteristic of distinguishable populations in relation to their weight. In many measurements on wild animals true basal conditions have not been ascertained, but the rates are acceptable if consistently obtained with animals at rest and in temperatures warm enough to elicit no elevation of metabolic heat production. We have seen (Chapter 8) that the heat production of arctic mammals was not elevated by increasing coldness that extended to much colder levels than would produce a change in tropical mammals. I have compiled in Table 9.1 the lower critical temperatures (at which produc-

Table 9.1. Lower critical temperatures of some mammals

Species	Weight	Location	Crit. Temp., ° C	Reference
Lepus americanus (Varying hare)	1.38 kg (winter)	Anchorage (60 °N)	− 8	IRVING et al., 1957
Citellus undulatus (Arctic ground squirrel)	0.87–1.25 kg	Barrow (71 °N)	8	ERIKSON, 1956
Tamiasciurus hudsonicus (Red squirrel)	165, 185 g (summer)		20	
	228, 230 g (winter)	Anchorage (60 °N)	20	IRVING et al., 1955
Dicrostonyx torquatus (Varying lemming)	45–65 g	Barrow (71 °N)	14	SCHOLANDER, HOCK, WALTERS and IRVING, 1950
Erethizon dorsatum (Porcupine)	4.3, 6.8 kg (summer)		7	
	3.2., 6.7, 7.7 kg (winter)	Anchorage (60 °N)	–12	IRVING et al., 1955
Canis familiaris – pups (Sled dog)	9–15 kg	Barrow (71 °N)	<–20	SCHOLANDER, HOCK, WALTERS and IRVING, 1950
Canis familiaris (Dog)	8.5–10.5 kg	Philadelphia	27	HAMMEL et al., 1958
Canis dingo (Dingo)		kept at 30°	30	
		kept at –20°	5	SHIELD, unpublished
Alopex lagopus (Arctic fox)	3.8–5.5 kg	Barrow (71 °N)	<–30	SCHOLANDER, HOCK, WALTERS and IRVING, 1950
Vulpes fulva (Red fox)	4.4 kg (summer)		8	
	5.0 kg (winter)	Anchorage (60 °N)	–13	IRVING et al., 1955
Mustela rixosa (Least weasel)	38–70 kg (winter)	Barrow (71 °N)	17	SCHOLANDER, HOCK, WALTERS and IRVING, 1950
Ursus maritimus (Polar bear cubs)	8.5, 9.5 kg	Barrow (71 °N)	0	SCHOLANDER, HOCK, WALTERS and IRVING, 1950
Phoca vitulina (Harbor seal)	23–33 kg (summer)	in water (42 °N)	22	HART and IRVING, 1959
		in air	0	
	27–41 kg (winter)	in water	12	IRVING and HART, 1957
		in air	<–10	
Phoca groenlandicus (Harp seal)		St. Andrews (45 °N) winter, in water	0	IRVING and HART, 1957
Oreamnus americanus (Mountain goat)	32 kg (winter)	Anchorage (65° N)	–20	KROG and MONSON, 1954
Lapps naked			27	SCHOLANDER et al., 1957
Norwegians naked			27	ERIKSON et al., 1956
Norwegians acclimated to cold			24	SCHOLANDER et al., 1958

tion of heat increased) reported in several species of wild mammals and in men native or living in cold northern and arctic conditions. For comparison, lower critical temperatures of some tropical mammals are referred to in Table 9.2.

Table 9.2. Lower critical temperatures of some mammals from warm climates

Species	Weight	Critical temperature °C	Reference
Tachyglossus aculeatus (Spiny anteater)		26	MARTIN, 1902
Ornithorhynchus anatinus (Platypus)		22	MARTIN, 1902
Aotus trivergatus (Night monkey)	820 g	26	SCHOLANDER, HOCK, WALTERS, JOHNSON and IRVING, 1950
Leontocebus geoffroyi (Marmoset)	225 g	24	SCHOLANDER, HOCK, WALTERS, JOHNSON and IRVING, 1950
Homo sapiens (Man)		26	
Choloepus hoffmanni (Sloth)	3.8 kg	29	SCHOLANDER, HOCK, WALTERS, JOHNSON and IRVING, 1950
Proechimus semispinosus (Jungle rat)	265 g	24	SCHOLANDER, HOCK, WALTERS, JOHNSON and IRVING, 1950
Procyon cancrivorus (Raccoon)	1.16 kg	26	SCHOLANDER, HOCK, WALTERS, JOHNSON and IRVING, 1950
Nasua marica (Coati)	4.5 kg	22	SCHOLANDER, HOCK, WALTERS, JOHNSON and IRVING, 1950

Variation in Critical Temperature

Red squirrels did not change critical temperature from winter to summer (Table 9.1), nor was there noticeable thickening of their fur in winter. Red fox and porcupine lowered their critical temperature in winter about 20°, changing in conformity with mean environmental temperatures of the seasons in their boreal climate. Prime winter fur of large furbearers is much thicker than their meager fur after molting in summer and is an obvious factor providing superior insulation in winter. The seasonal change of critical temperature has not been related to the temporal programs of the large seasonal change in arctic climates nor to the stages of molting and growth of fur. For example Arctic brown bears (*Ursus arctos*) retain thick prime coats well into warm summer before molting. The schedule of insulating fur that is out of phase with seasonal temperature might permit an analysis of the role of fur in the complex of processes included in the overall insulation of mammals.

Dog-like species (Canidae) are notable for their distribution from arctic over tropical lands. They are versatile in adjustment to climate. Domesticated dogs, developed morphologically to suit human fancy or neglect, illustrate variability within the species by critical temperatures such as the 27° of small dogs kept at that temperature by HAMMEL (1958) in Philadelphia (lat. 40°N) and −20° for pups of sled dogs in spring at Barrow (lat. 71° N) (Table 9.1).

Dingos (*Canis dingo*) are reputedly descended from canid stock imported into Australia by ancient people some 15000 years ago. They have become differentiated as a feral species in Australian deserts with hot summer days and occasional chilly nights. Even there some dingos range into mountain areas that are covered with snow in winter. Stock from dingos imported and inbred as captives at San Diego, California, and Sacramento were exposed to regimes of several temperatures by Dr. JOHN SHIELD while at the University of Alaska, and I am indebted to him for comments reflecting upon their adaptability.

After being maintained warm (30°) for three months the critical temperature of the dingos was +30° (see Table 9.1). After being kept at –20° their critical temperature was 5°. Part of the depression of critical temperature was assignable to elevation of resting metabolic heat production in the animals subjected to the cold regime. Another part was in the obviously thicker insulation afforded by their underfur.

After the regime of heat, the dingos in that group increased metabolic rates five times when exposed at –70°, maintaining body temperature by exhibiting metabolic vigor as great as has been reported in any truly northern mammal. The superior insulation of the dingos from the cold regime was shown by their maintenance of bodily warmth at –70° with only 2 1/2 times resting metabolism. If we presume that dingos passed through 7000 generations in warm Australia, the vigor of their metabolic reaction to cold must have persisted as long, although it was not exercised. A relatively brief experimental sojourn in air colder than the species has ever encountered evoked visible and protective growth of underfur, showing that ability to make insulative compensation for cold also persisted in the dingos without being exercised.

Speculating afar from these few examples it could be surmised that animals of wide climatic range like dogs (Canidae) and deer (Cervidae), retain the ability to adapt for cold even in climates where it is not evoked by circumstances. The few illustrations of critical temperature in northern people (Table 9.1) suggest that residence in cold climates has not modified this indicator of their reactiveness to cold. But later (Chapter 12) we shall discuss some examples of compensatory changes in human reaction to cold that are produced among people motivated or forced by exceptional circumstances to undergo exposures to cold exceeding the conventions of desirability.

A View of Behavior of Wild Mammals

The large mammals in the arctic do not appear more intent upon obtaining food than their relatives in a milder climate. Conspicuous caribou, foxes, and wolves, while capable of rapid action, nevertheless are often seen at rest on the snow, and their tracks and resting places demonstrate observance of times for rest and sleep. One or several wolves may be seen exposed for hours, quietly resting among caribou that move, rest or feed around them at a safe distance of a few hundred yards. In the pauses of a moving herd of caribou, the young animals may play in emulation of adult conflict as their elders quietly ruminate. During the rut, bulls are so concerned for rivalry in procreation and the attendant strife that during several weeks they scarcely feed as they subsist on fat accumulated during earlier summer. Bull fur seals (*Callorhinus arctocephalus*) are so intent upon maintenance of their stations and associated cows that during summer months they maintain guard and engage in ferocious displays and occasional combat without leaving their territories for the sea. During sunny days of spring many ringed seals *Phoca hispida),* bearded seals *(Erignathus barbatus)* and walrus *(Odobenus)* rest for long periods on the ice of arctic seas. These examples illustrate the variety of activities as well as the extent of rest involved in maintenance of a natural population. Only a limited time is available for feeding if the population is to maintain the habits of its members, their social organization and annual relation to a suitable range. These requirements of the species for maintenance of a successful, coherent population are much alike in all climates. Even if food were abundant, time is not available for obtaining a large increment in the use of food for production of heat, and I would be surprised if a wild mammal could persistently exert itself metabolically at a high rate just to keep warm.

Heat of Small Mammals

Among the small mammals, ground squirrels (*Citellus*) and marmots (*Marmota*) evade the issue of cold by the special process of hibernation. Varying hares (*Lepus americanus*) enter the arctic climate by extending barely beyond tree line in willow-filled valleys. Though no measurements are available from the actual Arctic, it seems that their insulation may be too small to withstand full exposure at basal rate without some shelter (see Fig. 9.1), and in their wooded and brushy habitat they are somewhat shielded from wind and radiative loss of heat to the cold arctic sky. Red squirrels *(Tamiasciurus hudsonicus)* dwell in nothern American timber, where they occasionally appear even in cold winter, but their cache of winter food is in burrows from which they do not often emerge in coldest weather. During these ventures their metabolism would need some four-fold elevation if the air was at −40°. In their burrows at the margin between snow and vegetation, arctic lemmings might encounter cold below freezing, with resultant expected production of heat at least twice basal, except as or if they occupy nests and huddle together for rest. We have to speculate further upon the habits of small mice and shrews, which are too small to possess insulation protecting them below probable critical temperatures about 25°. In their subnivean environment they would incur metabolic requirements three times basal until they could seek the contrived insulation of nests. Because their subnivean habits are so little known, I am doubtful about the reasonableness of speculation upon the extent of exposure of arctic mice in their winter habitat.

It is shown that mice and rats kept in air about freezing in the laboratory develop basal or resting metabolic rates which are increased up to 40%. House mice (*Mus musculus*, 15–30 g) can infest refrigerated stores of meat. When exposed to refrigerated air their production of heat would be expected to be some four times that expected from basal rates, but protection by huddling in nests is suspected of replacing metabolic production of heat adaptive to the cold.

During experimental confinement of small mammals in uniform cold, basal rates of heat production may be increased to supplement protection that cannot be provided by natural insulation. When they are kept out of doors in variable temperatures of natural winter the elevation of basal rates may not appear, making it seem that under natural conditions they are reluctant to make the increase and

125

instead, perhaps, prepare nests with better insulation. It is apparent that wild brown rats (*Rattus norvegicus*) infesting a northern garbage dump in winter had near normal basal metabolism (KROG et al., 1955). The wild and savage little (225 g) creatures could elevate their metabolism some sixfold at −40° compared with a limit of less than four times for white rats that had been warm or even somewhat acclimatized to cold. Respiratory quotients of the previously warm white rats rose at 0°, of those previously cold only at −30°, while this indicator of metabolic stability remained unaltered at −40° in the wild brown rats. Evidently the capability of the wild rats for accelerated heat production in winter exceeded the ability of white rats. Improved metabolic power in cold has frequently been observed in mammals of the laboratory after exposure to cold and in a few wild species in winter in comparison with their condition in summer.

Lower Critical Temperatures of Some Tropical Mammals

Lower critical temperatures of some tropical mammals are listed in Table 9.2. To this list could now be added other examples showing that generally the lower critical temperatures of mammals are near the temperature of their environments. As the elevation of critical temperatures observed in a few northern mammals in summer suggested that nature parsimoniously develops insulation just to suit conditions, we might expect similar parsimony in the maintenance of insulation in warm climates. In the Tropics, however, there may be little variation in seasonal conditions. As was demonstrated by the Australian dingos, the climatically versatile dogs in any climate retain the ability to make compensatory changes adaptive to cold.

Lest I too readily dismiss the need for thermoregulation in the Tropics, WRIGHT (1964) describes the considerable range in conditions for cooling from lowland tropical forests to high elevations in Africa, where rhinoceroses (*Ceratotherium sirnum* and *Diceros bicornis*) and hippopotamuses (*Hippopotamus amphibius*) occur. Under these conditions thermoregulation is more complicated by evaporation and radiation than in the Arctic and cannot so nearly be related to air temperature alone, as my discussion has so simply assumed.

Lower Critical Temperature of Birds

We can see that in winter insulation protects large arctic mammals for an economy of heat that is within their physiological competence and at not undue nutritional cost. We conclude that the smaller mammals with high critical temperature and meager insulation must commonly find shelter from cold in order to reduce their requirement of metabolic heat. Admittedly, our knowledge of the obscure behavior and circumstances of the small mammals is assembled with a large measure of imagination.

Behavior of birds is as open to our view as that of many mammals is concealed from our sight. In daytime during winter we see the arctic willow ptarmigan (*Lagopus lagopus*), snowy owl (*Nyctea scandiaca*) and raven (*Corvus corax*) fully exposed to cold and wind. If the snow is soft, willow ptarmigan dive into burrows where they remain sheltered during the long arctic nights. But when winds have hardened the snow, as is the condition over much of their arctic range, willow and rock ptarmigan roost in any slight depression, exposed above to loss of heat. Captive snowy owls remained visibly exposed in winter and we suspect that in their roosts ravens are exposed.

Among numerous species of birds wintering in northern forests, chickadees (Paridae) and woodpeckers (Picidae) can resort to roost in sheltering holes, but other wild birds, although not actually observed in darkness, we presume to roost exposed to cold. Captive small (40 g) snow buntings roosted exposed on an open shelf in winter at Barrow. Surprisingly, domesticated pigeons lived in open cages out of doors through late winter at Barrow. It does not appear that northern birds are generally able to find much shelter beyond the insulation that they naturally bear.

Basal metabolic rates of birds are in general accord with those of mammals of their size (see p. 118). There are no northern resident birds larger than a few kilograms and many, like redpolls (*Acanthis hornemanni*) and chickadees (Paridae), weigh only one or a few decigrams. Critical low temperatures of birds, where

Table 9.3. Lower critical temperature of some northern birds

Species	Season	Critical temperature °C	Reference
Branta bernicla (Black brant)		6	IRVING et al., 1955
Lagopus lagopus (Willow ptarmigan)	winter summer	−8.5 7.5	WEST, unpublished
Lagopus mutus (Rock ptarmigan)	winter	0	WEST, unpublished
Lagopus leucurus (White-tailed ptarmigan)		6.5	JOHNSON, 1967
Nyctia scandiaca (Snowly owl)	winter	4.5	GESSAMAN, 1968
Corvus corax principalis (Raven)		0	SCHOLANDER, HOCK, WALTERS, JOHNSON and IRVING, 1950
Parus major (Great tit)	winter	28	HISSA and PALOKAREGAS, 1970
Perisoreus canadensis (Gray jay)	summer winter	30 5	VEGHTE, 1964
Acanthis flammea (Common redpoll)	winter spring summer autumn	9.2 20 23 24.8	WEST, unpublished
Plectrophanax nivalis (Snow bunting)	winter	10	SCHOLANDER, HOCK, WALTERS, JOHNSON and IRVING, 1950
Pygoscelis adeliae (Adelie penguin, long captive at Baltimore)		−4.5	LERESCHE and WEST, 1967
Spheniscus demersus (African penguin long captive at Baltimore)		11.7	LERESCHE and WEST, 1967

determined (Table 9.3), are not low and many are enough higher than common temperatures of winter that it appears likely that they would need continuously to maintain metabolic rates two or three times basal. At the rate extrapolated from measurements in air at 4° in Turku, Finland, the great tit *(Parus major)* would require metabolic heat about double or three times the basal rate to maintain body temperature in winter air about –30° (Hissa and Palokaregas, 1970).

Several species of birds (see Table 9.3) have been found to have a considerably lower critical temperature in winter than in summer. The implication is that their insulation changes seasonally as does the pelage of large mammals. But the feathers are not conspicuously thicker in winter, except in comparison with the brief period of molting in summer. A few small mammals that have been examined have not shown much lower critical temperatures in winter, and in many it would be hard to measure appreciable seasonal change in their pelage. The examples are still too few to imply that this difference between birds and small mammals is of general significance.

In spite of our misgivings, the small northern birds do exist, and it is evident that they evade some of the dire consequences of exposure that I have projected from consideration of mammals. They do not obey the rules that I have outlined for operation of mammals in cold. For example, the tits at Turku dropped somewhat in body temperature in experimental cold and were found to be internally at 37° (5° cooler than in thermoneutral condition) when sleeping outdoors in a cage at –15°. At Oslo, Steen (1958) likewise found that under experimental observation tits cooled by night in cold winter air.

In the system where temperature of the body of a mammal is maintained by metabolic heat escaping through an insulative barrier, I have chosen to believe that temperature of the body is prescribed by some specific requirement and that deviation represents a perturbation not long tolerable and not usable for adaptation to a cold climate. At Turku the tits in winter experiments increased metabolism much more slowly as they were cooled than they did in summer experiments (Fig. 9.4). Projection along the line, which usually intercepts the abscissa at body temperature, in winter would intercept at an impossibly high temperature of the body. In such cases it could be suspected that the tits cooled, diminishing both their production of heat and the gradient that would lead to loss of heat. But I would not know how to examine a physical system in which all three factors

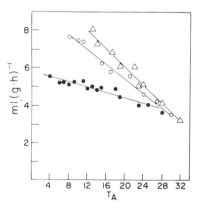

Fig. 9.4. Metabolism of the titmouse in summer and winter: ●, in winter; ○, in summer; ▽, winter, without feathers. Each point represents the average of three to five measurements. (From Hissa and Palokaregas, 1970)

in the equation comprising temperature, heat and insulation were changing. Some tolerance of hypothermia may be utilized by small homeotherms in arctic life to moderate somewhat the requirement of exaggerated metabolism and the enlarged requirement of food, but I am not satisfied with the attempts to rationalize upon metabolism and heat of arctic birds.

Effect of Wind

Except in the quiet subnivean haunts of small northern mammals, wind exerts a strong cooling effect. Locomotion also disturbs the insulation afforded by fur and feathers in addition to creating effects of wind. The cooling effect of wind, which is so readily felt, is difficult to measure and analyze. GESSAMAN'S (1968) measurements of snowy owls in a wind tunnel at Barrow showed their metabolism to increase about as the square root of wind speed (from 0 to 2 3/4 m/sec), and at −40° it was about double the levels observed at −10°. If extrapolation can be made from these modest wind speeds (about 10 km/hr) to the much higher velocities of natural winds in which the owl stands exposed, it is suggested that at 30 km/hr (8.4 m/sec) metabolism might increase six times in maintaining temperature of the body. The owls did maintain an even temperature, except for occasional and unexplainable lapses.

Conversion of Food to Heat and Activity

Calorimetry over short periods is convenient and provides the physiologist with hard numbers for the production of energy by oxidative metabolism. Assumptions such as that measured consumptions of oxygen represent stable processes, that brief periods can be extrapolated to days, and that a few individuals characterize a population, can arouse skepticism about the validity of drawing general conclusions from indirect calorimetry about the metabolic cost of natural living. But the large consistency among many measurements on numerous species establishes comparative significance of basal rates and critical low temperatures. They still deal only with metabolism at rest, under imposed conditions, without the calorigenic effect of food, and neglect activity, seasonal changes in weight, and periodic processes like reproduction and molting. As we try to formulate production of heat in the simplest of physical models we disregard the complexity of the animal as a producer of heat.

Daily Activity of Arctic Willow Ptarmigan

The habits of arctic willow ptarmigan (*Lagopus lagopus*) at Anaktuvuk Pass (lat. 68°N) could be observed well throughout several years with help from the resident Eskimos, who are familiar with the birds through their own lifelong experience and knowledge derived from ancestors. In mid-winter, flocks of ptarmigan are seen and heard in the few hours of twilight around noon. On dark stormy days observation is difficult. We have occasionally seen them standing in the lee of a snow bank and sometimes by day they are flushed from burrows under the snow. As days lengthen, flocks in migration trend northward, reaching a crescendo of conspicuous migratory activity late in May, when they may be seen or heard at any hour. Shortly after pairing they settle for nesting. Individuals may, however, be seen in activity at any time of day in summer. As nights begin to darken, signs of nocturnal activity diminish as migration starts southward by day until we believed that in midwinter the duration of activity extended for only a few hours about noon.

In winter the ptarmigan leave signs to extend our visual and auditory observation. Tracks can be seen in snow and feces accumulate in burrows in snow from which birds are flushed in early morning. These have indicated to the observant Eskimos that ptarmigan of a flock had remained through long winter nights in place in the burrows into which they had plunged from flight at dusk and from which they emerged in flight when aroused. Another trace of the regime of feeding is provided by the amount of buds and twig tips of willow contained in crops of ptarmigan taken by day for specimens and by the Eskimos for food. In mid-winter the crops contained a homogeneous collection of willows of only one or two species. Their weight is an indicator of the intensity and extent of feeding. As is shown in Fig. 9.5, weights of crops increase in midwinter and decline in summer. In midwinter the weight of crops increased during the day from empty at dawn until they reached maxima exceeding 10% of the ptarmigan's weight at 1500 h, at about the end of 'civil twilight'.

These indications of the natural program of activity and feeding were analyzed in captive ptarmigan kept free from disturbance out of doors at Fairbanks (65°N).

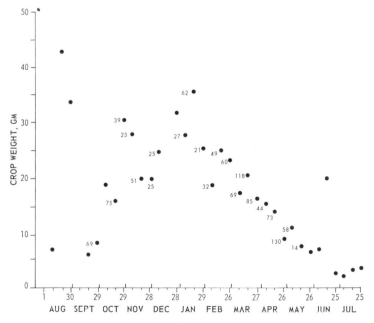

Fig. 9.5. Average weight of crops of willow ptarmigan in each 10-day interval. Number of crops weighed is shown by numeral under point. Points without figures represented fewer than 10 birds. Total = 1192 birds collected from localities between the Koyukuk River and Umiat. (From IRVING et al., 1967)

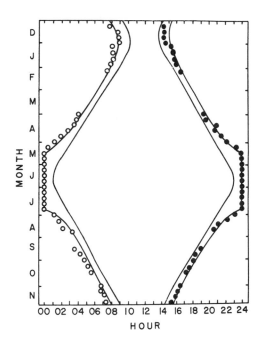

Fig. 9.6. Onset (○) and cessation (●) of activity of captive willow ptarmigan under natural conditions of temperature and photoperiod at College, Alaska. The outer lines indicate beginning and end of civil twilight; the inner lines indicate sunrise and sunset at College, Alaska. (From WEST, 1968)

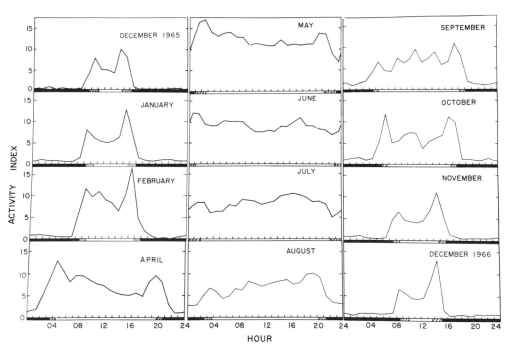

Fig. 9.7. Seasonal changes in pattern of gross activity of captive willow ptarmigan at College, Alaska. Activity index is defined as the average number of 3-min intervals in which a bird is active/hr. The activity from 2 to 4 birds each day is averaged over each month in the figure. The dark base line indicates night; the cross-hatched line, civil twilight; and the open line, day-light. (From WEST, 1968)

131

Recorded daily activity in the morning preceded the time of civil twilight by about an hour and ceased about an hour after civil twilight ended throughout the year (Fig. 9.6). The intensity of activity, as shown by recorded movements, varied in extent throughout the year in relation to daylight (Fig. 9.7). Seldom is it possible to analyze an annual program of behavior of captive animals so clearly in relation to the known behavior of their wild population.

The calorific energy available to the captive ptarmigan from their consumed food (less the energy in excrement) increased from about 100 kcal/ bird/day at 20° in summer to 130 kcal at –35° in winter. The increase in winter was apparently conserved by the improvement of insulation that is illustrated by the considerably lower critical temperature in winter (–8.5°) than in summer (+7.5°) (see Table 9.3). But changing seasonal activity of ptarmigan (see Fig. 9.7), breeding and molting also vary the flow of metabolic energy through the bird in such manner that molting and laying eggs are more demanding in warm summer when less energy is required for thermoregulation. As a result of compensating savings and expenditures, the flow of energy metabolized was not much altered during the

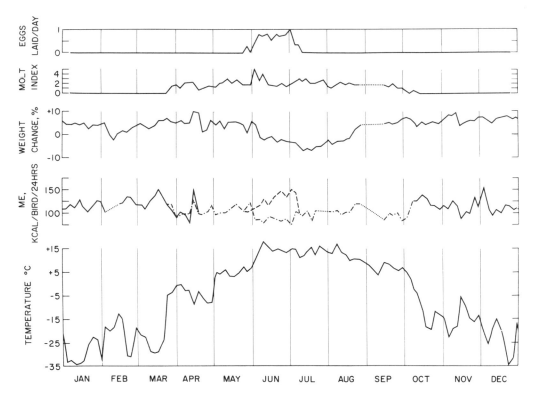

Fig. 9.8. Seasonal pattern of egg laying, molt, weight change, metabolized energy and ambient temperature in caged willow ptarmigan at College, Alaska. All data are expressed on a per-bird basis.
Weight change is expressed as percent change from the birds initial weight recorded in September, 1965. Fine dotted lines indicate lack of data; the dashed line is the metabolized energy of females during egg laying; the dotted and dashed line is the metabolized energy of males and non-laying females during molt. (From WEST, 1968)

year (Fig. 9.8). It is a satisfaction to see that experimental analysis of cyclic activity and flow of metabolic energy are in reasonable accord with observed behavior of a wild population of the species.

Bioenergetics of Snowy Owls

In his studies of captive snowy owls GESSAMAN (1968) found the flow of energy through snowy owls kept outdoors in varying wind and temperature, by the metabolic utilization of a diet of rats, was reasonably consistent with extrapolations from metabolic rates, lower critical temperature and effect of velocity of wind as measured by indirect calorimetry. With a few not unrealistic assumptions he estimated that four lemmings (4x60 g) per day might be required by an owl weighing 2 kg in weather at Barrow during October, and near seven lemmings during the coldest December. Factors in the comparatively low requirement are the rather low basal metabolic rate and sedentary habits of the owl. A good guess, based on reported observations, is that free owls generally stand quietly and, if undisturbed, are on the wing only some 5% of the time. In a spring and summer with abundant lemmings capture of the daily ration would be quite feasible with this modest activity. In cold winter, when lemmings are concealed and when a few owls are seen apparently subsisting on ptarmigan, I have thought that the owls had to hunt vigorously to capture this swift and alert prey. In the years of abundance of arctic lemmings it seems feasible for owls to multiply as they do to numbers that must disperse southward in the cyclic winters of very few lemmings. I have not seen evidence to determine whether these dispersed owls return northward, or whether the few that remain in the Arctic reconstitute the populations.

Summary

Internal Temperature

Warm-blooded animals preserve internal temperatures characteristic of each species (Chapter 7); temperature of the body is not adaptable to circumstances. Rather, in meeting the requirements of innate specific characteristics, the mode of life under varying circumstances must be adapted to that thermal requirement set in a remote past.

Basal Metabolic Production of Heat

The rate of generation of metabolic heat by birds and mammals at the basal level for existence seems also to be related to the size of each species (p. 118), although some categories of species exceed by twice or fall to half the so-called normal rate for their size. The relation of basal metabolism to size varies in some strains of domesticated animals even within a species. In general the basal level appears to be genetically established. In its relation to internal temperature, the animal

adjusts to its inherited metabolic requirement and adapts its ways to that requirement set by its past. To speculate about evolution we must look backward in
order to project from the origins of adaptations to their present operation.

Resting Metabolic Production of Heat

Resting metabolic production of heat is a more vague characteristic, and in cold
winter climates small birds seem not to be able naturally to relax the rate of resting
metabolism to the basal level. Some adaptation of persistent resting metabolic
rate is possible to suit climate (HART, 1964), but it is limited in amount, time
required for its establishment, by the availability of food and capability for its
utilization to produce heat. Adaptation of resting metabolic production of heat
for arctic life is slow and of limited extent.

Metabolic Thermogenesis Induced by Cold

In circumstances colder than permit basal metabolism, or when the less well definable resting metabolic rate does not suffice to maintain bodily warmth, birds and
mammals shiver to provide supplemental heat by muscular activity that does not
produce locomotion. Mammals can also generate heat by its direct evolution from
metabolic chemical reactions that do not result in muscular contraction. Chemical
thermogenesis appears not to occur in birds. Muscular exertion also adds to the
generation of heat. Any of these reactions is, as we all know, better than freezing,
but they are costly. A human athlete can run or swim for some hours generating
heat at ten times the basal rate, and a sled dog or wolf can do at least as well.
Since motion diminishes the insulation of clothing, feathers, or fur, not all of
this heat is applicable for maintaining warmth. In short, during experimental tests
of an hour or so in cold some vigorous mammals can counteract cooling by producing heat at six times the basal rate, but few of us are in such good condition.
Wolves, dogs, feral brown rats and human athletes have such capabilities. For
various reasons some species of mammals are not capable or inclined to long-sustai-
ned high rates of thermogenesis. In experiments several species of northern birds
in winter maintained such surprisingly high production of heat in cold as to cause
us to wonder about the metabolic capability and nutritional economy of such
a way of life under natural arctic conditions.

Insulation

The obvious adaptation in thermoregulation in the arctic is effected by resistance
to escape of heat. To express this resistance as insulation according to its proper
physical definition, or as its reciprocal, conductance, requires reference to the
area of the surface through which heat is emitted. The geometry of surfaces of
animals is hard to measure, their insulative fur and feathers differ topographically,
and the emission of heat through conduction, convection, evaporation and radia-

tion is a further complication. I prefer not to make the assumptions necessary for designating insulation or conductance in proper thermal dimensions, but to rest on the scheme of relative resistance to escape of heat in the designation of overall insulation used by SCHOLANDER, HOCK, WALTER, JOHNSON and IRVING, (1950).

References

BENEDICT, F. C.: Vital Energetics. Publication No. 503. Washington: Carnegie Inst. 1938.

BRODY, S.: Bioenergetics and Growth, with Special References to the Efficiency Complex in Domestic Animals. New York: Hafner Pub. Co. 1964.

DAVYDOV, A. F., MAKAROVA, A. R.: Changes in heat regulation and circulation in newborn seals. Fed. Am. Soc. Exp. Biol. Proc. Trans. Suppl. **24** (II), 563–566 (1964).

ERIKSON, H.: Observation on the metabolism of arctic ground squirrels (*Citellus parryi*) at different environmental temperatures. Acta physiol. scand. **36**, 66–74 (1956).

ERIKSON, H., KROG, J., LANGE ANDERSEN, K., SCHOLANDER, P. F.: The critical temperature in naked man. Acta physiol. scand. **37**, 35 (1956).

GESSAMAN, J. A.: Metabolism and Thermoregulation of the Snowy Owl. Ph. D. Thesis, Univ. of Illinois, Dep. of Zoology (1968).

HAMMEL, H. T., HOUPT, T. R., LANGE ANDERSEN, K., SKJENNEBERG, S.: Thermal and metabolic measurments of a reindeer at rest and in exercise. Techn. Doc. Report AAL-TDR-61-54, Arctic, Ft. Wainwritht, Alaska (1962).

HAMMEL, H. T., WYNDHAM, C. H., HARDY, J. D.: Heat production and heat loss in the dog at 8–36° environmental temperature. Amer. J. Physiol. **194**, 99–108 (1958).

HART, J.S.: Insulative and metabolic adaptions to cold in vertebrates. In: Proc. 18th Symp. Soc. for Exp. Biol. Cambridge (England): Cambridge Univ. Press 1964.

HART, J. S., IRVING, L.: The energetics of harbor seals in air and in water with special consideration of seasonal changes. Canad. J. Zool. **37**, 447–459 (1959).

HEROUX, O.: Seasonal adjustments in captured wild Norway rats. I. Organ weights, ear vascularization, and histology of epidermis. Canad. J. Biochem. Physiol. **39**, 865–870 (1961).

HISSA, R., Palokaregas, R.: Thermoregulation in the tit mouse (*Parus major*). Comp. Biochem. Physiol. **33**, 941–953 (1970).

IRVING, L., HART, J. S.: The metabolism and insulation of seals as bare-skinned mammals in cold water. Canad. J. Zool. **35**, 497–511 (1957).

IRVING, L., KROG, H., MONSON, M.: The metabolism of some Alaskan animals in winter and summer. J. Physiol. Zool. **28**, 173–185 (1955).

IRVING, L., KROG, J., KROG, H., MONSON, M.: Metabolism of a varying hare in winter. J. Mammal. **38**, 527–529 (1957).

IRVING, L., PEYTON, L. J., MONSON, M.: Metabolism and insulation of swine as bare-skinned mammals. J. App. Physiol. **9**, 421–426 (1956).

IRVING, L., SCHMIDT-NELSON, K., ABRAHAMSON, N.: On the melting points of animal fats in cold climates. Physiol. Zool. **30**, 93–105 (1957).

IRVING, L., SCHOLANDER, P. F., GRINNELL, S. W.: The respiration of the porpoise (*Tursiops truncatus*). J. Cell. Comp. Physiol. **17**, 145 (1941).

IRVING, L., SOLANDT, O. M., SOLANDT, D. Y., FISHER, K. C.: The respiratory metabolism of the seal and its adjustment to diving. J. Cell. Comp. Physiol. **7**, 137–151 (1935).

IRVING L., WEST, G. C., PEYTON, L. J.: Winter feeding program of Alaska willow ptarmigan shown by crop contents. The Condor **69**, 69–77 (1967).

JOHNSON, R. E.: Temperature regulation in the white–tailed ptarmigan, (*Lagopus leucurus*). Comp. Biochem. Physiol. **24**, 1003–1014 (1967).

KANWISHER, J., SUNDNESS, G.: Thermal regulation in cetaceans. In: Whales, Dolphins and Porpoises. Ed. by K. S. NORRIS. Berkeley: University of California Press 1966.

KLEIBER, M.: The Fire of Life: An Introduction to Animal Energetics. New York: John Wiley & Sons Inc. 1961.

KROG, H., MONSON, M.: Notes on the metabolism of a mountain goat. Amer. J. Physiol. **178**, 515–516 (1954).

KROG, H., MONSON, M., IRVING, L.: Influence of cold upon the metabolism and body temperature of wild rats, albino rats, and albino rats conditioned to cold. J. Appl. Physiol. **7**, 349–354 (1955).

LASIEWSKI, R. C., DAWSON, W. R.: A re-examination of the relation between standard metabolic rate and body weight in birds. The Condor **69**, 13–23 (1967).

LE RESCHE, R. E., WEST, G. C.: Acute metabolic responses of antarctic and subtropical penguins to temperature. Unpublished preliminary report (1967).

MARTIN, C. J.: Thermal adjustment and respiratory exchange in Monotremes and marsupials. Phil. Trans. Roy. Soc. London. B. 195, 1 (1902).

McEWAN, E. H.: Energy metabolism of barren ground caribou (*Rangifer tarandus*). Canad. J. Zool. **48**, 391–392 (1970).

SCHOLANDER, P. F.: Experimental investigations on the respiratory function in diving mammals and birds. Hvalradets Skrifter No. 22. Oslo: Jacob Dybwad 1940.

SCHOLANDER, P. F., HAMMEL, H. T., LANGE ANDERSEN, K., LYMING, Y.: Metabolic acclimation to cold in man. J. Appl. Physiol. **12**, 1–8 (1958).

SCHOLANDER, P. F., HOCK, R., WALTERS, V., IRVING, L.: Adaptation to cold in arctic and tropical mammals and birds in relation to body temperature, insulation, and basal metabolic rate. Biol. Bull. **99**, 259–629 (1950).

SCHOLANDER, P. F., HOCK, R., WALTERS, V., JOHNSON, F., IRVING, L.: Heat regulation in some arctic and tropical mammals and birds. Biol. Bull. **99**, 237–258 (1950).

SCHOLANDER, P. F., IRVING, L.: Experimental investigations on the respiration and diving of the Florida manatee. J. Cell. Comp. Physiol. **17**, 169–191 (1940).

SCHOLANDER, P. F., LANGE ANDERSEN, K., KROG, J., VOGT LORENTZEN, F., STEEN, J.: Critical temperature in Lapps. J. Appl. Physiol. **10**, 231–234 (1957).

STEEN, J.: Climatic adaptation in some small northern birds. Ecology **39**, 625–629 (1958).

VEGHTE, J. H.: Thermal and metabolic response of the gray jay to cold stress. Physiol. Zool. **3**, 316–328 (1964).

WEST, G. C.: Bioenergetics of captive willow ptarmigan under natural conditions. Ecology **49**, 1035–1045 (1968).

WRIGHT, P. G.: Wild Animals in the Tropics. Proc. of Symposium of the Zool. Soc. of London. London and New York: Academic Press 1964.

Chapter 10

Heterothermic Operation of Homeotherms

Gradients of Temperature from Depth to Surface

As generators of heat with well sustained internal operating temperatures, birds and mammals maintain thermal gradients from the interior to surrounding cold air or water. I will forego discussion of evaporative cooling by breathing and panting, which are not especially illuminated by arctic studies, to speak of regulation of warmth by thermal gradients from the warm interior to cold surroundings. Without much analysis of the methods of transport of heat I shall point to thermal gradients and consequent conditions that are emphatically revealed in arctic birds and mammals.

Arctic birds and land mammals covered with feathers or fur characteristically keep the skin on their bodies warm. Over the body the skin does not usually cool more than 6 or 7 degrees below the interior. In air at −40°, the gradient from skin through fur or feathers may be 70°, some 10 times the gradient through bodily tissues to the skin. A comfortable man keeps the skin on his trunk above 30° by adjusting his clothing and thus, like fur-bearers, referring the largest gradient outside of his skin.

Eyes, mouths and bills, ears, feet and hands would not be perceptive under a covering of fur or feathers, so their sensitive living tissues are bare. Thick insulation of limbs would hinder swiftness of movement of long-legged caribou. Bears have thick fur on their massive legs, illustrating that insulation of extremities differs among species, but considerable surfaces of arctic birds and mammals protrude exposed from the effective insulation covering their bodies.

Insulation by fur (or feathers) is lacking from the beaver's large bare tail and from the feet of aquatic birds. The skin of whales and walrus is devoid of insulating hair. The arctic and antarctic phocid seals (Phocidae), comprising the major numbers of the world's seals, have only short hair of small insulative value in air in comparison with a caribou's fur. In water the seal's hair is wet and skin is directly exposed to its powerful cooling effect. Maintenance of warm skin in icy water would cause an insupportable drain of heat. By allowing skin to cool, heat is conserved, but the thermal gradient regulating the flow of heat is within living superficial tissues. Distributed over the whole body, as well as in bare appendages, the insulative system of seals operates quite differently from insulation by fur and feathers. This method of insulation by thermal gradients through sensitive living tissue is employed with striking success by arctic marine mammals. The cold, bare extremities of arctic land mammals and birds illustrate the localized employment of thermal gradients through living tissues for insulation.

Bare Legs of Arctic Aquatic Birds

Wondering about the loss of heat that might occur through the large surfaces of the webbed foot of an arctic duck or gull swimming in icy water, we immersed the foot of an arctic glaucous gull (*Larus hyperboreus*) in a calorimeter. The heat emitted was so small that it could only mean that the tissues of the foot were near freezing temperature, some 40° colder than the internal temperature of the body (SCHOLANDER, WALTERS, HOCK and IRVING 1950). We were skeptical about how to describe the physiological processes and states involved.

Circulation through Cold Webbed Feet

Observation through a binocular microscope of the webbed foot of a boreal glaucous-winged gull (*Larus glaucescens*) showed rapid flow of corpuscles through fine blood vessels when the foot was cooled on a cold plate until the internal temperature, indicated by a thermocouple inserted adjacent to the active circulation, was near 0° (IRVING and KROG, 1955) (Fig. 10.1). If warm blood were cooled in the large area of the gull's foot, escape of heat to the great cooling power of ice water could amount to an insupportable loss of metabolic heat. Temperatures

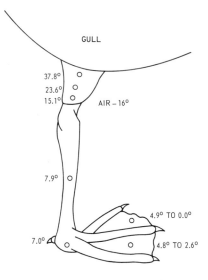

Fig. 10.1. Topographic distribution of superficial temperatures in the leg of a gull (*Larus glaucescens*). (From IRVING and KROG, 1955)

along the skin of the leg showed a gradual rise from the web and a sudden rise as the distal portion of the tibia became covered by thick contour feathers, under which the skin reached the warmth (38°) characteristic of feather-covered skin over the body. The abrupt rise in temperature in the proximal part of the leg suggested that an arrangement of veins with reference to arteries allowed heat from arterial blood to warm cold returning venous blood, and in this manner conserved heat while permitting continuing circulation in the cold extremity.

138

Observing the veins intimately surrounding arteries flowing toward the extremities, CLAUDE BERNARD (1876) remarked that the veins were in a position suitable for warming blood as it returned cool from the periphery. Operation of vascular heat exchangers was first demonstrated in the femoral region of dogs and in man by the large gradient of temperature falling distally along the artery (BAZETT et al., 1948; BAZETT, 1949).

Vascular arrangements suitable for countercurrent heat exchange have been described and their operation has been indicated by measured thermal gradients in a few birds. The STEENS (1965 b) showed that as the air surrounding a gull (*Larus marinus*) cooled to 5°, only a few percent of the total heat produced was emitted from a leg that was immersed in water. In air at 30° from 25 to 40 percent of the metabolic heat was emitted from a single immersed leg. In contrast, about 1/16 of the metabolic heat was emitted from one immersed leg of a heron (*Ardea cinerea*) in air below 20°. In air at 30° nearly 3/4 of the metabolic heat was emitted to water from a single leg. The gull remains on the Norwegian coast in winter; the heron migrates to warmer climates. The legs of the gull conserved heat in a cold environment more effectively than did the legs of the heron. Both are effective in dissipating heat to cooler water when the birds are in warm air, but the migratory heron's legs appear to be adapted for heat regulation under warmer conditions.

In several contexts I have mentioned the use of vascular countercurrent heat exchangers in the regulation of warmth in arctic animals. Usually their employment as essential variable insulators is implied by temperature gradients and by the presence of vascular devices that appear to be suitable for regulation. Seldom is their operation to regulate emission of heat as clearly shown as in the gulls and herons of the Steens. I suspect that these variable vascular insulating devices are widely employed. Their actual operation and regulation is much more complex than is shown by the measurement of their net effects. Analysis of their function, which will bring out some new physiological processes, should be favored in the arctic animals in which thermal gradients and amounts of heat exchanged are large and in which effective variable insulation is of such importance.

Adaptation of the Gull Foot for Cold

A dramatic illustration of adaptation of a gull foot for cold was afforded at Barrow when a glaucous gull that had been kept captive during winter in the warm laboratory escaped to stand on snow in air –20°. Within a minute its feet had frozen and parts of the outer web and toes subsequently became gangrenous and were lost (SCHOLANDER, WALTERS, HOCK and IRVING, 1950). Several other captive gulls living outdoors walked unconcerned on boards and ice in air often colder than –30°. The adaptation of the gulls for winter cold had been lost in several weeks of warm life indoors.

Adaptation of Peripheral Nerve for Cold

Another illustration of flexibility of adaptation to cold was provided in herring gulls (*Larus smithsonianus*) captured on the coast of Maine and examined during winter in Boston (CHATFIELD et al., 1953). Distal metatarsal sections of peroneal nerves excised from gulls kept outdoors (air –1° to 6°) responded to electrical stimulation as they were cooled down to about 4°. The more proximal tibial part failed at a temperature about 8° warmer. Nerves from gulls kept in cages where they waded in water at 37° ceased conducting at about 10° in the distal metatarsal portion and at about 12° warmer in the proximal part. The metatarsal temperatures of the gulls adapted to heat were warmer than 25° while those of the cold adapted gulls were between 6° and 13°. It appears that the nerves became adapted by their environmental temperature only in the distal parts that were exposed and cold. The adaptation of nerves to cold occurred in the distal parts of continuous axons that proximally, being warm, did not become adapted.

Thermal Gradients Over the Body

Temperatures on the skin of arctic birds under their thick contour feathers have been found to be commonly only a few degrees cooler than in the interior of their bodies. As in temperate regions, the thermal gradient between interior and skin is small; through the thick feathers of large arctic birds to the air (–40°) the gradient may be 20 times as great. In none of the arctic birds (Table 9.3) is the reported critical temperature so low that birds could maintain internal warmth without elevating their production of metabolic heat. For small birds, with their relatively high lower critical temperature, the insulation of thin plumage appears to be insufficient for preservation of warmth without a large metabolic expenditure. By endurance of some hypothermia at rest they may effect some reduction of heat loss.

By reference to the accelerated heat production among southern birds in cold air, the increment of metabolic heat may be supposed to result from shivering. It seems as though the lives of arctic birds would be restless, the demands upon their metabolic processes excessive, and the requisite amount of food too large to obtain by foraging in the short winter twilight. These speculative problems are the result of ignorance, for the birds do not exhibit ill effects from the stresses that we imagine.

Persistence of Cold in Extremities

Cooling of the feet is a conservative device that seems particularly suitable for arctic birds and which we think is probably widespread among aquatic birds. Since we have been unable to record continuously the temperature of feet, we do not know to what extent the metabolism of their tissues is sustained while cold. We do see that excised nerves can operate while cold and we suspect that during swimming in icy water and walking on ice or snow the feet operate as effectively as in warm conditions of summer. It can be suspected that growth and maintenance of tissues may be confined to periods when feet can be withdrawn among feathers for warmth. This manoeuver would be a deferment of metabolism during hypothermic depression. Its postulation, however, is our speculative evasion of the prospect that peripheral parts of homeothermic animals do operate in the cold. Not only do they operate for locomotion when cold, but they are also equal to locomotion when warmed, and so the feet are adapted to work under heterothermic conditions.

Heterothermic Operations in Mammals

Feet of Porcupines and Dogs

I was impressed at seeing porcupines (*Erethizon dorsatum*) walking slowly through snow, in air at –20°, above treeline in the Talkeetna Mountains (lat. 60°N). Tracks of their slow progress showed the prolonged exposure of the large bare pads

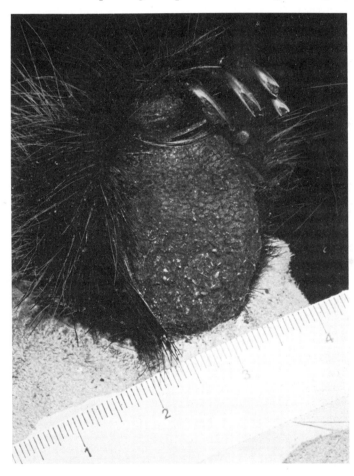

Fig. 10.2. Foot of a porcupine (*Erethizon dorsatum*). (From Irving and Krog, 1955) Scale in inch: 1 inch = 2,5 cm

of their feet (Fig. 10.2). These animals were easily captured and are of gentle disposition. Application of a thermocouple to the large bare pad of the foot showed temperatures as low as 0° while under the fur the skin was from 25° to 36°, and rectal temperatures were 36° to 38° (IRVING and KROG, 1955). While measuring temperatures I noticed that falling snow flakes remained on the bare cold pad of the foot. The snow falling on my bare hands melted and rendered them unusable.

Arctic sled dogs may become completely covered with snow that falls when they are asleep, a condition that demonstrates the small loss of heat through their thick fur. Cold footpads not only conserve heat but by preventing melting of snow in contact they prevent magnified extraction of heat by its melting. If contact with snow brought about even occasional melting there would be the further peril of formation of ice that would encase the toes and freeze fur or feathers to the lair in which the animals rested. I have examined many beds of animals in snow without finding hairs or feathers torn out by freezing. I must admit that many views upon the warmth or coldness of tissues are prompted by teleological opinions as to the usefulness of conditions that are observed or only suspected. Experimental testing of animals not adapted for cold, like the gull that had been kept indoors, might show the rather delicate balance of warmth and cold that I suspect is maintained in the surfaces of adapted animals.

Extremities of Arctic Mammals

In a number of arctic and northern mammals cool or cold temperatures were recorded in bare footpads and hooves. Gentle, well mannered resting arctic sled dogs not only held up their paws to show the cold suface of the bare footpads,

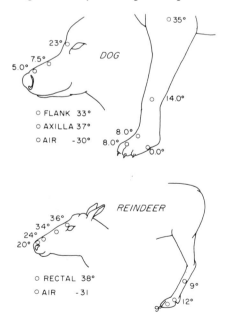

Fig. 10.3. Topographic distribution of superficial temperatures in a dog and in a reindeer. (From IRVING and KROG, 1955)

but the dogs so well appreciated human attention that they allowed insertion of needle thermocouples to show that subcutaneous tissues were, within a degree or so, as cold as the skin. Proximally along the leg, skin under thin fur was cold (Fig. 10.3). Deep in the legs of caribou and reindeer killed instantly, inserted thermocouples showed that temperatures around 8° occurred. Capability for cool operation has also been noticed in deep tarsal bones of animals from temperate climates, but the degree of coldness and its apparent usefulness are conspicuous in arctic species.

Variable insulation provided by gradients in bare extremities can indicate conservation of heat. Warming of extremities can also help to dissipate excessive heat. Warming of the extensive suface of the bare tail of the muskrat (*Ondatra zibethicus*) (JOHANSEN, 1962) is an essential means for dissipation of heat in warm air, indicating little flexibility in reducing the insulation on its fur covered body. The large bare tail of the beaver (*Castor fiber*) can also conserve or dissipate heat by cooling or warming (STEEN and STEEN, 1965 a). HAMMEL (1968) has listed some extremities that, by their variation in temperature, can serve for thermoregulation:

Wood ibis (*Mycteria americana*)	legs
Ostrich (*Struthio camelus*)	legs
Jack rabbit (*Lepus californicus*)	ears
Beaver (*Castor fiber*)	tail
Muskrat (*Ondatra zibethicus*)	tail
Domesticated Norway rat (*Rattus norvegicus*)	tail
Fur seal (*Callorhinus ursinus*)	flippers
Domestic goat	horns

I am certain that this list can be greatly extended.

Maintenance of Warmth in Feet Standing on Ice

Bypass of a vascular countercurrent heat exchanger plausibly explains its employment for increased dissipation of heat. Likewise, full employment of the exchanger plausibly explains its use for conservation of heat. The tolerance of cold by warm-blooded tissues, however, can scarcely extend much below their freezing point, which is not known to be below –1°. In colder air or in contact with cold ice and snow, the bare feet of arctic birds and mammals often touch surfaces as cold as –50°. Although the conduction of heat by dry snow may be small, at these low temperatures it would seem likely that increased provision of heat through the circulation would be required to prevent the extremities from freezing. HENSHAW and FOLK (1969) and HENSHAW et al. (1972) proposed that in the feet of arctic wolves vasodilatation occurred in cold, increasing the transport of heat from the body to avoid freezing of tissues of the foot. Measurements of skin temperature on bare foot pads showed 0 to 5° on cold snow. The foot of an anesthetized wolf did not freeze during one and a half hours while it was immersed in a cold bath (–34°).

The common view, obtained from man and laboratory animals that are not adapted for cold, is that exposure to increasing cold progressively emphasizes vasoconstriction in the extremities. At some low temperature, however, sustained vasoconstriction would amount to autotomy of the limb. In fact, this is the result of cooling beyond ability for compensation, as is shown by the development of 'trench' or 'immersion' foot, a disorder resulting from prolonged exposure to wet cold but without actual frostbite.

In a man exposed to cold within the range of his usual experience, the vasoconstriction in the hand that is induced by cold is periodically released to permit transient rewarming (see also Chapter 12). It is still debated whether the restoration of circulation is effected by relaxation of vasoconstriction or by the active antagonistic process of vasodilatation. In a well ordered (i.e., adaptive) vascular reflex the operation of vasodilatation would inhibit antagonistic vasoconstriction. We may imagine that the feet of arctic animals are truly adapted to endure exposure to the intense cold that they would encounter. The adaptive compensation would be effected by relaxation of vasoconstriction and further facilitated by active vasodilatation. In order to provide the large outflow of heat shown to occur in the feet of HENSHAW's and FOLK's wolves, they reasonably postulate the operation of a very effective vasodilator system. I anticipate that they will point out some of the intricate components of vasodilatation in the hands and feet of arctic animals, with important illumination of an operation that has been so obscure in studies on animals not adapted to cold because vasodilatation in the extremities of man is relatively feeble.

We have to make several assumptions in order to explain the avoidance of damage to feet from arctic cold, and these may conceal the actual regulation of circulated heat by blood that must proceed with high accuracy when external contacts are so cold, tissues are so critically sensitive, vascular operations in these conditions are so unexpected, and the disposable supply of heat is not unlimited. The delicacy of the situation is illustrated by the opinion that if the feet become much warmer than freezing they will melt snow and cause an insupportable drain of heat amounting to 80 calories per gram of snow that is melted. On the other hand, we suspect that living tissues cannot endure a temperature below their freezing point. A very sensitive and effective vascular regulation seems to be the requirement for maintenance of warmth between these narrow limits.

The feet of native arctic birds and mammals do not suffer injuries from freezing unless injured or caught in traps. When weather is colder than −30°, working sled dogs lift their feet during a halt as if to reduce contact with cold snow, and they soon lie down in their traces with feet covered by their coiled bodies. Short-haired beagle dogs imported to Alaska in winter and released in cold outdoor pens for some days lifted their feet from the cold snow, yelped as if in pain and occasionally rolled on their backs with feet in air (DURRER and HANNON, 1961). After longer exposure the feet of the beagles appeared to become adjusted to contact with cold snow.

We all know that even in moderately cold weather cold hands and feet are awkward and a source of misery. The physiological processes that protect the arctic animals must be so intense and accurate that their study may well relieve the obscurity of the small and imprecise reactions to cold of animals unaccustomed to it.

Operation of Nerves in Heterothermic Mammalian Extremities

MILLER and IRVING (1967) found that excised sections of caudal nerve from beaver and muskrat were still operational when cooled to –5.0° and –4.4° respectively. Nerves from the thick-furred tail of Alaskan red fox (*Vulpes fulva*) and coyote *(Canis latrans)* could be cooled only to 3.1° and 1.0°, respectively, before becoming unexcitable (MILLER, 1967). The tail of the coyote, when exposed for one and one-half hours at –25°, remained within 10° of rectal temperature. In cold air the tissues of the tail of an Alaskan marten (*Martes americana*) and red squirrel (*Tamiasciurus hudsonicus*) became cold. The tails of both of these species are only thinly covered by hair. When caudal nerves excised from the marten and squirrel were cooled they continued to conduct at about the cold temperature (–4°) that was tolerated by nerves from bare tails of muskrats. In summary, nerves from tails that naturally cooled over a large range conducted impulses even at subzero temperatures, while nerves from well-furred, warm tails ceased operation at warmer temperatures.

Comparison of Homeothermic Internal and Heterothermic Peripheral Nerves

In spinal nerves from three locations in the beaver (*Castor canadensis*), caudal, tibial and phrenic, cold blocked the operation in the order shown (Fig. 10.4):

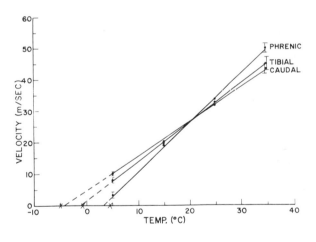

Fig. 10.4. Conduction velocity as a function of temperature in beaver caudal, tibial, and phrenic nerves. Bars indicate plus or minus standard error of mean values. Dotted lines are extrapolations to zero conduction. (From MILLER, 1970)

Nerve	Extinction
Caudal	–5.0°
Tibial	–0.7°
Phrenic	4.5°

Phrenic nerves of the thoracic region are kept at normal body temperature; tibial nerves may encounter some, but little cooling; caudal nerves are from a region normally operating from very cold to warm temperatures (MILLER, 1970).

145

Peripheral and Internal Nerves of Seals

An impressive comparison was made of spinal nerves from the hind flipper, tibial region and thoracic phrenic section of seals *(Phoca vitulina, Phoca fasciata, Erignathus barbata)* taken from cold waters of Bering Sea during a cruise of R/V *Alpha Helix* (MILLER, 1970). As in the other mammals, the temperature of extinction of function by cold was lowest in the section of the nerve of the phalanges, higher in the tibial region and warmest in the phrenic sections, in order as these parts are normally exposed to cooling in thermoregulation. These differences were already visible in nerves from newborn pups. To that degree the adaptation was innate, but seals from warm waters have not been examined in order to consider whether life in a warm environment modifies their operation in cold.

Velocity of conduction in nerves slowed with cooling (Fig. 10.4). Perhaps more relevant than temperature of block by cold of the nerve is the frequency at which impulses may be transmitted. Estimated from refractory periods in fast-conducting myelinated fibers of these spinal nerves, frequencies transmissible at 5° would be 99/second in caudal nerve; 56/sec in tibial; 28/sec in phrenic (MILLER, 1970). We suspect that these ranges represent orders of capabilities for transmission of information by frequency modulation in these fast-conducting myelinated nerve fibers. It is clear from observed reactions that the beaver's tail is sensitive at 0°, and that the regulation of circulation proceeds effectively, as in the foot of gulls; but the regulator nerves of vascular function are as yet inaccessible to observation by electrical stimulation.

Reactivity of Heterothermic Arteries to Adrenaline

JOHANSEN (1969) observed that arterial preparations from smooth muscle excised from the flippers of seals *(Phoca vitulina)* taken during a cruise of R/V *Alpha Helix* within the late-winter ice of Bering Sea responded to adrenaline by vasoconstriction at 1°, whereas preparations from arteries of the kidney, deep in the homeothermic body, became refractory to adrenaline at 15°. Electrical stimulation of peripheral nerves has been observed only in the large myelinated fibers which would mediate certain fast sensory and motor impulses. The slow unmyelinated nerve fibers concerned with regulation of circulation had not been considered until JOHANSEN's observations on reactivity to adrenaline were related to persistence of excitability of vascular regulation in heterothermic arteries when very cold.

Tolerance of Cold by Nerves

I have often found that speculation upon the usefulness of a physiological reaction may lead to the design of studies that can examine origins and consequences of the isolated reaction in the life of a species. We have speculated in this manner upon the ability of the phrenic nerve to retain excitability at 4.5°, whereas in fetal and adult life it never cools more than a few degrees. At birth, the infant hair seals *(Phoca vitulina)* born south of the ice pack and having shed the white lanugo coat *in utero*, are well prepared for thermoregulation, but they probably have a reserve capability for enduring transient accidental hypothermia. Whether or not operation while cold is advantageous, we can see from examples listed that some large myelinated spinal nerves of mammals can conduct impulses even at −5° or until the nerve actually freezes. Below −1° the nerve is supercooled, and in course of time or by seeding with an ice crystal, it freezes. After freezing, if the excised nerve is rewarmed to 25° it soon recovers normal characteristics of excitability and conduction, and these faculties persist under experimental conditions for more than a day.

This tolerance of low temperature, supercooling and even brief freezing recalls the frequent use of cooled or, with cryoprotective agents, frozen spermatozoa of bulls, red blood cells, corneal tissue of the eye and some other tissues for artifical insemination or surgical replacement of damaged tissues (SMITH, 1961). This empirically determined tolerance of cold by preserved mammalian and avian tissue has been of great practical value, which in turn has excited theoretical speculation in cryobiology to establish the better preservation and uses of preserved tissues. In the case of nerves, the preservation of function while supercooled shows that in supercooled solutions of the cells and tissues the condition of membranes of nerves that produce action potentials indicative of impulses persists until freezing and may be restored after brief freezing. Adaptation to cold was shown better in heterothermic than in homeothermic nerves, and experimental exposure of the animal to cold has been shown in peripheral nerves of birds (p. 140) to bring about operational capability at colder temperature.

Cellular Activity in Heterothermic Tissues

One of the advantages attributed to homeothermy is preservation of a milieu in which cellular reactions may be conjoined in thermal conditions suitable for optimal operation. Many aquatic poikilothermic organisms and tissues are retarded if cooled only a few degrees, and your goldfish will be seriously injured by sudden cold 10 degrees below the usual range. Some poikilotherms can become acclimatized to operation in cold, but the procedure must be gradual and slow. In general, poikilotherms and their tissues will not stand the sudden changes of some 40° that are tolerated normally by peripheral heterothermic tissues of birds and mammals. The view, though disturbing, is real.

In fishes acclimatized to a new and colder temperature, affinities of enzymes for their substrates may become altered to states permitting more effective operation in cold. With this background in mind, SOMERO and JOHANSEN (1970) found that lactate dehydrogenase and pyruvate kinase of arterial smooth muscle from flippers of harbor seals (*Phoca vitulina*) taken within winter ice of Bering Sea preserved affinities for their substrates with little change by temperature. This step plausibly illustrates one of the sequences of essential enzymatic reactions that could remain effective over the wide range of temperature in which the arctic seal's flippers operate. Enzymes of muscle of rabbits cooled from 27° to 17° increased affinity for substrate so much as to appear ill-suited to heterothermic operations. When a similar preparation of enzymes from the homeothermic interior of the seals was examined, it proved to resemble peripheral preparations from heterothermic tissuess in smallness of depression of activity by cold. These early

147

results of analysis of heterothermic enzymatic reactions open further sequences of interesting biochemical research in the description of cellular processes pertinent to arctic life as well as raise difficult speculations upon the lack of parsimony that seems to have preserved unnecessary adaptation.

I have mentioned that we do not have records showing persistence of cold in peripheral tissues beyond a few minutes or hours. A question arises whether the cold tissues of skin can effect cellular division for replacement of wear while cold, or if they periodically rewarm to allow the essential division of cells. FELTZ and FAY (1968) found that cell cultures prepared from web epidermis of the flipper of a northern harbor seal did not effect cellular division below 17°, the temperature at which division ceased in cultures from skin of other seals and walrus; their ability to divide in cold did not differ from that of cultures prepared from a seal's kidney or of cultures of two human tissues.

After storage at 4° for 26 weeks, the cultures from skin of harbor seals and sea lions (*Eumetopias jubata*) resumed cellular division when returned to 37°. Two cultures from human tissues did not recover the ability to divide after three weeks of cold storage. Tolerance of cold storage by cultures from seal epidermis suggests ability of skin to resume functions of maintenance after cold intervals. Since regulated circulation persists in cold skin, since it is sensitive and some essential enzymatic operations are possible, I am inclined to believe that the search for continuous comprehensive cellular activities in cold will importantly extend knowledge of these extremely heterothermic tissues. For the sake of relevance to actual life, the regime of temperature in arctic seals must be monitored through long periods in winter.

Melting Points of Fats from Heterothermic Tissues

Fats stored by bull caribou over the lower back in summer and over the visceral organs solidify at room temperature. These hard fats of the large herbivores are conveniently stored by Eskimos, for in cold they become brittle hard. Thinking that in the cold extremities such fats would immobilize joints and tissues, we found that the melting points of marrow fats extracted from the femur were about body temperature. Distally the melting points of marrow fats declined until in the phalanges they remained soft near freezing temperatures (IRVING et al., 1957). Low-melting fats were found in distal extremities of carnivorous arctic wolves, foxes and dogs, and it seemed that this was a condition essential for their arctic life. But when the gradient in melting temperature of fats extracted from marrow of the leg of a tropical Panamanian (lat. 11" N) brocket deer (*Mazama americana*) proved indistinguishable from that of fats from arctic caribou, we had to dismiss the notion that the distal gradient of melting points was developed as an adaptation for arctic life. It might be that only with such physical properties of substances in the extremities could warmblooded animals enter the arctic, but the origin of the condition probably long preceded the appearance on earth of the present arctic climate.

The occurrence of low-melting fats in hooves of cattle has been ancient knowledge of European farmers, who used neat's-foot oil to soften and waterproof leather. Mutton tallow of perivisceral origin was used to give hard glossy finish on their old-time leather boots. Based on traditional Eskimo knowledge, fluid fats from the phalanges of caribou were used for maintaining the flexibility of bow strings of twisted sinew.

For many years reports have suggested that fats from mammalian peripheral tissues exposed to cold have lower melting points than fats from the warm interior. Some analyses show increases peripherally in iodine number of fats, in degree of unsaturation and perhaps in lower-melting short-chain acids in human legs in comparison with fats from the body. But these reports concern people and mammals from temperate climates under conditions in which exposure to cold is limited. In view of specific geographical variations in diets and in the metabolism of adipose tissue, I do not think it clear how mammalian fats vary adaptively in relation to climate.

Oils prepared from blubber of seals and whales are notably fluid at room temperatures. Oil from arctic seals has been an ancient food and fuel for Eskimos. Seal oil includes unsaturated fats that oxidize in air. According to Eskimos, and perhaps associated with the unsaturation of seal oil, native-made skin boots and their seams treated with oil from seal blubber remain waterproof during several weeks of wear. If they are greased with the fat from land mammals the waterproofing lasts for only a short time.

In addition there have been studies of melting points and iodine numbers of fats of poikilothermic animals and plants showing lower melting in colder or more northern climates, apparently leading to the idea that fluid fats would be more flexible and chemically more reactive than hard fats at low temperature. Analysis of the fatty acids of marrow from the caribou leg showed a notable increase in oleic (18 =) acid in metacarpals, metatarsals and phalanges, with a distal decrease in palmitic (16) and stearic (18) acids (MENG et al., 1969) (Fig. 10.5).

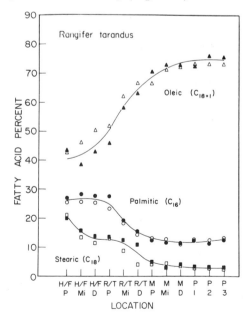

Fig. 10.5. Changes in three fatty acids of caribou leg bone marrow. Closed symbols are for the front legg; open symbols are for the hind leg. Curves are fitted by eye. H, humerus; F, femur; R, radius; T, tibia; M, metacarpal or metatarsal; P, phalange. Proximal, middle and distal sections of each vone are indicated. (From MENG, WEST, and IRVING, 1969)

Carnivorous species derive their fats from the diversity found in species of their prey. Herbivorous caribou are restricted in the species of plants consumed in each season so that their diet is generally low in fat, constraining them to synthesize the fats that they deposit. Furthermore it is to be expected that in ruminant caribou synthesis of fatty acids proceeds from acetate produced by microorganisms acting in the rumen. The elaborate array of fatty acids, varying with anatomical situation in the leg, would seem to furnish an excellent opportunity for observing to what extent depot fats are selected from blood-borne lipids synthesized elsewhere and/or synthesized in the cells of adipose tissues. This situation might offer a chance to demonstrate cellular specialization serving an apparently useful function.

A man whose body contains 40% fat is obese and inclined to certain pathological impairments of circulation. Marine mammals in winter, birds in preparation for long migrations and arctic ground squirrels (*Citellus undulatus*) prepared for hibernation may accumulate more than 40% of their weight as fat. Examinations of arteries of these fat animals have not revealed signs of fatty deposits such as are likely to occur in the arteries of obese man. We must conclude that the cyclical and biologically purposeful transport, deposit and utilization of large amounts of fat are unlike the accumulations of lipids in obese man.

Insulation of Mammals without Fur

Arctic mammals on land are conspicuously and effectively insulated by fur, with only extremities protruding with thin covering. The mass of the thinly covered tissues of extremities is not a large proportion of their whole bodies and the surfaces are not great, but the extent and proportionate participation of these heterogeneously insulated tissues in regulation of heat would defy calculation. Only man among native arctic mammals on land is bare of fur and his insulation will be a special problem. Domesticated swine are nearly devoid of insulating hair. In arctic seas, whales, seals and walrus are practically unprotected from cold by hair. It is commonly remarked that the fat covering swine and, as blubber, covering marine mammals serves as insulation. These coverings of adipose tissue are insulators, but they also serve as reserves of nutrition that change in thickness cyclically with season and habits. According to our usage of the variable insulation of animals, blubber is an insulator fixed in thickness for considerable periods and unable to vary its insulative value in response to rapidly changing metabolic heat and externally changing weather.

Adipose Tissues as Insulators

In domestic swine, seals (Phocidae) covered only with short, wettable hair, whales (Cetacea) and walrus (Odobenidae) the muscular body is invested in an envelope of adipose tissue from which the head and appendages protrude (Fig. 10.6). Considering blubber as an insulating system, it exposes the skin in the coldest situation, whereas under fur and feathers skin is kept almost as warm as the interior. We do not need to imagine existence of a naked northern bird.

150

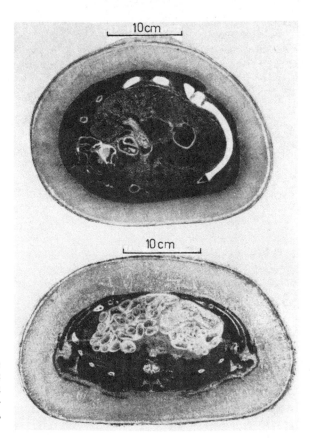

Fig. 10.6. Cross sections of two frozen seals (*Phoca hispida*) shot in March, 1948, showing the thick layer of blubber. From SCHOLANDER, WALTERS, HOCK, and IRVING, 1950)

Insulation of Swine

Domestic swine are kept in regions with cold winter climate. Although they require a certain amount of care, dry litter, and shelter, in Alaska large swine occupied unheated buildings in which air temperature fell below −30°. In September two young boars (50 kg) living outdoors at Anchorage (mean temperature about 5°) showed low critical temperatures about 0° (p. 122). As shown in Fig. 10.7, while the pigs were being experimentally cooled, the skin on their bodies cooled progressively below 10°. In winter at Fairbanks (65°N) skin on large hogs (140–180 kg) became colder in cold air in their unheated pens than did that of the pigs under experimentation. The degree of cooling of skin in the Alaskan hogs exceeded that reported for hogs from the warm climate of California, from which we surmise that seasonal variations in relation of their skin to cold would be shown to be adaptively varied in correspondence with their common climatic experience.

Thermocouples inserted to various depths under the skin demonstrated gradients of temperature which in cold air might extend for 100 mm before reaching internal temperature. In warmer air thermal gradients were less steep and shorter. As air was cooled the thin lean mass of tissue of a pig's ear cooled precipitously, reaching a lower limit about 0° from which it rose intermittently to 10° (Fig.

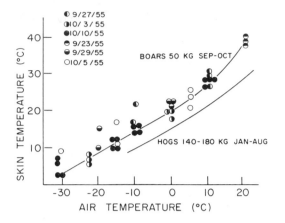

Fig. 10.7. Skin surface temperatures in young boars and hogs, related to air temperature. (From IRVING et al., 1956)

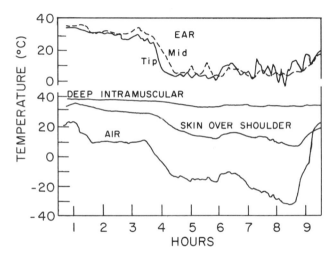

Fig. 10.8. Skin temperature and body temperature of young boars in air between 20° and −30° (From IRVING, PEYTON, and MONSON, 1956)

10.8). So we see that over the body there is a degree of topographic regularity in variation of temperature of skin, gradients in depth through fat which also vary, and distinct thermal behavior of the relatively small mass in peripheral tissues of the ear. In coordinated action the various heterothermic conditions of superficial tissues of swine effectively regulate their economy of heat.

Insulation of Seals by Heterothermic Tissues

The greatest insulation afforded by blubber would occur if no heat were transported to the skin by the circulation. As activity changes the metabolic production of heat or as the animal emerges from icy water into warmer air and sunshine the conducted flow of heat through blubber can be increased by transport through the considerable circulation of blubber and skin. Its operation is conspicuously effective in thermoregulation of seals in water. In icy arctic seas, they encounter the greatest capacity for removal of heat of any environment. We have shown (p. 122) that the overall insulation of small northern harbor seals in winter is so effective that their critical temperature in water is about 12°, and that of young arctic harp seals, 0°.

Unlike an animal in air, a seal in water is surrounded by a uniform environment to which its heat passes without complication by cutaneous evaporation or radiation. In their humid environment evaporation through breathing is not large. As the surrounding water cools, transport of heat to the skin from the warm interior is reduced toward the rate of conduction through blubber and tissue, supplemented by the least transport of heat by the minimum circulation that is acceptable for maintenance and repair of skin and subcutaneous tissues. As in the pig, various cooling of skin and the shell of adipose tissue effectively regulate dissipation of heat.

The extremities, protruding from the envelope of blubber, operate somewhat differently. Seals also effectively regulate economy of heat in the complex conditions in air, when naturally their underparts are in contact with ice while on their upper surfaces variable temperature of air and insolation require changes of insulation with wide topographic variation (RAY and SMITH, 1968).

Thermal Gradients through Blubber

Gradients of temperature through blubber are shown in Fig. 10.9, illustrating variations in several environmental conditions. Regulated variability of temperature in the envelope of blubber is illustrated in Fig. 10.10. As an illustration of

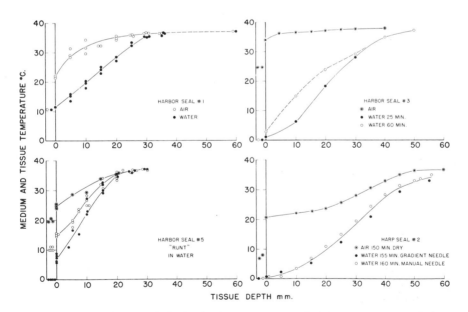

Fig. 10.9. Temperature gradients in the body of seals at various air and water temperatures. Ordinates give both medium temperature (outer line) and tissue temperature (inner line). (From IRVING and HART, 1957)

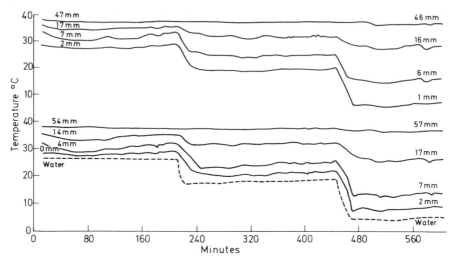

Fig. 10.10. Simultaneous records of temperature gradients of a seal at points separated by 16 mm on back over thorax. Upper record, point embedded in rib; lower, point intercostal. (From HART and IRVING, 1959)

localization of regulation of cutaneous temperature, a 5x10 cm area of skin on the back of a seal immersed in ice water protruded into air at 12°. The wet hair in air dried quickly and the skin warmed to 17° while adjacent submerged skin was 2°.

Thermal Gradient in Flippers

It might appear that the common heterothermic operation of bare extremities is extended over the entire body in those mammals possessing little insulative fur. Like ears of pigs, flippers are heterothermic, but the lability of their temperature, revealed by the limited damping effect of their small mass, is greater than on the body and subject to a different system of control (Fig. 10.11). Large and rapid changes in temperature can appear in the web of flippers, even though not obviously related to the thermal states of the body. A disturbing noise or vibration irrelevant to heat regulation sometimes caused a sudden transient, localized warming in the flipper. Localized peripheral vascular reactions unrelated to thermoregulation are familiar evidences for the multiple stimuli that may bring them into view, as in the cutaneous reaction of face and neck when blushing was the proper expression of a meiden's embarrassment.

The gradient in the flippers is axial instead of vertical as on the body. Deep among the metacarpal bones 5 cm from the body the temperature was 9° to 15° (skin on body 7.8°, web between phalanges 6° to 7.8°); 2.5 cm from the body and deep among metacarpals it was 22°, and deep in the body 37°. With this steep axial gradient, we suspect the existence in flippers of a countercurrent heat exchanger. Proper arrangement of veins investing arteries for a heat exchanger has been shown to exist in the 'fins' and flukes of a porpoise (SCHOLANDER and SCHEVILL, 1955). The dorsal fins of whales are not supported by an appendicular

154

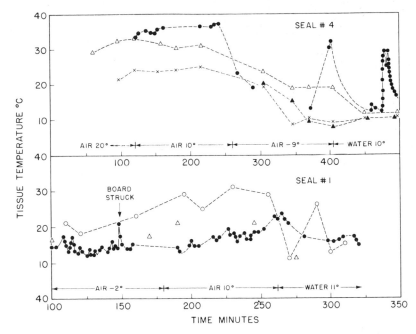

Fig. 10.11. Tissue temperature variation with time in harbor seal No. 4 (upper) and No. 1 (lower) under various temperature conditions indicated.
(●) Subcutaneous, web of hind flipper.
(×) Surface, over metabasal bones of hind flipper.
(△) Body skin on back.
(○) 5 mm deep on body.
(From Irving and Hart, 1957)

skeleton, and vascular specialization is not restricted to skeletal extremities. In fact in the maze of subdermal vascularity of mammals, veins and arteries can be seen adjacent to each other in proximity that would permit their operation as countercurrent heat exchangers.

Contrast between the thermoregulatory operation of flippers and body was nicely shown in the large bare flippers of northern fur seals (*Callorhinus ursinus*) on their breeding grounds in the chilly but not arctic Pribilof Islands. When driven to slaughter overland, some fur seals became prostrated by hyperthermia (Irving et al., 1962). The flippers were then warmer than air and felt warm to the hand. The surface of fur of the body at the same time was not warm. Through the dense fur but little emission of heat occurred and it was scarcely variable enough for thermoregulation. The variable insulation of flippers extends over a bare area that is about 1/3 of the total surface of a fur seal. Under the fur of a fur seal in cold water, the unwetted skin remains rather steadily warm.

Topographic Variation in Surface Temperature

By recording temperature photometrically on the surface of a harp seal (*Pagophilus groenlandicus*) in air, Nils Øritsland (1968) observed that in air −13° suface temperature on flippers and nearby body remained 5° to 10°. When the seal was

155

caused to exercise on a treadmill these surface temperatures increased to 22° and the warm area increased. At rest the surface (as scanned from above) that warmed with warming air amounted to 10–20% of the upper surface of the seal. During exercise at 0° the warmed suface increased to 70–90% of the area scanned from above. ØRITSLAND remarked that in some cases the warming areas extended in an irregular pattern from the region of the flippers over the surface of the body. There is, accordingly, variability in topographic extent as well as temperature on the surface in regulation of emission of heat.

Topographic variations occur in amount of sweating in areas over the human body. These are in part related to the exposure of the skin to evaporation, but not all parts are anatomically alike in ability to sweat. For a seal in water, which, we presume, does not sweat, the topographic variations are damped to small differences in temperature by the large heat capacity of its watery environment. When the seal is exposed to air, particularly when observed by optical recording of skin temperature, surface temperature gradients are less damped and indicate the temporal and topographic complexity of thermoregulation in skin that results as local conditions for emission of heat differ with exposure to heat loss of the various parts of the skin.

Insulation of Polar Bears

It may appear out of order to consider the insulation of polar bears (*Ursus maritimus*) along with bare-skinned aquatic mammals. A bear in water about 10° cooled internally from 36.5° to 35.5° during 3 h while the subcutaneous temperature on the flank cooled to about 25°. Subcutaneous layers of blubber covered the body of the bears with layers of fat of various thickness. We have already remarked that the fur of bears is wettable and loses most of its insulation in water (p. 105). It seems that the insulation of bears in water operates by thermal gradients from the cool skin to the warm interior, passing in part through blubber. The system, as far as it has been observed, appears to operate in water like the insulation of bare-skinned mammals (ØRITSLAND, 1970); in air the dry fur probably preserves the warm skin that is usual among arctic land mammals.

Seasonal Change of Insulation

Harbor seals (*Phoca vitulina*) in warm water in summer had critical temperatures at 22°, the temperature prevailing in warm coastal waters at Woods Hole, Massachusetts (see Table 9.1). In winter their critical temperature had been about 12° at St. Andrews, New Brunswick (HART and IRVING, 1959). They showed a parsimony of insulation in summer that we believe, from a few measured examples, should characterize adaptive thermoregulation in northern regions of considerable seasonal climatic change. The comparatively simple conditions for heat flow from seals in water indicated that in summer metabolic production of heat rose with skin temperature below 22°, while in winter the increase in metabolism took place with skin temperature only about 15° (Fig. 10.12), a seasonal shift in the reference of metabolic heat to temperature of the skin (HART and IRVING, 1959).

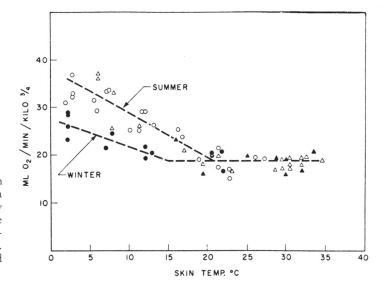

Fig. 10.12. Oxygen consumption as a function of body skin temperature for seals during winter and summer. (From HART and IRVING, 1959)

Thermoregulation in Walrus

From the time of birth, walrus (Odobenidae) are essentially bare-skinned and possess only the insulative capacity of thermal gradients through their thick blubber and large flippers. But walrus differ from seals in their very large size (500 to 1500 kg) and consequently in their smaller ratio of surface to mass. They also differ in behavior related to temperature and toward each other. Information about their thermoregulation is derived largely from interesting observations on their behavior in the zoo at New York and on arctic ice floes and from measurements of temperatures on their skin (FAY and RAY, 1968; RAY and FAY, 1968).

Walrus are not only gregarious but unlike seals, deliberately make contact with each other, varying proximity and contact with temperature of air. If air is warm and sun is bright they sprawl extended and separate on ice. When weather is cold and windy they huddle together and reduce the exposure of their skin. In real cold (below –20°) they enter the water, which is never colder than freezing. During immersion, skin temperature was within 3° of the water. The thermal gradient through thick skin and blubber of a large walrus was about three times as long as in our young harbor seals. In shade and still air above 18° pups and adults had rising skin, flipper and body temperatures, with visible cutaneous hyperemia.

Nursing pups are solicitously attended for more than a year by the mother, who in cold weather places them in her lee and enfolds them in her large front flippers. Altogether walrus are gentle and sociable animals that exhibit behavior varying with thermal requirements. Their apparent upper limit for comfort of 15° in shade unsuits them for warm climatic conditions. When molting in summer their skin reddens as if hyperemic and they appear sensitive both to solar heating and to cold. The period of molting apparently imposes a critical requirement for some seasonal warmth in their otherwise chilly circumstances.

157

Thermoregulation in Whales

We can only speculate on thermoregulation in whales. It has been mentioned (p. 117) that in bottle-nosed porpoises (*Tursiops truncatus*, 150 kg) resting metabolic rates were about double the expectation from the common relation to size in mammals. Even in warm seas the envelope of blubber of whales is thick. Large whales that migrate to antarctic waters replenish blubber that had been expended during migration in temperate waters. Thickening of the passively insulating blubber would elongate the vascular bed required to transport heat for dissipation from skin, but seasonal thickening of superficial adipose tissue appears to be a reserve for meager feeding in migration. In view of their large mass relative to surface in comparison with seals, our imagined problem is not for their conservation but for their dissipation of heat. We mentioned that in 'fins' and flukes of a porpoise (p. 154) investment of arteries by veins provides structures suitable for countercurrent heat exchangers. By increasing arterial flow in the exchanger the conservative action could be diminished, as it could be affected also by diversion of returning blood from venae commitantes to separate and more superficial veins, as is effected in the warm human arm.

Filtering small euphausids from sea water by whalebone whales (Mysticeti) passes large volumes of water through the huge cavities of their mouths. In speculating upon devices that might serve in the economy or effectiveness of animals I have tried to point to situations favorable for demonstration of actual function. I cannot see how the participation of the mouth of the whalebone whale in exchange of heat could be tested in the present state of the art of physiology.

In whatever way their thermoregulation is effected, bowhead whales (*Balaena mysticetus*) and narwhals (*Monodon monoceros*) are regarded as residents in the margins of arctic ice. Gray whales (*Eschrichtius gibbosus*) migrate in summer into the marginal leads of arctic ice, as do some belugas (*Delphinapterus leucas*), some of the killer whales (*Orcinus*) and one of the smallest whales, the harbor porpoise (*Phocoena*, 30–50 kg). Not only is there diversity among the species with regard to their use of arctic habitats, but several species show their climatic versatility by annually migrating between warm and cold waters.

In Africa, Wright (1964) found the internal temperatures of wild amphibious hippopotamuses (*Hippopotamus amphibius*) to be unvaryingly about 35.4°. Cena (1964) observed temperatures in skin in the mouth and on the body of a hippopotamus (2000 kg) raised in the zoological park at Warsaw, Poland. In cool (9°) water, the skin within the huge mouth cooled to 10°, and nearly as much cooling was found in parts of the skin on the body. The huge hippopotamus and several other tropical mammals are devoid of hair. Although we have dismissed consideration of tropical animals except, for comparison, those of equally warm regions, many kinds extend into chilly highlands and some, like the hippopotamus, that have lived in captivity in cool climates, doubtless possess and utilize defenses against cold that we have described among arctic residents.

158

Ontogeny of Effective Thermoregulation in Seals

Arctic programs and circumstantial conditions for reproduction in marine mammals have been discussed in Chapter 6. Four species of seals that bear young on the ice of Bering Sea give birth to fur-covered young on ice that is covered with cold, dry snow. The fur (lanugo) of pups of these species is an effective insulator when dry, but it is wettable and in that condition loses insulating ability. Pups of antarctic Weddell seals (*Leptonychotes weddelli*) are likewise covered with dark-colored lanugo that provides serviceable insulation when dry but is inadequate when wet. The pups avoid water, and if their fur becomes wetted they show their discomfort and suffering from cold. (RAY and SMITH, 1968).

The transition of thermoregulatory capability of seal pups from adequacy in air to effectiveness in water was elegantly demonstrated by DAVYDOV and MAKAROVA (1964) with pups of harp seals (*Pagophilus groenlandicus*) obtained during a Russian sealing expedition in the ice of the White Sea. Four stages in growth were selected: 1) up to seven days of age, weighing 7–12 kg, possessing practically no subcutaneous fat and thick, white fur coat; 2) 8–15 days, weighing 15–25 kg, with developing subcutaneous blubber; 3) increasing in weight to 36 kg as the layer of blubber thickened and they rapidly began to shed infantile fur; and 4) at age 30–40 days, pups that had been weaned, possessed only thin, wettable adult hair and had lost weight.

Temperatures of skin were measured in each age group while in cool air (0°) and after immersion during 30 min in ice water. As is shown in Fig. 10.13, in cool air the skin of the youngest pups under their fur was above 30°, as it is in land animals with thick fur. Progressively with growth of blubber and molting of fur, in cold air the skin cooled. After immersion in ice water the skin likewise cooled more with increasing age.

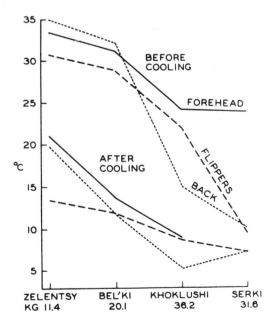

Fig. 10.13. Skin temperature of young harp seals in cool air (above) and after 1/2 hour in ice water. (From DAVYDOV and MAKAROVA, 1964)

159

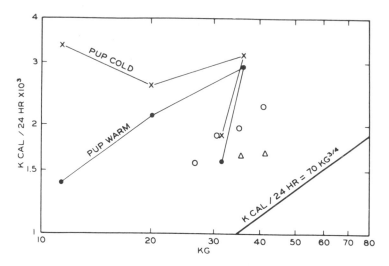

Fig. 10.14. Metabolism in ice water and cool air during growth and molt to adult hair coat and blubber in young harp seals. (From figures of DAVYDOV and MAKAROVA, 1964; rates for ○ *Phoca vitulina* and △ *Pagophilus groenlandicus* from IRVING and HART, 1957)

The relation of skin temperature to metabolic production of heat was nicely shown in the tabulation of DAVYDOV and MAKAROVA (1964), which I have plotted from their tables in Fig. 10.14. We see the rather high metabolic rate of the small pups, dry and in cool air, progressing as they grew with little change per unit of weight until after weaning it declined toward the level common to seals of that size. After immersion in ice water the metabolic rate of smallest pups was more than double the rate while warm. As they grew the metabolic rates when cold from immersion increased less until in the oldest, weaned pups, ice water did not significantly elevate the production of heat.

The large harp seal pups of DAVYDOV and MAKAROVA agreed well in metabolism in ice water with the harp seals of that size from the breeding population of the western Atlantic (IRVING and HART, 1957). We can see that the lanugo, quite inadequate for aquatic life because it is wettable, is replaced during growth by the insulative gradient through blubber which is an effective insulator in air and water. The developmental process involves, beside the loss of fur, transition of the operating temperature of skin from the usual rather even warmth that prevails under fur of land animals and feathers to the heterothermic condition of the seal's skin after weaning. This transformation in cutaneous and subcutaneous operating conditions might well show interesting cytological and vascular alterations as well as changes in the regulatory processes during growth.

Youngest pups of northern fur seals (*Callorhinus ursinus*) born in the boreal summer of the Pribilof Islands are initially awkward swimmers, and when wetted by accidental immersion or rain they shiver and cry dolefully. After immersion a young pup (3.9 kg) gained 12% in weight, in spite of shaking vigorously after it emerged. An older pup (10 kg) gained only 2.3% after being soaked (IRVING et al., 1962). Under dry fur the skin of young pups was warm (above 35°), but within a few minutes after experimental immersion the wetted skin on the posterior part of the body and flippers cooled nearly to the temperature of the water. Adult fur seals when immersed maintained warm dry skin under fur over the body, thus operating quite differently from hair seals in regard to the situation of tissues involved in insulation.

160

By and large it appears that the reproductive processes and habits of some mammals are suitable for their life in the arctic climate. All must make concessions to seasonal climatic conditions by timing dates of birth within a season when the condition of the newborn will permit the development of infantile thermoregulation to a degree of independence compatible with the weather and the varying degrees of specific parental care. Conspicuous transitions in the operation of cutaneous insulating systems appear in the seals that breed on ice.

Size and the Use of Adipose Tissue for Insulation

Knowing the insulative value of blubber and taking the observed metabolic rates of production of heat by several species of seals, we could calculate the smallest size of bare-skinned mammals suitable for life in arctic seas. Such a calculation would have to include estimates without basis in measurement on the flux of heat from the head, where the brain of a seal is separated from the sea by only a centimeter of tissue practically devoid of blubber. Nature seems to have performed the trial by providing no seal smaller than the arctic ringed seal (*Phoca hispida*), which at the time when it becomes fully capable of aquatic operation weighs over 20 kg. The smallest porpoise *(Phocoena)* is of about the same size as a ringed seal. Whether smaller seals or whales occurred in warm ancient seas I do not know. I am surprised, however, that we have not examined the flux of heat from the thin tissues that cover the dorsal aspect of the large brain of seals, which is about as poorly protected as the human brain.

References

BAZETT, H.C.: In: Physiology of Heat Regulation. Ed. by L.H. Newburgh. Philadelphia: Saunders 1949.
BAZETT, J.C., MENDELSON, E.S., LOVE, L., LIBET, B.: J. Appl. Physiol. 1, 169 (1948).
BERNARD, C.: Leçons sur la chaleur animale. Libr. J. Paris: D. Bailliere et Fils 1876.
CENA, K.: Thermoregulation in the hippopotamus. Int. J. Biomet. 8, 57–60 (1964).
CHATFIELD, P. O., LYMAN, C. P., IRVING, L.: Physiological adaptation to cold of peripheral nerve in the leg of the Hering gull *(Larus argentatus)*. Amer. J. Physiol. 172, 639–644 (1953).
DAVYDOV, A. F., MAKAROVA, A. R.: Changes in heat regulation and circulation in newborn seals on transition to aquatic form of life. Fiziologischeskii Zhurnal ssr imeni 1. Msechenova (Fed. Proc. 24, Trans. Suppl., No. 4, Part II. T563–566) 50, 894 (1964).
DURRER, J. L., HANNON, J. P.: Seasonal variation in the caloric intake of dogs living in an arctic environment. Tech. Report 61–63. Arctic Aeromedical Laboratory, Ft. Wainwright, Alaska (1961).
FAY, F. H., RAY, C.: Influence of climate on the distribution of walruses, *Odobenus rosmarus* (Linnaeus). I. Evidence from thermoregulatory behavior. Zoologica 53, 1–18 (1968).
FELTZ, E., FAY, F. H.: Thermal requirements *in vitro* of epidermal cells from seals. Cryobiology 3, 261–264 (1968).
HAMMEL, H. T.: Regulation of internal body temperature. Ann. Rev. Physiol. 30, 641–710 (1968).

HART, J. S., IRVING, L.: The energetics of harbor seals in air and in water with special consideration of seasonal changes. Canad. J. Zool. **37**, 447–459 (1959).

HENSHAW, R. E., FOLK, G. E.: Peripheral circulation mediated resistance to freezing in arctic wolves. Fed. Proc. **29**, 791 (1969).

HENSHAW, R. E., UNDERWOOD, L. S., CASEY, T. M. Foot temperature in two arctic canines. Science **175**, 988–990 (1972).

IRVING, L.: Physiological insulation of swine as bare-skinned mammals. J. App. Physiol. **9**, 414–420 (1956).

IRVING, L., HART, J. S.: The metabolism and insulation of seals as bare-skinned mammals in cold water. Can. ad. J. Zool. **35**, 497–511 (1957).

IRVING, L., KROG, J.: Temperature of skin in the arctic as a regulator of heat. J. Appl. Physiol. **7**, 355–364 (1955).

IRVING, L., PEYTON, L. J., BAHN, C. H., PETERSON, R. S.: Regulation of temperature in fur seals, Physiol. Zool. **35**, 275–284 (1962).

IRVING, L., PEYTON, L. J., MONSON, M.: Metabolism and insulation of swine as bare-skinned mammals. J. Appl. Physiol. **9**, 241–426 (1956).

IRVING, L., SCHMIDT-NIELSEN, K., ABRAHAMSON, N.: On the melting points of animal fats in cold climate. Physiol. Zool. **30**, 93–105 (1957).

JOHANSEN, K.: Heat exchange through the muskrat tail. Evidence for vasodilator nerves to the skin. Acta Physiol. Scand. **55**, 160–169 (1962).

JOHANSEN, K.: Adaptative responses to cold in smooth muscle from heterothermic tissues of marine mammals. Nature **223**, 866–867 (1969).

MENG, M., WEST, G. C., IRVING, L.: Fatty acid composition of caribou bone marrow. Comp. Biochem. Physiol. **30**, 187–191 (1969).

MILLER, L. K.: Caudal nerve function as related to temperature in some Alaskan mammals. Comp. Biochem. Physiol. **21**, 679–686 (1967).

MILLER, L. K.: Temperature–dependent characteristics of peripheral nerves exposed to different thermal conditions in the same animal. Canad. J. Zool. **48**, 75–81 (1970).

MILLER, L. K.: Temperature adaptation in peripheral nerves of northern hair seal. M.S.

MILLER, L. K., and IRVING, L.: Temperature-related nerve function in warm and cold-climate muskrats. Amer. J. Physiol. **213**, 1295–1298 (1967).

ØRITSLAND, N. A.: Variations in the body surface temperature of the harp seal. Acta Physiol. Scand. **73**, 35 A (1968).

ØRITSLAND, N. A.: Deep body temperatures of swimming and walking polar bears. J. Mammal. **50**, 380–382 (1969).

ØRITSLAND, N. A.: Temperature regulation of the polar bear (*Thalarctos maritimus*). Comp. Biochem. Physiol. **37**, 225–233 (1970).

RAY, C., FAY, F. H.: Influence of climate on the distribution of walruses, *Odebenus rosmarus* (Linnaeus). II. Evidence from physiological characteristics. Zool. **53**, 19–32 (1968).

RAY, C., SMITH, M. S. R.: Thermoregulation of the pup and adult Wedell seal, *Leptonychotes weddelli* (Lesson) in Antarctica. Zool. **53**, 33–46 (1968).

SCHOLANDER, P. F., SCHEVILL, W. E.: Counter-current vascular heat exchange in the fins of whales. J. Appl. Physiol. **8**, 279–282 (1955).

SCHOLANDER, P. F., WALTERS, V., HOCK, R., IRVING, L.: Body insulation of some arctic and tropical mammals and birds. Biol. Bull **99**, 225–236 (1950).

SMITH, A. U.: Biological effect of freezing and supercooling. Baltimore: Williams & Wilkins 1961.

SOMERO, G. N., JOHANSEN, K.: Temperature effects on enzymes from homeothermic and heterothermic tissues of the harbor seal *(Phoca vitulina)*. Comp. Biochem. Physiol. **34**, 131–136 (1970).

STEEN, J., STEEN, J. B.: Thermoregulatory importance of the beaver's tail. Comp. Biochem. Physiol. 15, 267–270 (1965a).

STEEN, J., STEEN, J. B.: The importance of the legs in the thermoregulation of birds. Acta Physiol. Scand. **63**, 285–291 (1965b).

WRIGHT, P. G.: Wild animals in the tropics. In: The Biology of Survival, 17–28. Proc. Symp. Zool. Soc. of London, May 1964.

162

Chapter 11

Size and Seasonal Change in Dimensions

Temperature and Production of Heat

Temperatures in the bodies of birds and mammals are specifically established and regulated to within a few degrees. Heat is produced by metabolism that, except in hibernation, does not normally fall below a basal level. As temperature of the environment changes, the various components of overall insulation vary the escape of metabolic heat in a manner that regulates the body temperature. Basal metabolic rates are related to size and they show no relation to climates. One component of overall insulation, the fur, is limited in thickness by the short stature of the small mammals, and the overall insulation of these small mammals is correspondingly limited. Among arctic mammals the size of a fox *(Alopex lagopus),* greater than 4 kg), fur and overall insulation suffice to maintain normal body temperature in any arctic weather.

The view of constant basal metabolism and variable overall insulation leads to interesting and useful formulations of the economy of animal heat. But experimental conditions under which basal metabolism is measured are quite unrepresentative of natural life. I will attempt to describe some of the characteristics of size and behavior of arctic populations that appear to be significant even though measurements do not completely serve to integrate those characteristics into the formulation of metabolic economy.

Size of Animals and Their Economy of Heat

At a date when ideas about the production and flux of heat of animals were only vague, BERGMANN (1847) pointed out that since, according to Newton, warm objects lose heat from their surfaces, the extent of surface of an animal determines the rate of its cooling. With increasing size the surface of a spherical body increases as mass to the 2/3 power. Consequently warm animals of increasing sizes would apparently have an advantage in cold climates. BERGMANN speculatively remarked that in some examples larger birds and mammals did occur in northern climates. Subsequently, as KLEIBER (1961) elegantly discusses, many physiologists have tried to relate metabolic production of heat to areas of surfaces of animals.

The surfaces of some mammals can be measured although the geometric task is formidable. The heat emitting surface of a bird is even more difficult to determine. Some who were critical of the appropriateness of considering the geometric surface of the animal body as the emitter of heat tried to relate metabolism to alveolar area of lungs, amount of blood or other systems that might be involved in emission of heat. Now more than a century after BERGMANN's publication, biologists continue to employ confused experimentation and dubious logic in trying to relate heat production and metabolism to the suface areas of animals. As we have discussed, weight to the 3/4 power provides a rather satisfactory empirical basis

163

for comparing basal metabolic rates (Chapter 9). The bare-skinned animals show that their bodies do not emit heat from a homogeneous mass or through a uniform surface that is definable.

Climatic Rules

Biologists have extensively referred to the relation between size and surface that BERGMANN discussed as conveying an advantage to animals of larger size that would be seized upon by natural selection in favoring the establishment of larger forms in the north from clines within species distributed over areas extending over a range from north to south (see MAYR, 1963). SCHOLANDER (1955 and 1956) aroused a storm of protests (and some support) when he proclaimed that the climatic rule or law, commonly referred to as BERGMANN'S , was not reasonably based, nor was it regularly born out by the natural distribution of animals.

I agree with SCHOLANDER that it is illogical to conclude that size is adaptive to climate. On a given day, size is a rather steady character of an adult individual, but it varies with age, sex, season and nutritional state. Metabolic heat production varies according to momentary fluctuations in the activity of the individual and sudden external variations in exposure to cooling. On the other hand, insulation varies visibly and with nicely measurable influence upon the economy of heat in a series of mammals from cold and warm climates. In birds the quantitative nature of variations of insulation in relation to climate is less clear.

I suppose that, in a narrow view of evolution, for natural selection to operate it is implied that the clinal variants were components in a competing population. If that supposition is correct, the variants first came into existence in circumstances in which they did not compete. In view of the uncertainty about the circumstances, localities and times at which components of species became segregated into differentiated developing subspecies, I find it difficult to speculate about the steps by which adaptations became established.

Such an eminent and interesting authority on ecology as ALLEE (ALLEE et al., 1949) illustrates ALLEN's rule, as a derivative of BERGMANN's rule, by the diminishing outlines and sizes of the ears of hares *(Lepus)* from *L. californicus* of Arizona, through *L. californicus* of Oregon, and *L. americanus* of Minnesota to *L. arcticus* of the Barren Grounds. I agree that the ears of the arctic hare appear smaller, but the insulative fur on ears and body of hares increases markedly in the series from the south to the north. The overall insulation would better designate the climatic adaptations of these three species. Allee did not speculate upon the evolution of the three species, which are not related within an intraspecific cline, but the series illustrates in general the variation in insulative characters that are adaptively useful in the climates occupied by each species.

Many references to BERGMANN's rule do not confine its application to intraspecific clinal variations. The distribution of sizes in American caribou *(Rangifer)* show that the largest animals occur at the southern part of their range in British Columbia; small Peary caribou are found on Canadian arctic islands. That there is debate over whether these caribou are of one or several species illustrates a real difficulty of taxonomic definitions that could suggest when, how and where the taxa evolved to their present differentiation. If we cannot presently see the processes through which adaptations have occurred we can see and often analyze the operation of insulation that adaptively affects the economy of heat.

Seasonal Flexibility of Insulation

I have alluded to the change of insulation from winter to summer that raised the critical temperature of several species in summer above its winter value (Table 11.1). In some of these examples the critical temperature in each season was near the mean temperature of the locality. HART and POHL (1965) also measured by heat flow the insulation of sections of pelts of several fur bearers, with results similar to the earlier measurements by SCHOLANDER, WALTERS, HOCK and IRVING (1950) of insulation of pelts of northern and arctic mammals. HART and POHL remarked that the noticeably lesser winter insulation of pelts of hares from Ottawa (lat 45°N) than of Alaskan hares (lat 65°N) might represent the milder southern conditions of winter at Ottawa.

HART and POHL calculated that the increased insulation measured in the winter fur would by itself provide for the better conservation of heat shown by the lower critical temperature of hares in winter. Evidently the peripheral circulation was not involved in the seasonal change of insulation of the hares. In the virtually hairless harbor seal regulation of the peripheral circulation accounted for the lower critical temperature that was shown in winter.

The arctic jays and willow ptarmigan (Table 11.1) demonstrated seasonal changes in the insulation of birds (see also Table 9.3). Although the small mammals seem to find winter shelter that supplements their meager insulation, the small

Table 11.1. Seasonal changes of insulation indicated by critical temperatures

Species	Location	Critical temperature °C		Reference
		Winter	Summer	
Lepus americanus (Varying hare)	Ottawa (45 °N)	0°	10°	HART and POHL, 1965
Tamiasciurus hudsonicus (Red squirrel)	Anchorage (60 °N)	20°	20°	IRVING et al., 1955
Erethizon dorsatum (Porcupine)	Anchorage (60 °N)	−12°	7°	IRVING et al., 1955
Vulpes fulva (Red fox)	Anchorage (60 °N)	−13°	8°	IRVING et al., 1955
Phoca vitulina (Harbor seal)	St Andrews in air	−9°	0°	HART and IRVING, 1959
	Woods Hole in water	13°	22°	
Branta bernicla (Black brant)	Anchorage (60 °N)	6°	6°	IRVING et al., 1955
Lagopus lagopus (Willow ptarmigan)	Fairbanks (65 °N)	−8.5°	7.5°	WEST (unpub.)
Corvus caurinus (Northwestern crow)	Anchorage (60 °N)	−7°	−5°	IRVING et al., 1955
Perisoreus canadensis (Gray jay)	Fairbanks (65 °N)	5°	30°	VEGHTE, 1964

birds that remain exposed in winter cold appear to rely upon production of metabolic heat at rates elevated above the common capability of mammals.

In his pioneering, experimental studies of the influence of lengthening day in inducing the condition of birds for migration, ROWAN (1928) kept juncos *(Junco hyemalis)* in open cages during winter at Edmonton (lat 53° N), where air sometimes cooled to –40°. He remarked that the birds became quiet at –30° and scarcely moved at –40°. Nevertheless during several winters there were few casualties. Although the wild birds normally migrate southward, in captivity they survived in a climate colder than that of their natural winter resort. More remarkable, however, was the existence at Edmonton of 30 domesticated canaries through winter in open cages.

These little birds of subtropical stock successfully encountered the cold winter of the Canadian prairies. Rowan remarked that the gonads of his canaries expanded under the influence of lengthened artificial illumination, but even in the normal short winter days of that latitude (53°) the gonads of canaries began to develop earlier than the gonads of juncos.

Use of Posture to Vary Insulation

I have mentioned changes in the posture of several animals that would conserve heat in cold, and there are well measured examples of increased elimination of heat by change in posture of birds and mammals in hot climates. In very cold weather arctic gray jays *(Perisoreus canadensis),* when perched on a branch, expand their feathers until in silhouette the jay appears nearly spherical. Barbules of the contour feathers cohere so that the volume of air that they contain is greatly increased and the insulation is correspondingly enlarged. In this shape the bird could not fly.

In cold weather sled dogs coil with feet against the belly and bushy tails over noses. In this position a thermometer inserted in the center of a coiled dog registered 32° while in the open air the temperature was –25° (Fig. 11.1). In cold air the dog's exposed surface is very much reduced.

Fig. 11.1. Drawing from a photograph of thermometer in the center of a coiled dog. Air temperature −25° C

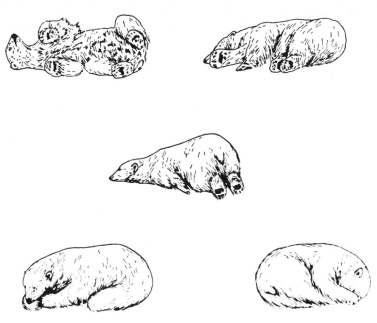

Fig. 11.2. Polar bears' postures at mean windchills 830 W/m² (I), 1410 W/m² (II) and 1910 W/m² (III). (ØRITSLAND, 1970)

Large polar bears *(Ursus maritimus)* (280 kg), observed during sunny days with temperatures from –8° to –20° and moderate winds, were seen lying sprawled on their backs or sides with legs extended in order to expose extensive undersurfaces and bare paws (ØRITSLAND, 1970). On cloudy days with stronger winds their posture was more compact, and in strong winds the bears coiled like sled dogs with paws against their bellies (Fig. 11.2). Evidently the bear's fur affords good insulation in air; in fact, its effectiveness requires modified behavior in strong solar heating. On the flank exposed to strong insolation, subcutaneous temperature rose about two degrees above internal temperature. The flank on the shady side remained about 32°, which is within the usual range of temperature under fur.

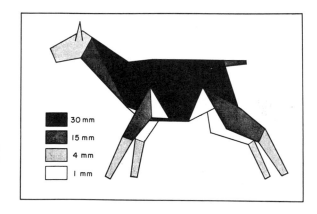

Fig. 11.3. Diagrammatic representation of fur distribution on guanaco. Areas on chart are proportional to measured areas on male animal. (From MORRISON, 1966)

167

Differences in the Distribution of Fur

I have not seen the differences in the distribution of fur and posture so well documented in a northern animal as MORRISON (1966) portrayed in a South American guanaco *(Lama guanicoe)*. His diagram (Fig. 11.3) shows the varying thickness of fur on parts of the body and appendages. Conductance of heat has been found to vary inversely with the thickness of fur in many measurements on pelts of mammals. Over the total surface of the guanaco thermal conductance will vary as the area of each fur type shown in Figure 11.3 divided by the thickness of fur, or as meters^2/cm of thickness. The guanaco may stand with all bare surfaces exposed (I in Table 11.2) or stand with bare areas covered (II in Table 11.2). It may further reduce flow of heat from the extremities by the cooling that is discussed in chapter 10 (III in Table 11.2). If the guanaco lies with maximal cover and minimal exposed surfaces, conductance can be further reduced (IV in Table 11.2). Finally, the speed of wind encountered by running at 50 km/hr would increase conductance as indicated in line V in Table 11.2.

Employment of these five patterns of exposure of its surfaces would change the outflow of heat as is shown in Fig. 11.4. Coiled in the best insulated condition in still air (I), heat production at the basal rate would maintain normal body temperature at 0°, which is about the coldest temperature in its warm northern range. Running at 50 km/hr (V) would be likely to elevate heat production ten times. Regardless of the accuracy with which the various emissions of heat are estimated, the effect of changing insulation of the fur by posture and activity shows the degree of flexibility of insulation that is available to the guanaco. Distribution of fur over the guanaco seems to provide unusual flexibility of regulation of heat flow through the fur as a component of overall insulation. In winter caribou have thicker fur over the body than the guanaco and no truly bare areas except for hooves and eyes, but the slender legs are only thinly covered. The procedure

Table 11.2. Estimated thermal conductance factors for guanacos[a]

Posture	Condition		Bare	Short	Med.	Long	Sum	Change[b]
			— Pelage type					
I	Total surface exposed	M²/cm	1.0	0.5	0.2	0.2	1.9	
		fraction	1/2	1/4	1/10	1/10		
II	Cover bare area	M²/cm		0.5	0.2	0.2	0.9	×1/2
		fraction		1/2	1/4	1/4		
III	+ Cool extremities	M²/cm		(0.2)	0.2	0.2	0.6	×1/3
		fraction		1/3	1/3	1/3		
IV	+ Curl	M²/cm			0.2	0.2	0.4	×1/5
		fraction			1/2	1/2		
V	Run, 30 MPH[c]	M²/cm	8	2	0.4	0.2	(11)	×(5)
		fraction	4/5	1/5	1/25	1/50		

[a] Factors represent quotient of values for and depth from Fig. 11.3.
[b] Referred to condition I with total surface exposed.
[c] LENTZ and HART (1960) measured the effect of 30 MPH wind on caribou fur: 2-fold increase over 13 mm fur; 12-fold over bare surface. We may consider the "effective thickness" of the fur reduced by these same factors and the conductance factor increased correspondingly.

(From MORRISON, 1966)

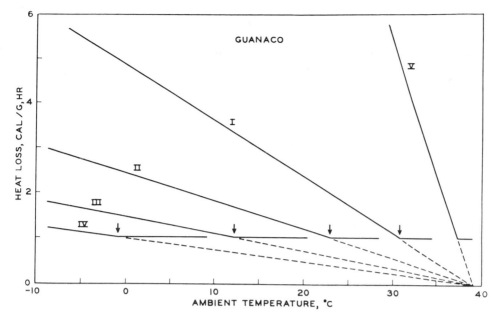

Fig. 11.4. Calculated relationship between ambient temperature and conductive heat loss. Heat loss represents the product of the conductance factor (Table 11.2), the conductivity of the fur and the temperatur differential (body temperature-ambient temperature). 20% of the heat has been taken as dissipated by evaporation. Mean conductivity of fur taken as $\dfrac{3.1.\ \text{kcal cm}}{\text{hr} \,^\circ\text{C M}^2}$ (LENTZ and HART, 1960); BMR (horizontal curve), 3.8 W $^{0.27}$ ccO$_2$/g hr (BRODY, 1945). Conditions I–V correspond to Table 11.2; body temperature, 39°. (From MORRISON, 1966)

used by Morrison nicely illustrates the topographic variability of insulation that can be attributed to fur as a physical insulator. It demonstrates the flexibility in the employment of fur, as posture varies that component of the overall insulation, in regulating the emission of heat from a mammal.

Small Mammals in Winter

I have mentioned that many small mammals live beneath arctic snow in conditions that we think temper the cold to which they are exposed. They follow prepared runways to areas with available vegetation or stores of gathered food, entering well built nests and associating huddled together in behavioral procedures that mitigate the effects of cold and substitute for the shortness of their insulative fur.

The smallest of mammals, shrews (Soricidae), dwell in cold arctic lands. In fact, in a paper kindly translated for me by W. O. PRUITT, Jr., MEZHZERIN (1964) pointed out that in several northern Asiatic species of the genus *Sorex* the weights of adult individuals in winter diminished by 25 to 40% from their weights in summer. He argued that the diminution in size advantageously reduced the requirement for food in winter and intensified heat production in the diminished mass. Further, he pointed out that of several species of the Soricidae the average weights

169

of the species found locally increased as the average isotherm of January warmed with increasing distance from the center of extreme cold in northeastern Siberia.

January isotherm	Average Weights
–30°	5.0 g
above –30°	6.2 g
warmer	7.7 g

MEZHZHERIN considered that this interesting seasonal change in stature and the relation of size to climate refuted Bergmann's law. Even in a mild climate the voracious captive long-tailed shrews *(Sorex cinereus,* 3 to 4 g) must feed at least every hour and daily consume meat nearly equal to the weight of their own bodies (MORRISON et al., 1959). The metabolism of shrews is impressive and the subnivean environment seems to be highly productive in sustaining its small denizens through eight or nine months of winter.

Weight and Stature of Arctic Willow Ptarmigan

Taking advantage of the great numbers of willow ptarmigan *(Lagopus lagopus)* snared and shot in Alaska in winter we were able to measure lengths of wings and tails, as indicators of stature, and net body weight (without crop) of 2600

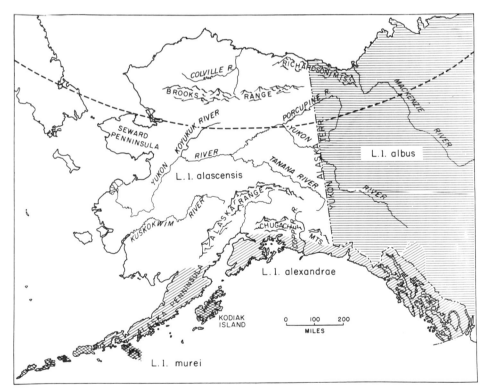

Fig. 11.5. Proposed distribution of 4 subspecies of willow ptarmigan in Alaska and adjacent Yukon Territory based on body size and weight measurements. (From WEST et al., 1970)

examples (WEST et al., 1970). Dividing these records into four categories of juvenile males and females and adult males and females, we found no significant differences during mid-winter in linear dimensions of each category over the area shown in Fig. 11.5 that is attributed to the range of *L. l. alascensis*. Weights were somewhat more variable than linear dimensions but not different enough to distinguish local populations. This population with homogeneous dimensions extends over 12° of latitude southward from Barrow, with mean annual temperature −12.5°, to Iliamna, with mean annual temperature 8.8°. In the northern range the photoperiod changes from 24 hours of sunlight in summer to none in winter. In the south the seasonal change is from 18 hours in summer to 6 hours in winter. The range of this homogeneous population of *L. l. alascensis* about coincides with the part of Alaska that was not covered by ice during the Wisconsin glaciation. Ptarmigan of adjacent races to the southwest, south and east were smaller in linear dimensions and mass.

African and South American Large Mammals

One condition for the present geographical distribution of animals is that they occur in regions that were accesible to their ancestors. It occurs to me to be relevant to the argument that there are probably a dozen or more species of mammals on warm lands of Africa that exceed in size the largest mammalian species of warm South America. Not only do they continue to live in the lands of their ancestors but through long extents of time they have retained their ancestral forms, in many cases existing through extensive climatic changes and even surviving considerable geological alterations in lands and waters.

Size and Reserves of Heat and Energy

There is a factor in size that importantly limits the way of life of a species. Some wild birds and mammals accumulate fat in advance of seasons when they may be unable to feed during periods in their reproductive cycles, in preparation for the sustained effort and uncertain supply of food during migration, and in preparation for fasting during hibernation. Before setting forth on a long migration the new accumulation of fat in a bird may equal its lean weight. Similar accumulation of fat occurs in an arctic ground squirrel *(Citellus undulatus)* during the last weeks of August before it enters hibernation.

MORRISON (1960) has shown an interesting way to consider the relation between size of an animal and its reserve of energy in the form of fat. The maximum amount of fat (F_M) stored in a bird or mammal is about equal to its fat-free body weight W (in grams). Fat in adipose tissue can provide about 7 kilocalories per gram. Consequently the metabolic equivalent of fat possessed by a fat animal is:

$F = 7\ W$ kcal

basal metabolic rate is:

$M_B = 0.44^{3/4}$kcal day^{-1} x W

with maximum storage of fat:

$F_M/M_B = 16\ W^{1/4}$ days.

171

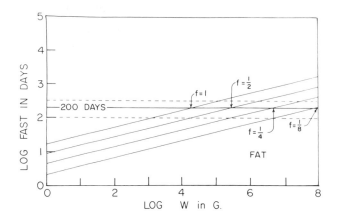

Fig. 11.6. Influence of body fat on fasting time in mammals of different size. (From MORRISON, 1960)

The relation between provision for fasting, weight and fatness can be shown in Fig. 11.6. A beaver (20 kg) might provide for basal metabolism during 200 days with fat equal to its lean weight; a bear (300 kg) might last 200 days with half as much fat; a huge (100 metric tons) whale might require use of only 1/8 of its weight in fat for the same fast.

Natural Fasting in Hibernation

Only a few animals are disposed to endure prolonged rest. A man resting in a bed in hospital deteriorates as his inactivity is prolonged. The weightlessness of astronauts outside of the field of gravitational force brings about changes in composition of the body that are worrisome concerns for travel in space. Arctic brown bears *(Ursus arctos)* are able to rest through winter and emerge about the end of April from their shelters still possessing enough fat to sustain themselves on roots of willow and the meagerly available carrion or infrequent capture of living animals. Not until July is growth of vegetation sufficient to provide them with ample nourishment. Feeding is terminated when ground freezes in September and by then they must have prepared their dens for winter. In the wild arctic condition the bulk of the annual nourishment of these large arctic mammals is provided in only a few months of summer.

An arctic ground squirrel (500 – 1000 grams) could not outlast eight months of winter when food is not available without shelter in a nest living at greatly reduced metabolic rate in hibernation. LYMAN and O'BRIEN (1969) remarked that with only their feeble metabolic power (and small heat content) to apply to maintain body temperature just above freezing, hibernating arctic ground squirrels must be hypersensitive to change in temperature of the air and of their bodies.

Fasting Periods in Normal Life Cycles

Only arctic bears, marmots and ground squirrels appear disposed to prolonged inactivity and hibernation. Several other species of arctic birds and mammals pass through prolonged fasts that permit special and often very active attention for

172

events in their life history. I have remarked that some small-sized species of migratory birds arrive on their nesting grounds with a suply of fat which becomes
diminished in the males during the intensive activity of claiming territory and
mate, while the less harried females only later lose their fat (See Chapter 5).

The smallest birds, however, with high metabolic rates in relation to their small
mass, seem to have scant reserve for unseasonable arctic weather. Their prediction
of seasonal conditions must be as accurate as their reserves are small. Prediction
must be especially precise in the variable arctic weather. Male antarctic emperor
penguins *(Aptenodytes forsteri)* arrive on their nesting grounds in March weighing
over 45 kg and lose half as much during three or four months' fasting during
the first spell of incubation that they undertake in antarctic winter (PRÉVOST, 1961).
It is reported that nestling fulmars *(Fulmarus glacialis)* attain weights exceeding
those of the adults while still inadequately feathered for flying or swimming. The
adults then abandon the young birds, which during three weeks of fasting develop
plumage suitable for swimming before they leave the ledges for the sea (FREUCHEN
and SALOMONSEN, 1958).

Fasting by Mammals

During the rut in autumn arctic bull caribou are so impelled toward procreation
that they scarcely eat, but utilize their extensive deposits of fat accumulated during
summer. Male black-tailed deer *(Dama hemionus)* in British Columbia may lose
40% in weight during the rut. The intensive disposition of these species toward
breeding can lead them toward rapid local episodes of overpopulation if extrinsic
restraints become ineffective (KLEIN, 1970). The large bull fur seals *(Callorhinus
ursinus)* literally waste away while they claim and vigorously defend their breeding
territories during several months of summer without entering the water to feed.
Female seals, as was illustrated by the gray seals *(Halichoerus grypus),* shrink
as they provide milk of high fat content for the very rapid growth of their nursing
pups (see Chapter 6).

Only with the reserves consistent with large size could these populations maintain their habits. The period of fasting may make life difficult for arctic species;
for the male caribou enter winter lean after fasting through the rut, and not until
spring do they recover fat. The requirement of periodic fasts for completion of
the life history of some species may have precluded their meeting the circumstances
of the Arctic, but periodic fasting is by no means a peculiar arctic habit. How
the small birds and mammals make provisions for nutritional exigencies in their
arctic lives is an impressive mystery.

Seasonal Change in Myoglobin

In winter the amount of myoglobin increases in muscles of the leg, diaphragm
and heart of the snowshoe hare (*Lepus americanus*) in Alaska (lat 65° N). The
hemoglobin content of blood remains remarkably steady (ROSENMANN and MOR-
RISON, 1965). Increased myoglobin was most marked in the masseter muscle of

northern (lat 65°) red-backed voles (*Clethrionomys rutilus dawsoni*) in winter and the increase was less in leg and heart muscles. As in the hare, the hemoglobin in blood remained unchanged throughout the year (MORRISON et al., 1966). The winter habits of these mammals are obscure, but the special increase in the large gnawing muscle of the vole may be associated with the hardness of the dry, frozen bark on which the voles feed in winter.

The redness of the meat of game animals is associated with the myoglobin of their muscles. Training of horses and dogs to prolonged exertion increases the myoglobin in their muscles, especially in those muscles involved in sustained work. The dark red muscles of diving mammals are rich in myoglobin, which provides an appreciable store of oxygen for use in diving before the muscles begin to resort to anaerobic formation of lactic acid. Myoglobin probably serves in the intracellular application of oxygen for aerobic muscular work, but the actual use of the interesting substance is still too obscure for useful speculation on its role in adaptation to conditions in winter.

Ontogeny of Thermoregulation

Birds

Embryonic development of birds and mammals takes place in a maternal environment that maintains even warmth. To be sure, embryonic and newborn mammals and newly hatched birds tolerate greater and longer cooling than do adults, but this tolerance is not peculiar to arctic life, nor do I know that it is especially or adaptively developed among arctic animals. Annual programs of reproduction in arctic birds show the accuracy with which they prepare for laying at a season when the specific kind of parental care can be expected to (and does) permit successful provision of warmth that can shield the eggs and young (see Chapter 5). I am by no means sure that only programming of date of laying and intensity of care adapt birds for reproduction in the arctic, but I believe that it will be by first measuring these programs that special adaptations for reproduction in the Arctic may be discovered.

Altricial Young Mammals

In quite differing specific ways and for varying lengths of time carnivorous mammals and, in general, small herbivorous rodents care for their young until development of independent ability to maintain themselves. I believe that it is safe to generalize that carnivores, with usually small and feeble young, prepare shelter in dens where the mother can feed and warm the young. Season and locality of reproduction are rather accurately selected so that the young bears and foxes may emerge in a time of suitable warmth and adequate supply of food. Similarly, provision of shelter, care and some seasonal programming maintain reproduction in small herbivores, although information about their natural habits is even more scarce than for large carnivores. It may be related to their dependence upon man that domesticated dogs are erratic in selecting a season for reproduction.

174

Newborn Alaskan red-backed voles *(Clethrionomys rutilus dawsoni),* born as captives in summer, are completely bare and weigh less than one-tenth of their mother's weight. At first their intrinsic capability for heat regulation is feeble and they are kept warm in the nest by the mother. At 14 to 18 days of age and with half the mother's weight they can maintain normal body temperature of adults when alone for an hour in air at 0° (MORRISON et al., 1954). This rapid development of independent thermoregulation, even in voles raised in the laboratory, would early suit them for free existence.

Calves of Caribou

Arctic caribou calves are born at a season in spring when they can just survive the prevailing chilly weather. Although precocious at moving about, they are born moist and for a few days their fur is not thick enough for insulation in a cold spell, nor does it possess the order and texture necessary to resist wetting (LENTZ and HART, 1960; HART et al., 1961). The mother provides scarcely any sheltering warmth, and the young calves suffer from cold, rain and wind. It would seem to be a risky situation, and it has been met by capacities for thermoregulation that are especially marginal in arctic spring. I have been informed, however, that in milder climates of Scotland and Australia lambs of domesticated sheep are born in a precarious state for thermoregulation during the rain, wind and cool weather that occur in the season in which lambing is concentrated.

Some Conclusions

As a physiologist familar with some animals I am envious at reading the determinations of genetics of some physiological characters that clearly appear to adapt some populations of plant species to the different conditions in which they live in several latitudes and their related climates. As my discussions show I am puzzled by trying to find characteristics usefully indicative of a genetic definition of adaptations in populations of arctic birds and mammals. The best that I could do is to describe some characteristics of physiology, form, activity, behavior, and habits that appear to be utilized in sustaining arctic species. I consider it correct to call these useful, and in some cases, indispensable characters – adaptations in the common meaning of the word. Many of these adaptations are evidently not unique to arctic forms, or they differ only in degree of expression, or in time of operation from characteristics of comparable forms in other climates. That broad view of adaptations does not make them less real, and in fact a number of them can be quantitatively related through metabolism, heat, and by dimensions of size and time.

In order to regard adaptations in a perspective of evolution we would need more precise information about the genetic processes by which they are transmitted and how they have been geographically distributed, and some view of the manifestation of these adaptations in time. Through systematic relations and distribution we can carry out the awkward procedure of looking backward in time. But the circumstances of the past and the movements of original populations are vague. This may be in part because we are looking backward at operations of populations that were always in forward progress.

It is well to consider and discard speculations that have failed to attain to an essential theory of evolutionary adaptation. By viewing the lives of arctic animals we can describe many factors in their adaptation to the Arctic. In a general sense descriptions of some of these factors even explain how the existence of arctic animals is possible and how their lives proceed within the limits of the complex economy that is permissible for individuals and populations. In a few recent years we have gained much information about the animals and their environment. Even some of their past is becoming apparent and the picture of arctic life is becoming scientifically more real, intellectually more satisfactory and, above all, more interesting.

References

ALLEE, W.C.: Principles of Animal Ecology. Philadelphia: Saunders Co. 1949 (reprinted 1963).

BERGMANN, C.: Über die Verhältnisse der Wärmeökonomie der Thiere zu ihrer Größe. Göttinger Studien, pt. 1, 595–708 (1947).

FREUCHEN, P., SALOMONSEN, F.: The Arctic Year. New York: G.P. Putnam 1958.

HART, J.S., HEROUX, O., COTTLE, W.H., MILLS, C.A.: The influence of climate on metabolism and thermal responses of infant caribou. Canad. J. Zool. 39, 845–856 (1961).

HART, J.S., IRVING, L.: The energetics of harbor seals in air and in water with special consideration of seasonal changes. Canad. J. Zool. 37, 447–459 (1959).

HART, J.S., POHL, H.: Seasonal acclimatization in varying hare (Lepus americanus). Canad. J. Zool. 43, 731–744 (1965).

IRVING, L., KROG, H., MONSON, M.: The metabolism of some Alaskan animals in winter and summer. J. Physiol. Zool. 28, 173–185 (1955).

KLEIBER, M.: The Fire of Life: An Introduction to Animal Energetics. New York: John Wiley & Sons, Inc. 1961.

KLEIN, D.R.: An Alaskan population explosion. Explorers Journal 48, 162–172 (1970).

LENTZ, C.P., HART, J.S.: The effect of wind and moisture on heat loss through the fur of newborn caribou. Canad. J. Zool. 36, 679 (1960).

LYMAN, C.P., O'BRIEN, R.C.: Hyperresponsiveness in hibernation. In: Dormancy and Survival. Ed. by H.W. WOOLHOUSE. Cambridge (England) 1969.

MAYR, E.: Animal Species and Evolution. Cambridge, Mass.: Belknap Press of Harvard University 1963.

MEZHZHERIN, V.A.: Yavlenie Wenyela i evo vozmozhnoe obyasnenie. (Translation by W.O. Pruitt, Jr.) Acta Theriologica 8, 95–114 (1964).

MORRISON, P.: Mammalian hibernation: IV. Some interrelations between weight and hibernation function. Bull. Mus. Comp. Zool. Cambridge, Mass. (1960).

MORRISON, P.: Insulative flexibility in the guanaco. J. Mammal. 47, 18-23 (1966).

MORRISON, P., ROSENMANN, M., SEALANDER, J.A.: Seasonal variation of myoglobin in the northern red-backed vole. Amer. J. Physiol. 211, 1305–1308 (1966).

MORRISON, P., RYSER, F.A., DAWE, A.R.: Studies on the physiology of the masked shrew, Sorex cinereus. Physiol. Zool. 32, 256–271 (1959).

MORRISON, P., RYSER, R.A., STRECKER, R.L.: Growth and the development of temperature regulation in the tundra redback vole. J. Mammal. 35, 370–386 (1954).

ØRITSLAND, N.A.: Temperature regulation of the polar bear (Thalarctos maritimus). Comp. Biochem. Physiol. 37, 225–233 (1970).

PREVOST, J.: Ecologie du Manchot Empereur. Actualitées scientifiques et industrielles, 1291. Mission Paul Emile Victor, No. 222. Paris: Hermann 1961.

ROSENMANN, M., MORRISON, P.: Seasonal augmentation of myoglobin in the snowshoe hare. J. Biol. Chem. **240**, 3353–3356 (1965).

ROWAN, W.: Bird migration. Proc. Bost. Soc. Nat. Hist. **39**, 151-205 (1928).

SCHOLANDER, P.F.: Evolution of climate adaptations in homeotherms. Evolution **9**, 15–26 (1955).

SCHOLANDER, P.F.: Climate rules. Evolution **10**, 339–340 (1956).

SCHOLANDER, P.F., WALTERS, V., HOCK, R., IRVING, L.: Body insulation of some arctic and tropical mammals and birds. Biol. Bull. **99**, 225–236 (1950).

VEGHTE, J.H.: Thermal and metabolic response of the gray jay to cold stress. Physiol. Zool. **3**, 316–328 (1964).

WEST, G.C.: Seasonal changes in resting metabolic rates of Alaskan ptarmigan. Unpublished data.

WEST, G.C., WEEDEN, R.B., IRVING, L., PEYTON, L.J.: Geographic variation in body size and weight of willow ptarmigan. Arctic **23**, 240–253 (1970).

Chapter 12

Insulation of Man

Historical Use of Clothing

There appear to be no indications of existence of arctic people without clothing. DARWIN was impressed by the meagerness of clothing worn by the people of Tierra del Fuego, but in the account of BRIDGES (1949), who lived in long association with them, their culture and shelter were much more elaborate than DARWIN's low estimate. The coastal Yaghans swam naked in the cold sea, but the coastal water was above freezing, and some urban people regularly practise swimming in icy winter water. The old Aleuts of the Aleutian Islands had highly developed techniques and good material for making clothing of fur and feathered skins but did at times go barefooted. With competence for preparing footgear, they nevertheless sometimes elected to go without, probably because the wet snow of the Aleutian Islands is hard on skin boots and, at least transiently, tolerable for the naked foot.

From my little acquaintance with the history of ancient man I cannot recall descriptions that show the insulation provided by clothing of ancient people in cold weather. Illustrations of statuary of the time (400 B.C.) do not show clothing that would have protected the 10,000 Greek mercenaries led by Xenophon in their winter retreat through the snows of mountainous Armenia after the defeat of the insurrection of Cyrus. Hannibal's army from Spain crossed the Alps in winter, with elephants, to surprise the Roman army, who thought that winter protected their northern flank. Roman legionnaires marched, lived and occasionally fought in lands north of the Rhine, but the clothing depicted seems inadequate even for those hardy men. Old Norsemen crossed the North Atlantic in small open Viking ships that would seem to have been extremely uncomfortable. The Norse settlement in southwest Greenland subsisted by farming in the European manner, wearing clothing of woolen fabrics. As their pastoral economy failed in the secular course of cooling climates after the 11th century they did not adapt their ways to those of Eskimos. The Norse colonists disappeared, while the Eskimos of Greenland lived on.

Early Contact with Arctic Eskimos

Early explorers on arctic seas confined themselves to their ships in winter, while observing that small groups of Eskimo men, women and children could move freely after the game on which they subsisted. Only when PEARY was drawn by Eskimo dogs and clothed in fashion was the North Pole attained by travel over the ice. In America and probably in Europe and Asia a few early traders for fur scarcely operated beyond the forests. They depended on imported manufactured goods and supplies of food prepared by importation through organized commerce and stored in well constructed depots. These schemes for storage and distribution were beyond attainment by aboriginal societies in the Arctic.

At the time of contact between arctic aboriginal people and strangers with technology for utilizing metal and possessed of extensive political and commercial organization, the aboriginals dressed in fur, utilized skins, wood, earth and snow for shelter, and obtained heat by burning wood or animal fat. Communication and transport covered only short distances and involved few people in limited organization that could not project its effort to obtain subsistence from other than current local sources; nor had they structures to safeguard storage. Existence was maintained from adjacent animals and material in almost immediate supply.

Shelter and Clothing of Eskimos

Many Eskimos now aged 50 grew up in clothing and shelters of the aboriginal design and construction of their ancestors (Fig. 12.1). Twenty years ago inland Eskimos of Alaska lived during winter in dome-shaped tents covered with thick furred skins from the bodies of winter caribou. Within these small, well insulated enclosures a small fire of twigs or animal fat maintained warmth. Heat from a few sleeping people in winter could keep water from freezing over night. A variety of other local designs of structures partly below ground and covered with well chosen dry sod conserved heat. Narratives of arctic travellers often dwell upon the heat in old-fashioned arctic dwellings. Warmth was much appreciated, but the small shelters could also be chilly and draughty because of poor housekeeping or insufficient supply of fuel.

I have mentioned that earliest relics of arctic people show their possession of kinds of implements of stone and bone with which older Eskimos of modern times could fabricate clothing warm and light enough for work in coldest winter. Most exacting requirements are for clothing and footgear during the seasonal changes from cold dry to wet snow. A large array of arctic clothing and footgear is required for the varying seasons and different conditions of terrain, snow and water. Needles, knives and shears, that reached arctic people through trade before description of their ways entered history, must have modified fabrication of fur garments, but reports from old people and examples of clothing indicate that aboriginally developed fashions persisted with the use of imported metallic implements.

Fur was selected from various animals and from skins of aquatic birds for the different requirements of each garment and its component parts. For an active hunter on land, clothing must be light in weight and supple, qualities especially served by skins of caribou that differed according to age, sex and season in which the animal was taken. Portions of skins from a half dozen species, of several sizes and ages for each, might enter the costume of each wearer. Trousers made from skins of wolves and bears provided warmth with too much weight for free hunting, but were good for waiting in cold wind.

Fashion of garments, footgear and mittens was commonly utilitarian. A variety of intricate patterns of stitching with threads or cords of sinews served functional seams. In fact there may be more methods of aboriginal stitching than are now utilized in manufacture of garments by artfully programmed machines. Useless or fanciful decorations embellish clothing in some arctic societies. The labor, inge-

Fig. 12.1. A. FRANK RULLAND before his caribou skin tent home of eight, Chandler, Lake, 1947. B. Eskimos of Anaktuvuk Pass in winter with JOHN KROG. (From IRVING, 1968)

nuity and fantasy in decoration of skin clothing in eastern arctic America and Greenland impresses one with the attention to appearance among those people.

The eminent CHARLES BROWER of Barrow (BROWER, 1942) related that while travelling in winter in a cold arctic storm he split the seam of his fur trousers. Wrapping a caribou skin about the exposed limb he hurriedly prepared a snow shelter and searched in vain among the gear on his sled for his sewing kit. Lighted

180

by a hastily contrived lamp burning some fat, with that patient persistence that has sustained arctic people, he laboriously fashioned a needle of sorts from the unlikely material of a brass 45–70 cartridge. After he returned to his home with the makeshift repairs he remarked that for a long time his wife asked if he had his sewing kit whenever he prepared for a journey.

At night in an arctic camp after a day's travel, Eskimos carefully hang fur clothing wet with sweat where it will freeze. The frost can then be beaten out of the fur with a small stick. As moist skins dry, they become hard and brittle and must be scraped to restore pliability. Wet skin boots need to be reshaped and rubbed to restore softness.

Seams require examination and repair. For the woman of an arctic household care of the clothing of a hunter and children was a prolonged task. Only with these attentions will the light-weight and fragile garments of fur retain the condition and fit that are required for activity in freezing winter or wet cold of summer. Clothing of fabrics is durable but cumbersome and about twice as heavy as the old skin clothing.

Arctic Eskimo styles of fur clothing were extremely comfortable, if you knew how to wear and care for the fragile and perishable garments. Older northern Indians and Eskimos complain that modern garments of cloth used by their young people are inadequate for cold. As is usual among men, the dangerously thin nether clothing of young women comes in for special criticism. With acculturation the insulative value of arctic peoples' usual clothing has deteriorated without equally good manufactured replacements of the ancient styles. More in each year we may suspect that man will live in the Arctic without the adaptive value of the aboriginals' clothing.

Urban Man's Adjustment to Cold

Elevation of resting metabolism indicates that a little more metabolic heat is available in Eskimos and arctic American Indians than in urban white people, but in the amounts reported while at rest it can lower critical temperature only a few degrees. Metabolic power is not to be disparaged, for it is useful in emergencies of exposure. In man and probably in most mammals its employment as supplement to insulation is wasteful and imposes stress that can be met only by those possessing sufficient vigor.

SCHOLANDER et al. (1958) vividly described situations in which men became able to accept cold that before exposure would have been intolerable. Even coming from urban life, men walking afield in chilly weather can after a few days tolerate wet clothes and obtain rest in scant covering of blankets. Soldiers forced into exposure to cold become more enduring, provided that the exposure is not so severe as to be intolerable. Their suffering from cold becomes less, with the result that they remain effective and, perhaps above all, they become able to rest and sleep at night. The experience is not happy but it is endurable for a purpose worthwhile. These examples do not illustrate adaptation fully suitable for arctic cold, but they do show adjustments that are helpful.

Adjustments of Men Native to Cold Climates

Aboriginal people of the Australian desert, sleeping nearly naked in a chilly night, accepted a small decline in rectal temperature and cooling of their skin, particularly on their feet, to a degree quite unpleasant for white scientists. The aborigines rested quietly and apparently asleep, with resting rate of metabolism, while the disturbed white men shivered and thrashed about with resulting elevation of metabolism (SCHOLANDER et al., 1958). In their natural way the Australians maintained a fire between sleepers, alternately turning to warm back and front and occasionally adjusting the fire for burning evenly. This exercise recalls to me the first uncomfortable nights in a cold arctic camp when, even with a good sleeping bag, I would be disturbed frequently by the need to adjust head covering to allow breathing. Later I was undisturbed in making the frequent adjustments and rested well. A complex set of behavioral adjustments, and perhaps some modest acceptance of cooling, permits rest in cold with limited restlessness and reduction of the shivering that spoil the value of insulative covering and waste metabolic heat. Lying awake and cold I have enviously observed the relaxed rest of Eskimos in cold camps under covers less than mine.

Physiological Tests

Warmth in a Cold Night

Tests of men sleeping with insufficient covering have been carried out with Lapp men (who were still accustomed to life in cold camps as they herded their reindeer), Athapaskan Indian men of arctic Yukon Territory and Eskimo men on Baffin Island. While resting through a night in near-freezing air, covered inadequately with a light blanket, metabolism was measured, along with rectal temperature and temperature of skin in several places. The results are compared by HART et al. (1962). All of the arctic subjects, as well as white men, elevated their metabolism during the cold night and all were restless and uncomfortably cold. The Eskimos and Indians started with a resting metabolic rate some 25% above that of white men, and all increased metabolism during the cold experience. The feet of white subjects cooled somewhat more than those of Indians or Eskimos. None of the changes measured indicated significant general or special physiological adaptation of the arctic people for cold. Some of the native men remarked that in practical life they always took care not to be cold, by which they meant that the sensible man provided for the shelter, clothing and heat that are essential for arctic man. An Australian aboriginal might adapt to the experience of chilly nights; arctic people do not fight cold but accommodate in behavior, clothing and shelter.

Examples of Special Adjustment for Cold

A Nepalese Pilgrim

We must resort to narrative accounts for descriptions indicative of man's adjustment to cold in which a few physiological measurements provide bases on which to model pictures of extreme development of thermoregulation. Narratives of experience can provide real views that are not evident in experiments. PUGH (1963) described a Nepalese pilgrim who was about their mountaineering camp high in the Himalayas for a month wearing only thin clothing without shoes or gloves. He claimed to sleep comfortably. During a night that cooled to –1° his rectal temperature dropped only from 36.9° to 36.6° while his feet cooled to 13.5°. In various experimental observations his metabolic rate rose as he cooled and shivered, reaching from 1.5 to 2.7 times normal. His adjustment was by increased metabolism and insensitivity to discomfort from cooling skin. His shivering and elevation of metabolism to maintain rectal temperature indicated that, unaware of or undisturbed by the discomfort, he was nevertheless accurately monitoring his thermal state for good thermoregulation.

Immersion in Cold Water

CARLSON et al. (1958) measured factors involved in the insulation of men in water according to the formula: $I = \frac{T_b - T_s}{H}$ in which I = insulation in $°C/cal/m^2/h$, T_b and T_s-temperatures of rectum and skin and H = 0.76 X heat production, assuming 24% evaporative loss in respiration. In men of widely different fatness insulation varied some 4-fold in proportionate relation to thickness of superficial fat and indication of fatness by specific gravity (Fig. 12.2). The greatest insulation, which was scarcely increasing further as the water cooled to 10°, was achieved by bodies containing over 30% of fat. Seals with perhaps 40% of fat are not burdened while floating in water, but in air a fat man pays for his load.

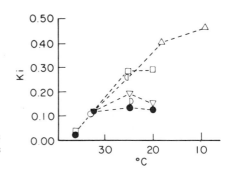

Fig. 12.2. Body insulation calculated at various water bath temperatures. Each symbol represents a separate subject. (From CARLSON et al., 1958)

Swimmers Racing Across the English Channel

Swimmers racing across the Channel traverse some 35 km of water around 16° to 15°, in from 12 to 17 h. All successful swimmers were above average in fatness. One who was relatively lean, but fast, had cooled to rectal temperature 34.1° at the finish of the race (PUGH et al., 1960). Some much fatter men scarcely cooled, and it is consistent with the calculated insulation of the fat distributed over their bodies that insulative fat was their protection. These swimmers are rare and unrepresentative individuals. Among other capabilities they probably expend nearly 10,000 kilocalories in the race (PUGH et al., 1960), three times the daily expenditure of a moderately active man. Certainly the swimmers are not exposed to arctic cold, and an occasional race is not the habit of a population.

Warm Hands of Arctic People

BROWN et al. (1954) remarked on the warm hands in cool weather of Eskimos of Southampton Island. Since that time warmer temperature and greater emission of heat to cold water have been ascribed to Alaskan Eskimos and Indians, northern fishermen and, with occasional uncertainties, to people accustomed to exposure to cold, compared with people unaccustomed to exposure. Exposure of a finger or hand and the recording of cooling and emission of heat are easily performed. But general warmth of the body, temperature of exposure, sex, mass of hand and age of subject, as well as experience and perhaps race, modify the reactions. Furthermore, manageable samples of subjects are often a few young people, from whom it is a dubious procedure to extrapolate to the reaction to cold by which a population of men, women and children succeeds or suffers in real life. I will, however, quote from examples which in my own experience and observation illustrate factors in successful and less successful reactions in cold.

True Tolerance of Cold Hands and Feet

Two students at the University of Alaska belonged to a sect consisting of men, women and children, which for simplicity wore only light clothing and walked barefooted in winter snow in manner quite shocking to observe. They kindly sat for me in a room about 0° while temperatures were recorded as represented for one young man in Fig. 12.3. The coldness that excited his fingers and toes to rewarm in cycles appeared to be around 10°, while his body (mid-back and over sternum) remained about 33°. Two bouts of moderate shivering were noted. In contrast, a vigorous young airman volunteered to sit in similarly light clothing and exposure (Fig. 12.4). The skin of his body cooled, as did his fingers and toes. Fingers and toes were not as reactive as those of the student subject. The airman's toes becam so painful and he began to shiver so violently that I caused him to terminate the test lest he shake himself apart. Although both students had been reading in preparation for examinations the airman remarked that he was completely unfitted for any use during the test. He suggested that infantry

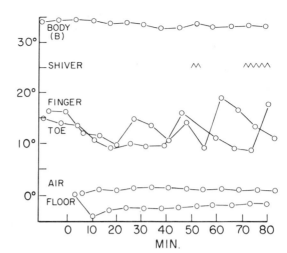

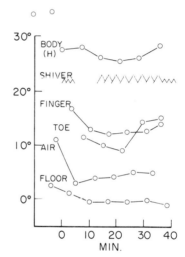

Fig. 12.3. Record of skin temperature in student B. Note the large swing of temperature in fingers and tees and the very slight shivering. (From Irving, 1960)

Fig. 12.4. Records of skin temperature in Airman Henson. Violent shivering with considerable fall of surface temperature. (From Irving, 1960)

soldiers prepared like the students for arctic action in light clothing would be extremely effective. I remarked that for air service personnel to adopt similar light clothing would effect large economies and convenience, at which he asked to withdraw his comments about the infantry.

One of the students volunteered that a given toe was warming just as the cyclic recorder showed local warming of the skin by one degree, and repeated the remark of change when another location had cooled one degree. Thus we see that good endurance of cooling was attended by fine discrimination of consciously observed warmth in contrast to the useless numbness of the intolerant subject. The examples of the two subjects tolerant of cold and the Nepalese pilgrim illustrate conditions of human adaptation to cold tissues after practice.

Physiological analysis of the processes and location of adaptation becomes highly complex, and they are beyond comprehensive view in relation to arctic

185

life. We can see, however, that a measure of human adaptability for cold tissues exists that can be evoked by sufficient motivation. On the other hand, only through powerful motivation or by force of circumstances does urbanized modern man, as probably also the ancients, accept the regime of exposure that is required to evoke the latent adaptability. Although use of this adaptability would importantly reduce the labor and invention expended on clothing and shelter, people usually go to great pains to avoid exposure to cold.

Testing the reaction of a hand by immersion in cold water differs from general experience. A few Eskimos at Barrow, Alaska, were asked to sit outside in air within a few degrees below freezing temperature. They were well enough clothed for comfort except for their bare hands. Cooling of hands was slower in Eskimo and white men who worked outdoors than in white workers indoors and in children (Fig. 12.5). In spite of the small mass of the children's hands they cooled only as fast as the large hands of white indoor workers (Fig. 12.6). Both outdoor and indoor white men cooled progressively with time. Occasionally the indoor workers cooled below 10°, which was painful and numbing. The little hands

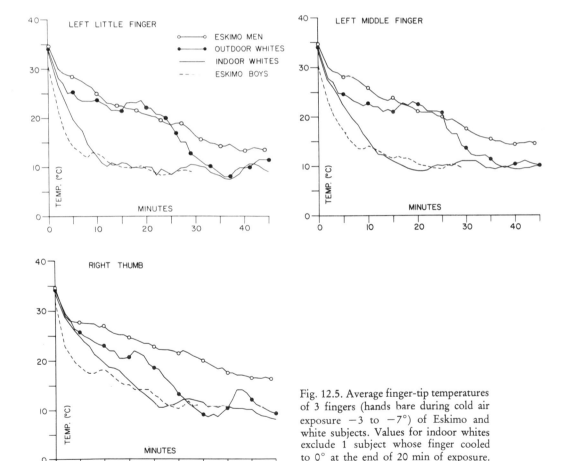

Fig. 12.5. Average finger-tip temperatures of 3 fingers (hands bare during cold air exposure −3 to −7°) of Eskimo and white subjects. Values for indoor whites exclude 1 subject whose finger cooled to 0° at the end of 20 min of exposure. (From MILLER and IRVING, 1962)

186

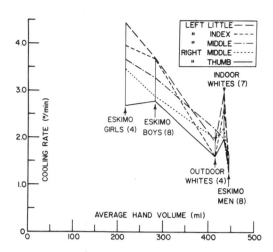

Fig. 12.6. Relationship between group average hand volume and average cooling rates for 5 fingers of Eskimo and white subjects during initial 5-min exposure to cold air (-3 to $-7°$). Numbers in parentheses are number of subjects in each group. (From MILLER and IRVING, 1962)

of the boys attained this temperature early and held near it, with individuals showing lively cycles of warming and cooling. The boys and girls reported some but not severe pain in hands that were so cold as to be very painful for the white men. We had remarked upon the heedless manner of the active Eskimo children when in noisy play they continued their sport after losing mittens from hands that then felt very cold to our touch.

MARSHALL (1969) noticed the dexterity of small children arriving at school in winter in Fairbanks, Alaska (65° N), with cold hands from insufficient or careless clothing. Temperatures of fingers were colder in younger children and warmer in older children. Fingers of children resident less than one year were colder in winter than those of children longer resident. At various ages the fingers of American Indian children at Old Crow, Yukon Territory (67° N) were warmer than fingers of the urban white children. It should not be surprising that children differ from adults. Processes involved in differences with age are more complex than growth in size of fingers and simple improvement in maintenance of warmth, but analysis of the steps by which that part of a child becomes adult in reaction to cold is insufficient for sensible review.

Comments on Insulation of Mammals without Fur

Experimental scientists are likely to forget that measurements of reactions to cold show only their selections from the physiological processes involved in adaptation for arctic life. Preparation of an experiment detaches an animal from its way of living. This detachment seems to make results of experimentation even more unrealistic for man than for other animals because we well know how complicated is the life of a population of humans. Not so well realizing the complexity in the life of other animals, we are inclined to consider their lives to be as simple as our limited characterization of their ways.

The insulation of furless mammals is interesting because it displays the rather surprising dependence of those warm-blooded animals on regulation of warmth by heterothermic gradients in peripheral tissues. The dimensions of these gradients and their changes are most conspicuous in the marine mammals of northern seas. Effective integration of the temporal and topographic processes involved is evident in the maintenance of steady internal warmth with metabolic expenditure that is not adaptively modified in an arctic environment.

This integration depends upon accurate perception of temperature and regulation of distribution of metabolic heat appropriate to the supply and suitable to the requirement of keeping the external tissues within the wide operational range that extends from near 0° to just above internal temperature. We can see some rough overall dimensions of the integrative process, but it is pointless to speculate beyond the illustrations furnished by a few measurements to the systems involved in integration. The physiological problem is peculiar to arctic life only in that the dimensions of thermal influences are so conspicuous.

Another likely approach to understanding heterothermic operations will be in seeing how some of the chemical processes and structures of cells, possessing rates of reaction considered to be highly sensitive to temperature, proceed effectively to sustain epidermal cells in even operation over a large range of temperature. Components are visible in some separable enzyme-substrate systems and possibly in some microstructural characteristics of cells.

I have spoken of the protection of arctic man from cold as if it were completely managed by his use of clothing and shelter. These shields, however, hinder man in observing his environment. Faces and hands must maintain perception of the surroundings; even with the best ordered regimes of clothing and housekeeping, exposure to cooling is a frequent or even prevalent arctic experience. The pathological consequences of frostbite are as severe in Eskimos as in other people, but I have remarked that only by accident do they incur frostbite. I believe that it it is to be suspected that some changes in exposed tissues of eyes, airways, and hands may result from exposure to cold. How far these influences can be countered by compensatory reactions before pathological results become overt, needs examination.

Protected by imported clothing and shelter, the new generation of Eskimos and newcomers to the arctic need not exercise the skills by which the ancients accurately appraised their surroundings and their ability to react to their influences. Will they suffer impairment from exposures that they do not properly appreciate, even if they can temporarily make compensations without overt pathology? I would think that studies of peripheral neurological conditions could give evidence for chronic effects of exposure to cold.

It will be a long process before societies of arctic people acquire the cultivated activities that urban people have developed to sustain their interest in life apart from a natural environment. As they become rapidly detached from their old concern and enjoyment for their physical and social surroundings, interesting replacements will be required if the arctic societies are not to become aimless and dull. For this substitution I have no ready suggestion, but history has shown that great changes in the ways of peoples can introduce damaging individual and social stresses.

188

References

BRIDGES, E. L.: Uttermost Part of the Earth. New York: E. P. Dutton 1949.

BROWER, C.: 50 Years Below Zero. New York: Dodd and Mead Inc. 1942.

BROWN, G. M., BIRD, G. S., BOAG, T. J., BOAG, L. M., DELAHAYE, J. D., GREEN, J. HATCHER, J. D., PAGE, J.: The circulation in cold acclimatization. Circulation 9, 813–822 (1954).

CARLSON, L. D., HSIEH, A. C. L., FULLINGTON, F., ELSNER, R. W.: Immersion in cold water and body tissue insulation. Aviation Medicine 29, 145–152 (1958).

HART, J. S., SABEAN, H. B., HILDES, J. A., DEPOCAS, F., HAMMEL, H. T., ANDERSEN, K. L., IRVING, L., FOY, G.: Thermal and metabolic responses of coastal Eskimos during a cold night. J. Appl. Physiol. 17, 953–959 (1962).

IRVING, L.: Human adaptation to cold. Nature 185, 572-574 (1960).

IRVING, L.: Adaptations of native populations to cold. Arch. Environ. Health. 17, 592–594 (1968).

MARSHALL, H. C.: Development of Human Adaptation to Cold. Ph. D. Thesis, Univ. of Alaska (1969).

MILLER, L. K., IRVING, L.: Local reactions to air cooling in an Eskimo population. J. Appl. Physiol. 17, 449–455 (1962).

PUGH, L. G. C. E.: Tolerance to extreme cold at altitude in a Nepalese pilgrim. J. Appl. Physiol. 18, 1234–1238 (1963).

PUGH, L. G. C. E., EDHOLM, O. G., FOX, R. H., WOLFF, H. S., HERVEY, G. R., HAMMOND, W. H., TANNER, J. M., WHITEHOUSE, R. H.: A physiological study of Channel swimming. Clin. Sci. 19, 257–273 (1960).

SCHOLANDER, P. F., HAMMEL, H. T., LANGE ANDERSEN, K., LOYNING, Y.: Metabolic acclimation to cold in man. J. Appl. Physiol. 12, 1–8 (1958).

Subject Index

191

P. J. Bentley: Endocrines and Osmoregulation

A Comparative Account of the Regulation of Water and Salt in Vertebrates

With 29 figures
XVI, 300 pages. 1971

(Zoophysiology
and Ecology, Vol. 1)

This new series will deal with subjects that are central to zoophysiology, ethology and ecology and that are of timely interest and not too narrowly conceived. As the title of the series indicates, the approach will be from the aspect of function and causality at various levels of organization: the organ, the individual, relations among individuals and, within a broader frame, within populations and communities. Zoophysiology and Ecology ist designed to foster mutual understanding between the disciplines involved. By sifting and summarizing the constantly increasing number of original publications, often widely scattered, these volumes will enable the reader to gain an overall view of the field. The monographs, which will be critical and concise, are equally intended for the advanced student and the specialist who welcome a new type of analysis of associated ideas, opinions, and conclusions.

W. B. Vernberg/F. J. Vernberg: Environmental Physiology of Marine Animals

With 116 figures
X, 346 pages. 1972

The oceans are vast in size and contain a rich diversity in biota and habitats. This textbook stresses the physiology of marine animals in terms of adaptations to various environmental factors in the sea.

Springer-Verlag
Berlin · Heidelberg · New York
London München Paris Sydney Tokyo Wien

Marine Biology

International Journal on Life
in Oceans and Coastal Waters
Editor in Chief: **O. Kinne**
1973, Vols. 18–22 (4 issues each):
DM 900,– plus postage and handling.

MARINE BIOLOGY is an international
journal on life in oceans and coastal
waters. It publishes original research
papers concerned with marine life,
such as those dealing with the
metabolism of organisms, the
interdependence of micro- and macro-
organisms, and alterations brought
about by environmental changes.
Studies on the physical, chemical, and
geological aspects of oceanography
relevant to marine biology are also
included. The journal serves throughout the world as an information
exchange for researchers in marine
biology.

Oecologia

In Cooperation with the International
Association for Ecology (Intecol)
Managing Editor: **H. Remmert**
1973, Vols. 12–13 (4 issues each):
DM 360,– plus postage and handling.

OECOLOGIA reflects the dynamically
growing interest in ecology. Emphasis
is placed on the functional inter-
relationship of all organisms and their
environment rather than their morphological adaptation. The journal
publishes original articles, short
communications, and symposia reports
that cover all aspects of modern
ecology, with particular emphasis on
physiological and experimental
ecology, population ecology, organic
production, and mathematical models

Journal of Comparative Physiology

Founded in 1924 as Zeitschrift für
vergleichende Physiologie by
K. von Frisch and **A. Kühn**
Editorial Board: H. Autrum, K. V. Frisch
G. A. Horridge, D. Kennedy,
A. W. Martin, C. L. Prosser, H. H. Weber
1973, Vols. 82–87 (4 issues each):
960,– plus postage and handling.

The increasing emphasis on the
comparative aspects in many branches
of biology plus the impetus derived
from new findings at the cellular and
subcellular level have led to a major
growth of comparative physiology.
Research results in molecular biology
often have a bearing for comparative
physiology studies dealing with more
complex organisms and even for
exploring ecological problems such
as temperature control or the physiological control of behavior. As its
broad coverage embraces new areas
of investigation and the still important
classical ones, this journal mirrors the
growing diversification of comparative
physiology.

**Springer-Verlag
Berlin
Heidelberg
New York**
London · München · Paris
Sydney · Tokyo · Wien